THEORY OF
NONLINEAR
CONTROL SYSTEMS

McGRAW-HILL ELECTRICAL
AND ELECTRONIC ENGINEERING SERIES

Frederick Emmons Terman, *Consulting Editor*
W. W. Harman and J. G. Truxal, *Associate Consulting Editors*

Seely · Electron-tube Circuits
Seifert and Steeg · Control Systems Engineering
Shooman · Probabilistic Reliability: An Engineering Approach
Siskind · Direct-current Machinery
Skilling · Electric Transmission Lines
Stevenson · Elements of Power System Analysis
Stewart · Fundamentals of Signal Theory
Strauss · Wave Generation and Shaping
Su · Active Network Synthesis
Terman · Electronic and Radio Engineering
Terman and Pettit · Electronic Measurements
Thaler · Elements of Servomechanism Theory
Thaler and Brown · Analysis and Design of Feedback Control Systems
Thaler and Pastel · Analysis and Design of Nonlinear Feedback Control Systems
Tou · Digital and Sampled-data Control Systems
Tou · Modern Control Theory
Truxal · Automatic Feedback Control System Synthesis
Tuttle · Electric Networks: Analysis and Synthesis
Valdes · The Physical Theory of Transistors
Van Bladel · Electromagnetic Fields
Weeks · Antenna Engineering
Weinberg · Network Analysis and Synthesis

THEORY OF NONLINEAR CONTROL SYSTEMS

NICOLAI MINORSKY

Former Professor
Stanford University

62482

McGraw-Hill Book Company
New York
St. Louis
San Francisco
London
Sydney
Toronto
Mexico
Panama

TO MADELEINE

NEW METHODS IN CONTROL THEORY

The title of the book reflects to some extent the present status of control theory. In fact, until the end of World War II, developments in control theory proceeded along a purely linear line of approach. This allowed a satisfactory codification of the young applied science on the basis of the theory of differential equations in the complex domain to be reached rapidly. The theorems of Cauchy, the earlier work of Heaviside, frequency methods, etc.—all these prepared a convenient ground on which scientists of that time (around 1925 to 1940) were able to build the fundamentals of linear control theory; even today, their work constitutes the standard theory of control systems.

At the end of this period some facts which could not be explained on the basis of linear theory began to appear; the most important of these was undoubtedly the existence of self-excited oscillations. There were some initial difficulties in understanding the nature of these oscillations (see the end of Chap. 1), but these difficulties were overcome by generalizing the theory of oscillations. As a result, control theory was enlarged, and the resulting new theory offered much broader vistas than did the original; this, in turn, permitted scientists and mathematicians to proceed with further generalizations.

In a sense, the title of this book—"Theory of Nonlinear Control Systems"—seems on a close examination to be not quite adequate, since new problems are very often found in a purely linear domain. In the last two decades the progress in this field (particularly in the U.S.S.R.) has been reminiscent of the development of a long war, in which a partial offensive is launched in a certain sector, reaches a limited objective, and then comes to standstill, only to be resumed later with better methods.   Meanwhile, other offensives develop in other sectors.   In this manner, the situation progresses through a series of local successes and temporary failures.

This comparison is probably justified by the fact that "scientific offensives" are leaning more and more on the elaboration of the mathematical tools needed for a given problem rather than on purely inventive activity.   Very often these mathematical tools need further extensions, and this results in delays.   Such programs are, however, justified in the long run, since, instead of developing one particular invention, one obtains a definite mathematical algorithm from which many applications (inventions) usually branch off.

This tendency toward generalization, while giving a broad view of a given problem, often results in a number of different theories, starting from different mathematical algorithms, which relate to the same subject.   It thus becomes necessary to "identify" different theories with regard to their relationship to a given particular.

A great deal of material in this book is taken from Russian sources.   Several reasons contributed to this choice.   In the first place, it is likely that the Russian contributions are less known than American or European contributions.   Second, because most of the Soviet contributions appear under the auspices of the U.S.S.R. Academy of Sciences or, more particularly, under the auspices of the Institute of Automatics and Telemechanics, a definite advantage results from the fact that an excellent bibliography is thus made available. Finally, Russian publications generally exhibit an excellent coordination of mathematical, physical, and engineering efforts.   It should be noted, however, that for the past few years this coordination has acquired a truly international character because of a closer cooperation between the American and Russian scientists in the field of control theory.

Chapter 1 gives a brief outline of the theory of nonlinear oscillations and its relation to nonlinear control problems.   This subject is explored further in Chap. 2, which deals with different forms of nonlinearities.

Chapter 3 deals with the important concept of *linearization*, which is still the dominant doctrine in all nonlinear problems; in Anglo-Saxon literature these problems are usually grouped under the *describing function method*.   Linearization methods have been recently extended to a form which absorbs different manifestations of discontinuities in control characteristics; this particular extension is generally called the *method of harmonic linearization* (Popov and Pal'tov [12]).   At present this method seems to be leading to a definite codification, since it is capable of handling almost any nonlinear problem (continuous or discontinuous) so long as it is *nearly linear*. Examples of the application of this method are covered in Chap. 7. Chapters 4 and 5 are concerned with Liapounov's second method. Chapter 4 deals with the theoretical part of the method; the first six sections follow closely the exposition of this subject by Lefshetz and LaSalle [7], and the rest of the chapter is devoted to a brief outline of recent advances in the theory of stability, (Aiserman [1], Aiserman and Gantmacher [2], R. E. Kalman [6], and Popov [11]). At the end of the chapter there is a brief survey of the theory of V. M. Popov.

Chapter 5 deals with the same subject as Chap. 4 but is limited to control problems only; its presentation follows closely the important work of A. M. Letov [8], which, in turn, is based on earlier contributions of A. I. Lur'e [9] concerning the reduction of differential equations of control theory to the so-called *canonical form*, which facilitates the application of Liapounov's second method.

Chapter 6 concerns the theory of relay systems. The beginning of this chapter (Secs. 6.1 to 6.15) gives an abridged presentation of Tsypkin's treatise [13], which outlines the subject in a concise manner; the end of the chapter discusses some more recent approaches to this subject. Chapter 7 discusses briefly some applications of the method of harmonic linearization (mentioned previously in Chap. 3). Chapter 8 is concerned with the so-called piecewise linear method, as described by Aiserman and Gantmacher [2]; this method deals with the quasidiscontinuous periodic processes *directly*, that is without any preliminary linearization procedure. The interesting point in these developments is the possibility of obtaining the *exact solution* in the form of a Fourier series. The problem is, however, essentially transcendental, and for the time being there are still certain difficulties in the last (computing) step of the method, which arise precisely from this transcendental nature. There is no doubt that this is only a temporary delay and that with the development of an appropriate computer the method will be complete. These piecewise linear systems (and phenomena) gradually have begun to play an increasing role in modern control systems with relays or exhibiting discontinuous behavior in general.

Chapter 9 indicates briefly the fundamentals of the point-transformation theory conceived by A. A. Andronov [3] about 1937; a number of years elapsed before this approach was further elaborated by N. A. Geleszov [4], who gave a topological analysis of trajectories of piecewise linear systems. The problems involved in these developments are practically the same as those outlined in Chap. 8, but here their treatment is topological rather than analytical.

This method was later applied (Gorskaya, et al. [5]) to an investigation of numerous nonlinear servomechanisms, which were treated on this basis topologically.

We should mention in passing that Chap. 9 offers a typical example of a "scientific offensive" which is handicapped occasionally by mathematical difficulties. In fact, the original work of Andronov (around 1937) broadly indicated the method, but some important points were still missing in the algorithm. When these additional details were explored and the algorithm of the point-transformation method was completed (about 1955), applications began to appear at once (1959).

Chapter 10 outlines a subject which at first glance may appear to be outside the scope of control theory—namely, the question of *analog computers and functional transformers*. With the rapid advance of control theory in recent years this subject has acquired considerable importance. The early period (1936) of these studies was initiated by the author [10], but the situation remained dormant for nearly 20 years; finally, around 1955, it began to develop with an ever-increasing tempo. The importance of this subject can be seen from the fact that analogs (particularly electronic ones) have begun to play a dominating role in modern control systems; in a recent publication ([2], Chap. 10) on this subject about 150 international references are cited for the last decade or so.

Considerations of space did not permit extending this material beyond these 10 chapters, although the material originally contemplated is considerably more extensive. Among the omitted topics are the following: (1) optimizing and gradient control, together with their ramifications (e.g., synchronous detection, dual theory, etc.); (2) the so-called theory of invariance; and (3) the most recent trend, which is to build up control theory on a deterministic-stochastic foundation.

All this would easily double the number of pages of this volume, which was unfortunately impossible; moreover, some of these topics are still evolving at such a rapid pace that their codification has not yet been achieved.

In view of this it is difficult to forecast the ultimate result of these various "scientific offensives," but it seems likely that they are directed toward the same goal—namely that of increasing the accuracy ("the quality") of control. In fact all these recent developments definitely pursue this purpose, although from somewhat different points of view. The deterministic-statistical foundations of control theory apparently have a still broader objective, but advances here are still too small to be discussed. In fact, there is no existing algorithm capable of combining the two widely different sets of variables—the deterministic and the stochastic—in one single control action.

Another important trend now under way is to ascertain the relative advantages of continuous and discontinuous control actions. Precedence is definitely in favor of the former, since originally the fundamentals of control theory were established on the basis of continuity (and often of analyticity) of functions. Chapter 1 shows that, in reality, the discontinuities, at least in derivatives of control actions, creep in, and appropriate generalizations are accordingly rather difficult. Usually any procedure of linearization eliminates some of these difficulties at the expense of shifting some other difficulties elsewhere; thus, for instance, although the investigation of amplitude and phase is facilitated, the question of stability is, on the contrary, complicated (Chap. 3).

On the other hand, there are some reasons for believing (Chap. 8) that periodicity can be obtained by means of a polygon of linear characteristics, provided that the transition times (from one linear stretch to the next) occur at strictly predetermined instants, which would permit "closing" the polygon and result, in turn, in periodicity. Unfortunately, the problem then becomes transcendental. The important feature in this case is the fact that no linearization is needed. It is not possible to forecast anything definite until this particular "offensive" begins again with better means.

These few remarks perhaps indicate the heterogeneous nature of the various topics involved. In some chapters, (for example, Chaps. 4 and 5) one finds oneself on the familiar ground of continuous theory; in Chap. 6, however, difficulties appear because of the introduction of discontinuities; these are particularly troublesome in connection with the question of stability of equilibrium, which is an essentially continuous concept.

In Chap. 7 the same difficulty appears, but in this case it is masked by the ingenious concept of *harmonic linearization*. This, as was stated previously, simplifies the problem with regard to amplitude and phase but complicates it with regard to stability.

In Chaps. 8 and 9 nonlinear problems are replaced by *piecewise linear* ones; the difficulty here is caused by the transcendental nature of such problems; their advantage is that no linearization is required. The difficulty at present seems to center on certain computational difficulties, and a computer capable of solving transcendental problems of a special kind must be used.

All this indicates that we are in the middle of a maelstrom of different ideas, which are resulting in different methods; all methods, however, aim toward the same goal—the improvement of the "quality" of control.   There is no doubt that eventually these various theories and methods will merge into a "final" theory, which will probably be a compromise among the different theories presently existing.   (Today's quantum theory is a good example of such a scientific compromise made among a number of different theories which existed prior to its advent.)   Control theory has not yet reached this stage.

It is interesting to note that the rapid progress of control theory in recent time concerns not only the problems of control themselves but also, occasionally, concerns the mathematical methods used.   In fact, in all developments of the past three decades or so nonlinear problems have been treated in terms of the real variable; this was because of Poincaré's theory.   Poincaré introduced the real variable for the sake of his theory of limit cycles insofar as in the theory of differential equations in the complex domain there exists no concept of limit cycles.   Since that time it has been usual to treat linear processes in terms of the theory of the complex variable and nonlinear processes in terms of the real variable.   The discovery of nonlinear processes in control systems introduced a series of difficulties in established engineering practice, since a number of simple graphical constructions (e.g., hodographs, Nyquist diagrams, etc.) had to be replaced by more elaborate analytical methods resulting from the theory of the real variable.   From this point of view, the recent theory of Popov [11] introduces a considerable simplification by justifying the return to graphical methods (under the condition that self-excitation is ruled out in the nonlinear system in question).   It is to be expected that the impact of these new ideas will probably be felt in control theory in the near future once these new methods are more developed and better adapted for control problems.

In summarizing this brief review of the topics treated in this book, one has the impression that control theory has entered a new phase, as evidenced by the various theories discussed.   Very likely, the main line of endeavor in the future will be to weld together the results of these different theories in order to form a "new" control theory incorporating the discoveries of the last two decades.

We assume that the reader is acquainted with classical (linear) control theory and also with the elements of the theory of differential equations.   A brief summary of the mathematical topics required is condensed in Chap. 1.

The chapters of this book can be read independently.   In the references, an attempt has been made to cite only the basic contributions or particularly those in which a complete bibliography appears.   It would be impossible to give a complete list of references in this book.

The author wishes to acknowledge with thanks the valuable cooperation and advice of Prof. Giovanni Sansone, University of Florence, on a number of mathematical questions encountered in this work. He also wishes to express his gratitude to his wife, whose continued effort considerably shortened the time of preparing the manuscript.

This work has been carried out under the auspices of the Office of Naval Research; the author is grateful for the opportunity to undertake this work as well as for the use of the many facilities that were available to him during its progress.

NICOLAI MINORSKY

REFERENCES[1]

1. Aiserman, M. A.: "Lectures on the Theory of Automatic Regulation," Fizmatgiz, Moscow, 1958.

2. Aiserman, M. A., and F. R. Gautmacher: "Absolute Stability of Control Systems," U.S.S.R. Academy of Science, Moscow, 1963. (This reference contains a complete bibliography covering the last 20 years.)

3. Andronov, A. A., and S. E. Chaikin: "Theory of Oscillations," Moscow, 1937 (in Russian); English translation by S. Lefschetz, Princeton University Press, Princeton, N.J., 1949.

4. Geleszov, N. A.: Editor, 2d ed. of Andronov and Chaikin, "Theory of Oscillations," Princeton Univeristy Press, Princeton, N.J., 1959.

5. Gorskaya, N. S., et al.: "Dynamics of Non-linear Servomechanisms," U.S.S.R. Academy of Science, Moscow, 1959.

6. Kalman, R. E.: *Proc. U.S. Acad. Sci.*, vol. 49, no. 2, 1963.

7. Lefshetz, S., and J. P. LaSalle: "Stability by Laipounov's Direct Method," Academic Press, Inc., New York, 1961.

8. Letov, A. M.: "Stability of Non-linear Control Systems," 2d ed., Moscow, 1958.

9. Lur'e, A. I.: "Some Non-linear Problems in Control Theory," Goztehizdat, Moscow, 1951.

10. Minorsky, N.: *Compt. Rend. Acad. Sci. Paris*, vol. 202, 1936; *Rev. Gen. Elec.*, vol. 34, 1936.

---

[1] For Letov, Lur'e, and V. M. Popov, see the bibliography in Aiserman and Gautmacher [2].

11. Popov, V. M.: *Akad. RPR*, vol. 10, nos. 1 and 3, 1960; *Avtomatika i Telemechanika*, vols. 22, 24, nos. 8, 1, 1961, 1963.

12. Popov, E. P., and I. P. Pal'tov: "Methods of Approximations in the Theory of Non-linear Control Systems," Fizmatgiz, Moscow, 1960.

13. Tsypkin, J. Z.: "Theory of Relay Control Systems," Moscow, 1955; Technical Cybernetics, *Dokl. Acad. Nauk SSR*, No. 3, 1963.

CONTENTS

CHAPTER ONE
FUNDAMENTALS OF NONLINEAR CONTROL THEORY

1.1 INTRODUCTORY REMARKS

Before studying the present approaches to the theory of nonlinear control theory, it is useful to outline briefly the principal parts of the classical nonlinear theory of oscillations. Although there are considerable differences between these two theories, many concepts are common to both, particularly with regard to certain physical phenomena. Thus a grasp of what has been done in the nonlinear theory of oscillations is helpful in analyzing analogous subjects in nonlinear control theory. It must be noted, however, that all such related topics are more difficult and less explored in nonlinear control theory than they are in the nonlinear theory of oscillations.

Three major aspects of the nonlinear theory of oscillations are also applicable to nonlinear control theory; they are (1) state of rest and its stability, (2) oscillations, and (3) the stability of oscillations. Although the fundamentals of these phenomena are similar in both theories, in certain cases the application of them is quite different. For example, in the nonlinear theory of oscillations, oscillations are useful phenomena, whereas in nonlinear control theory they are generally of an undesirable nature. This is a rather trivial matter, and merely indicates the light in which the phenomena are to be regarded. [It should be noted that occasionally the maintenance of oscillations is desirable in nonlinear control theory also (see Chap. 7); in such cases the subject matter of both theories is identical, although as a rule it is more complicated in nonlinear control theory.]

In general, however, these three basic topics are practically the same in both theories. Specifically, in both cases the state of rest and its stability find the same expression in the form of the singular points of the corresponding differential systems; the stationary state of oscillations is expressible in terms of the concept of *limit cycles*; and, finally, the stability of these stationary oscillations is governed by similar mathematical methods.

More important than the similarities are the differences between these two approaches that arise from the corresponding differences in the nature of the nonlinearities involved. A number of theorems in the nonlinear theory of oscillations do not hold in nonlinear control theory, and, conversely, a number of points definitely established in the latter do not hold for the former. These differences are of fundamental importance for this book; a great deal of confusion may result for those who try to follow too closely the nonlinear theory of oscillations in studying nonlinear control theory. In this chapter we shall outline the fundamentals of the nonlinear theory of oscillations (Secs. 1.2 to 1.4); Sec. 1.5 gives a brief account of the principal feature of nonlinear control theory. The remaining chapters are devoted entirely to nonlinear control theory.

1.2 ELEMENTS OF THE THEORY OF NONLINEAR OSCILLATIONS

We shall limit ourselves to a few of the most important points, since this subject is adequately covered in numerous texts (see Refs. 1 to 13).

Integral curves and trajectories We shall be concerned with differential equations of the form

$$\dot{x} = P(x,y) \qquad \dot{y} = Q(x,y) \tag{1.1}$$

in which $P(x,y)$ and $Q(x,y)$ are some regular functions of x and y. The solutions $x = x(t)$ and $y = y(t)$ of (1.1) are certain integral curves in the three-dimensional space (x,y,t) such that in projection on the x,y plane one has integral curves defined by the differential equation

$$\frac{dy}{dx} = \frac{Q(x,y)}{P(x,y)} \tag{1.2}$$

in which the parameter t (time) does not appear.

In this way system (1.1) gives the parametric representation of the integral curve C in which one can follow the motion of the representative point R defining the instantaneous state $x(t_0)$, $y(t_0)$ of the system at any instant $t = t_0$. Equation (1.2) gives only a geometric curve $C: y = f(x)$. We refer to (1.1) as defining a *trajectory* and (1.2) will be referred to as an *integral curve*. A system like (1.1) is designated as *autonomous*, since the independent variable t does not appear explicitly in this case.

For nonautonomous systems, instead of (1.1), one has

$$\dot{x} = P(x,y,t) \qquad \dot{y} = Q(x,y,t)$$

and in general it would be impossible to eliminate t as was done in (1.2). It is to be noted that in some *special* cases this system can be reduced to an autonomous form. In this chapter we shall be concerned only with autonomous systems such as (1.1).

Singular points   A particular case in which there exists a couple of values $x = x_0$; $y = y_0$ such that $P(x_0,y_0) = Q(x_0,y_0) = 0$ is called a singular point. In applications, such points determine the position of equilibrium (or state of rest).

Phase plane   The variable y is usually identified with $\dot{x} = dx/dt$, and the plane of the variables (x,y) is defined as the phase plane. The study of motion of the point R on trajectories is always studied in this plane unless specified to the contrary.

First approximation   Very often in applications one limits the functions P and Q to the linear terms only; such a case is termed the *first approximation* and (1.1) acquires a simple form

$$\dot{x} = ax + by \qquad \dot{y} = cx + dy \tag{1.3}$$

where a, b, c, and d are constants. In a great majority of applied problems Eqs. (1.3) are sufficient for a qualitative investigation of the phenomena involved, and this simplifies the problem. In some special cases the first approximation does not give any answer, and one has to go to approximations of higher orders, which introduces greater complications. In what follows we shall be mostly concerned with the first approximation.

Various types of singular points and their significance   Solutions of (1.3) of the form

$$x = c_1 e^{St} \qquad y = c_2 e^{St} \qquad S = \text{const}$$

require that S be a root of the *characteristic equation*

$$S^2 - (a + d)S + (ad - bc) = 0 \tag{1.4}$$

One can reduce any system (1.3) by means of the *canonical transformation* (Bieberbach [1] and Sansone and Conti [5]) so long as $ad - bc \not\equiv 0$.

The nature of singular points, as well as of their stability, reduces to the investigation of the roots S of (1.4).

1. If the roots S_1 and S_2 are real and of the same sign, the singular point is a *node*; it is stable if $S_1 < 0$ and $S_2 < 0$ and unstable if $S_1 > 0$ and $S_2 > 0$ (Fig. 1.1).

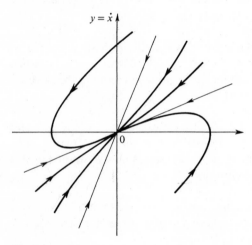

Fig. 1.1

2. If the roots S_1 and S_2 are real and of opposite signs, the singular point is a *saddle point* (Fig. 1.2).   This singularity is always unstable.
3. If the roots S_1 and S_2 are conjugate complex, the singular point is a *focus* (or a focal point); the motion of R in the neighborhood of a focus is shown in Fig. 1.3.   The focus is stable if Re $(S) < 0$ and unstable if Re $(S) > 0$.

The singular points appear both in linear and nonlinear differential equations, and their physical significance is as follows.

A *node* (Fig. 1.1) characterizes an overdamped motion such as that observed in the case of a pendulum approaching its equilibrium point without oscillations. The term "approaching" corresponds to the stable node; one encounters a similar situation if the motion creeps *away* from the unstable node.

A *focus* characterizes a similar, but underdamped, motion. This is the case of a pendulum approaching its equilibrium point with decaying

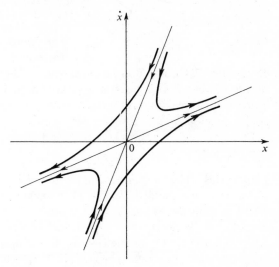

Fig. 1.2

oscillations if the focal point is stable; an unstable focus corresponds to a motion growing from rest with gradually increasing amplitudes.

A *saddle point* is an unstable singularity; its image can be given in terms of a pendulum in its upright (unstable) position.

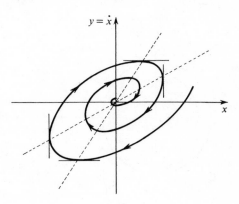

Fig. 1.3

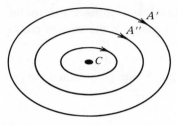

Fig. 1.4

Cases 1, 2, and 3 constitute the *simple* (or elementary) singular points. To these cases one can add:

4. If the roots S_1 and S_2 are purely imaginary, the singular point is called a *center* (Fig. 1.4).

The image of this case may be given in terms of the harmonic oscillator characterizing the motion in the neighborhood of a center.   It must be noted, however, that the first approximation fails to distinguish the center from a weak focus (that is, a focus corresponding to the complex conjugate roots S_1 and S_2 with a very small real part).   In this case one must go to higher approximations, and the problem becomes more complicated.

Limit cycles   The most important point in the modern nonlinear theory of oscillations is the discovery by H. Poincaré [4] of closed trajectories which he calls *limit cycles* (cycles limites).   They are characterized by the following property.

A limit cycle C_0 for the system (1.1) is a unique closed curve (in the phase plane) to which approach all other nonclosed trajectories C in the form of spirals winding onto (unwinding from) the limit cycle. In the first case (winding) (Fig. 1.5*a*), the limit cycle is said to be *stable*; in the second case (unwinding) (Fig. 1.5*b*), it is called *unstable*.   There is also a third (critical) case of a semistable limit cycle in which trajectories wind themselves onto limit cycles from one side (e.g., outwardly) and unwind themselves from the other side (e.g., inwardly), or vice versa.

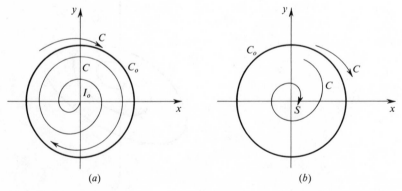

(*a*)   (*b*)

Fig. 1.5

A limit cycle is always an isolated closed trajectory in the sense that there is no other closed trajectory of a similar type in the small neighborhood of a limit cycle.[1] Since any point on nonclosed spiral trajectories C (which wind themselves on a stable limit cycle) may be regarded as certain "initial conditions," one can say that the motion on a stable limit cycle is *independent of the initial conditions*, since R will reach the limit cycle following a corresponding spiral; on the limit cycle the representative point will remain indefinitely if the limit cycle is stable.

Stable limit cycles have a definite physical meaning of trajectories characterizing self-sustained oscillations (e.g., those of an electron-tube oscillator). Unstable limit cycles have no physical meaning; they appear merely as "watersheds" separating the zone of attraction of two stable limit cycles (if they exist).

It is important to note that contrary to singular points (which exist also in linear systems), limit cycles are always due to the presence of *nonlinear terms* in the differential equation (1.1).[2]

Topological configurations   Poincaré has shown that singular points and limit cycles always form *topological configurations* (Poincaré [4]). The simplest such configuration (usually encountered in applications) reduces to that shown in Fig. 1.5a, in which I_0 is an unstable singular point and C_0 is a stable limit cycle. If I is an unstable focus, the trajectory unwinds itself from I and winds itself onto C_0 from the inside; the same holds for the outward trajectories C which wind themselves also on C_0 from the outside. One has thus a topological configuration IS, where the first letter always relates to the stability or instability of the singular point. One can also have an opposite configuration SI, where the singular point is stable and the limit cycle is unstable (Fig. 1.5b).

One may have more complicated configurations, such as ISI (Fig. 1.6a) and SIS (Fig. 1.6b). The configuration shown in Fig. 1.6b is known as a hard *self-excitation*. In fact, since the singular point (the state of rest) is stable, such a system is not "self-excited," but if an impulsive perturbation of some kind suddenly transfers R beyond the first unstable cycle I (for instance to the point A of the phase plane), the self-excitation develops toward the external stable cycle. Such

---

[1] Occasionally one encounters regions of accumulation of limit cycles (L. Bieberbach [1, page 87]), but such cases have no known physical significance.

[2] This holds in cases when $P(x,y)$ and $Q(x,y)$ in (1.1) are analytic functions of x and y. If P and Q are nonanalytic conditions, the matter is more complicated; this is discussed in Sec. 1.5.

phenomena are occasionally observed in control systems, and, if the external cycle S is located far enough from the unstable cycle I, dangerous effects may result. These "concentric" configurations are often encountered in applications and are always the same structure: either $ISIS \cdots$ or $SISI \cdots$.

In the case in which there are several singular points instead of one, the situation is more complicated and leads to the so-called *theory of indices* (H. Poincaré [4]), which we do not consider here.

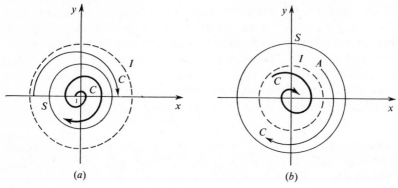

(a)   (b)

Fig. 1.6

Theorem of Poincaré-Bendixson   The direct theory of limit cycles is difficult, since for the determination of limit cycles it is not sufficient to know the parameters of the differential system, but it is also necessary to know the *solution* of the differential equation, which generally is not known.   One is thus caught in a vicious circle.

Poincaré approached this subject from his theory of "curves of contacts."   Bendixson completed Poincaré's work, and the result was the Poincaré-Bendixson theorem, which states:

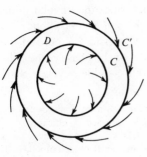

Given a domain D limited by two closed curves C and C' (Fig. 1.7) *such that no singular points of* (1.1) *exist either in D or on its boundaries C and C', then, if it is possible to show that the trajectories enter (leave) D through every point of the boundaries, one can assert that there exists at least one stable (unstable) limit cycle in D.*

This theorem gives both necessary and sufficient conditions for the existence of a limit cycle, but is difficult to apply because the "every point" condition must

Fig. 1.7

be satisfied.   In some special cases, when it is possible to assert this, the theorem gives an immediate answer.

We mention the Poincaré-Bendixson theorem because in nonlinear control theory it generally cannot be used because of *nonanalytic* nonlinearities.   These introduce certain *nonanalytic points* (on C or C') which preclude the use of this theorem.   This is one of the points at which the nonlinear theory of oscillations and nonlinear control theory diverge.   There are still further points of such situations which will appear later.

It must be noted, however, that these basic difficulties appear in the *exact* analytical theory; they are considerably reduced in the theory of approximations, in which the determination of limit cycles, particularly in the first approximation, does not present any difficulty.

Theory of bifurcations   It is well known (Poincaré [4] and [16] and Minorsky [9, Chap. 7]) that if a differential equation or a system of differential equations contains a variable parameter λ, its solution (trajectory in the phase plane) also varies; and, for some critical or *bifurcation* values $\lambda = \lambda_0$ of this parameter, the topological configuration (or "the phase portrait") may change *qualitatively*.   There are two principal kinds of such bifurcations:

1. The bifurcation of the *first kind* occurs whenever the nearest (to the singular point) limit cycle shrinks in size indefinitely when the parameter $\lambda \leqslant \lambda_0$; at the limit when $\lambda = \lambda_0$, the limit cycle coalesces with the singular point with the result that the latter changes its stability while the limit cycle disappears.   This phenomenon occurs according to one of the following two schemes

$$SIS \rightleftharpoons (SI)S \rightleftharpoons IS \tag{1.5}$$

or

$$ISI \rightleftharpoons (IS)I \rightleftharpoons SI \tag{1.6}$$

In these schemes S indicates stability, I indicates instability of the singular point, and the remaining letters designate analogous quantities for the limit cycle.   The letters in parentheses correspond to the elements undergoing the coalescence for $\lambda = \lambda_0$, and the double arrows show that these phenomena are reversible.

In scheme (1.5), the initial configuration SIS for $\lambda = \lambda_0$ undergoes the bifurcation of the first kind, the singular point S coalescing with the neighboring cycle I as the result of which the two disappear; instead, there appears a singular point I of opposite stability than that which existed previously.   Scheme (1.6) has an analogous meaning.

2. The bifurcation of the *second kind* occurs whenever two adjoining cycles (one stable and the other unstable) approach each other indefinitely and, for $\lambda = \lambda_0$, coalesce, giving rise to a semistable cycle which disappears thereafter.   One thus has a similar scheme, but only concerning the cycles:

$$SIS \rightleftharpoons S(IS) \rightleftharpoons S \tag{1.7}$$

$$ISI \rightleftharpoons I(SI) \rightleftharpoons I \tag{1.8}$$

These phenomena are often observed in electronic circuits and sometimes in control systems also.   For instance, in the case of a regenerative amplifier, schemes (1.5) and (1.6) can be interpreted as follows.   When the amplifier works in its amplification range (assuming that there is no signal), the circuit remains idle; this means that the singular point is stable.   If the parameter λ (the coupling between the anode and the grid circuits) is increased, the bifurcation value $\lambda = \lambda_0$ is reached for which SI coalesces, which gives rise ultimately (for $\lambda = \lambda_0$) to the configuration IS, which means that the circuit begins to work as a *generator* of oscillations and its amplifying property is thus lost.

Similar interpretations can be made in connection with other schemes.

1.3   STABILITY; VARIATIONAL EQUATIONS

We have already touched this subject in connection with the question of stability of singular points, but the question of stability of a stationary motion (for instance on a limit cycle) is more complicated, and it is useful to say a few words in order to prepare the ground for what follows.   (See also H. Poincaré [17].)

Since in control systems one always has several degrees of freedom instead of one degree of freedom, it is useful to consider instead of (1.1) a more general autonomous system

$$\dot{x}_i = X_i(x_1, x_2, \ldots, x_n) \qquad i = 1, 2, \ldots, n \tag{1.9}$$

We assume that the functions X_i are continuous and twice differentiable; x_i may still be regarded as certain *generalized coordinates* without attempting to attach to this term any geometrical significance.

Likewise, instead of talking of limit cycles, we must use an analytic term: the *periodic solution*.

Let us assume that we know that such a solution exists; for the time being we shall leave out the question of how it can be determined.

If such a solution exists and we indicate it as $x_{i0} = x_{i0}(t)$, we call it the *unperturbed solution*. Assume that the system has been perturbed somehow so that all coordinates become now

$$x_i(t) = x_{i0}(t) + y_i(t) \tag{1.10}$$

where the functions $y_i(t)$—the perturbations—are assumed to be small enough to be able to neglect $y_i^2, \ldots$. One can substitute (1.10) into (1.9); thus the expression

$$\frac{d}{dt}(x_{i0} + y_i) = X_i(x_{i0} + y_1, \ldots, x_{n0} + y_n) \tag{1.11}$$

being developed around the unperturbed solution, yields

$$\dot{y}_i = \frac{\partial X_i}{\partial x_1} y_1 + \cdots + \frac{\partial X_i}{\partial x_n} y_n \qquad i = 1, \ldots, n \tag{1.12}$$

or

$$\dot{y}_i = \sum_{j=1}^{n} \frac{\partial X_i}{\partial x_j} y_j \tag{1.13}$$

In these formulas $\partial X_i/\partial x_j$ are the partial derivatives of X_i with respect to x_j into which the unperturbed values have been replaced after the differentiations. Although the assumed smallness of $|y_i|$ permits the linearization of the problem (since the nonlinear terms $|y_i|^2, \ldots$ can be neglected), the problem in control systems is still very difficult because of the existence of many degrees of freedom and, particularly, because of the assumed smallness of y_i for which this procedure holds; as a matter of fact, in control systems perturbations cannot be considered small in the above sense.

Theoretically, at least one can see the origin of the modern theory of stability at this point. In fact, if it is possible to show that all initially small y_i remain small in the course of time, the system is called *stable*. If, moreover, all $y_i(t) \to 0$ for $t \to \infty$, it is *asymptotically stable*.

We need, however, more precise definitions (Chap. 4) in order to be able to specify the conditions of stability in a more definite manner. For the above reason, the problem so defined relates to the so-called *infinitesimal stability* or to the stability *in the small*.

These two limitations—(1) the difficulty (and often the impossibility) of integration of the variational system and (2) stability in the small—constitute a serious disadvantage for the use of this method in control systems, although in the astronomical calculations for which it was originally used, it is of a greater value.

1.4 DIFFICULTIES ENCOUNTERED IN STUDIES OF CONTROL SYSTEMS

We have outlined briefly in the preceding two sections a few of the most important aspects of the classical (analytical) nonlinear theory of oscillations. It will be necessary now to correlate this material to the analogous aspects of nonlinear control theory.

It is clear that the problems of nonlinear control theory are more complicated than those of the nonlinear theory of oscillations mainly because there are a greater number of degrees of freedom (or "dimensions") in nonlinear control theory. Although the fundamental concepts remain the same in both theories, the determination of the quantities involved becomes far more difficult in nonlinear control theory if one tries to follow the classical argument of the nonlinear theory of oscillations.

Thus, for instance, the position of equilibrium may still be regarded as a singular point of the system, but the simple geometrical interpretation is no longer available.

Still more difficult is to interpret the periodic solutions as certain closed curves in the phase space; this problem has been studied recently but with rather limited results. The major difficulty is that in the two-dimensional case (phase plane) the limit cycle bounds off two regions—the "inside" and the "outside" of the closed curve. Even in the three-dimensional case the difficulty appears on that account unless one introduces the separatrices, which are *surfaces* in this case. However, the problem of determining these surfaces is probably just as difficult as the determination of the cycles in the three space. One must admit that at present these studies have not resulted in anything that can be used in applied problems.[1]

In spite of these seemingly unsurmountable difficulties some points in common between the nonlinear theory of oscillations and nonlinear

[1] Strictly speaking, conditions also become more complicated in the nonlinear theory of oscillations for a greater number of degrees of freedom. However, most of the studies done so far in the nonlinear theory of oscillations relate to systems of the second order, that is, systems with one degree of freedom (Minorsky, "Theory of oscillations," Van Nostrand, 1962).

control theory can still be ascertained.   Thus, for instance, it is often observed that oscillations in control systems occur with *one single frequency* (Bogoliubor and Mitropolsky [12, Chap. 4]).   This permits us to conclude that, despite our total ignorance of the topology of the *n* space, everything happens as if the use of some kind of phase plane is still legitimate, although it is impossible to connect this observed effect with a more detailed analysis of the differential system in question. In what follows we shall return to this question.

Regarding the question of *stability*, the matter is less difficult but the analysis is still handicapped—certain drawbacks render the method of little use in problems of control.

Other manifestations of nonlinearities, such as the existence of a "hard self-excitation" and of "bifurcation" effects, have been definitely ascertained in nonlinear control systems.   Thus, for instance, it is often observed that a control system, which works without any oscillation as long as a certain amplification factor is small, begins suddenly to oscillate if this factor exceeds a critical value.

Similar effects are observed when a violent perturbation suddenly releases oscillations and thus evidences a kind of hard self-excitation.

However, to connect all these effects with the theory is impossible at present because of the lack of any connection with the topological concepts, on the basis of which all this becomes clear and simple in the two-dimensional space (as explained in Sec. 1.2).

There remains one factor which exists in nonlinear control theory and for which there is no counterpart at all in the classical nonlinear theory of oscillations.   This is the *nonanalytical* character of nonlinearities, which we shall investigate now.

1.5   NONANALYTIC NONLINEARITIES

Perhaps the most important factor in nonlinear control theory is the *nonanalytic form of nonlinearities*.   This feature was completely ignored in the classical nonlinear theory of oscillations.   Very likely this was the main reason why the studies of nonlinear control systems were initially handicapped.   In order to explain this point it is necessary to return to some fundamental points in the theory of differential equations.

It is recalled that a differential equation of the form

$$a_n x^{(n)} + a_{n-1} x^{(n-1)} + \cdots + a_1 x^{(1)} + a_0 x = f(t) \tag{1.14}$$

is called *linear* if its coefficients a_i are *continuous functions* of the *independent variable t* (usually time); in some particular cases these functions reduce to constants, in which case one has a linear differential equation with constant coefficients. If the right-hand term is absent, the differential equation is called *homogeneous*. (If $f(t) \neq 0$, it is nonhomogeneous, but this is of secondary importance here.)

Linear differential equations are characterized by the so-called *fundamental system* of solutions. This means that if one knows a certain number of particular solutions, the general solution is obtained as a linear combination of these particular solutions. There are a certain number of conditions to be fulfilled (e.g., nonvanishing of the Wronskian, etc.), but we shall not discuss these here.

This fundamental property of a linear differential equation finds its expression in physics in the form of the so-called principle of superposition. That is, in a physical system governed by a linear differential equation several oscillations (with different frequencies) can coexist without any interaction among themselves.

Linear systems have another important property, which can be formulated as a negative criterion. That is, *in linear differential systems self-excited oscillations (of the limit-cycle type) are ruled out.*

It is necessary to analyze closer *when a differential equation* (or a system) *can be considered as linear.* Here an important point intervenes which was not considered in the theory of differential equations prior to the advent of modern control systems.

It should be noted in passing that the converse of this property is not true; in fact, there are a considerable number of nonlinear differential equations in which such self-excited oscillations are absent.

Let us now return to the problem of nonlinear differential equations. The definition is as follows. A differential equation (1.14) is nonlinear if its coefficients a_i are *continuous functions of the dependent variable x.* Thus, for instance, the differential equation of Mathieu

$$\ddot{x} + (m + n \cos 2t)x = 0$$

is linear, whereas that of van der Pol

$$\ddot{x} + \mu(x^2 - 1)\dot{x} + x = 0$$

is nonlinear because of the term $(\mu x^2)\dot{x}$.

Whether a nonlinear differential equation has a periodic solution (of the limit-cycle type) or not is another matter. In fact, the establishment of conditions under which a nonlinear differential equation has a periodic solution constitutes the *problem of Poincaré* [17], which we do not propose to investigate here.

In both the linear and nonlinear cases the coefficients a_i [$a_i(t)$ for linear and $a_i(x)$ for nonlinear differential equations] are supposed to be *continuous* functions of the indicated variable with a certain number of continuous derivatives. This was the fundamental assumption in the classical nonlinear theory of oscillations.

The theory of automatic control introduced an entirely new feature of *discontinuity*, at least in some of their derivatives. In fact, control systems are full of such discontinuities resulting from the use of relays, contactors, lost motion, coulomb friction, saturation, hysteresis, etc. All these are idealized in one way or another in the form of certain discontinuities. We shall study these phenomena as well as their idealizations in more detail in Chap. 2, and shall investigate here only the theoretical side of these questions.

Assume that we have a linear homogeneous differential equation in which one of the coefficients a_i (we may just as well consider a differential equation with constant coefficients) undergoes a discontinuity of the first kind at $t = t_1$; in other words, for $t = t_1 - 0$ the value of a_i is a_i' and for $t = t_1 + 0$, it will be a_i'' with $a_i' \neq a_i''$. Clearly for $t < t_1$ we have one differential equation with certain constant coefficients and, for $t > t_1$, another one. In other words, for $t = t_1$ *the differential equation changes.*

Starting from this point it is possible to work out a further extension of the theory, which is useful here.

Andronov was probably the first to call attention to a rather special fact which seemed in 1937 to be a paradox but which is now completely explained.

Consider a system of two linear differential equations of the form (Andronov and Chaikin [6])

$$\ddot{x} + 2h\dot{x} + \omega_0^2 x = \begin{cases} \omega_0^2 & \text{for } \dot{x} > 0 \\ 0 & \text{for } \dot{x} < 0 \end{cases} \qquad 0 < h \leqslant 1 \qquad (1.15)$$

The change of the two equations occurs at the points when $\dot{x} = 0$. It is noted that these differential equations represent an oscillatory damped system whose trajectories are logarithmic spirals converging to a focal point, since the characteristic equation has two complex conjugate roots with negative real parts (Sec. 1.2). Physically these equations represent a damped oscillatory motion.

It should be noted, however, that the feature of interest here is that the focal points of the two equations—one for $\dot{x} > 0$ and the other for $\dot{x} < 0$—are displaced by the distance OO', as seen in Fig. 1.8, which shows for the sake of clarity the corresponding radii vectors r_i (for the upper arc AMB) and r_i' (for the lower arc BNA).

On the arcs themselves there is a continuous dissipation of energy, which is evidenced by the gradual decrease of energy when the representative point moves on the logarithmic arcs in the direction of the arrows.   It is recalled that

$$r = \sqrt{x^2 + y^2} = \sqrt{x^2 + \dot{x}^2}$$

in the phase plane may be regarded as $\sqrt{E}$, E being the *total* energy stored in the oscillation up to a certain constant factor and with a

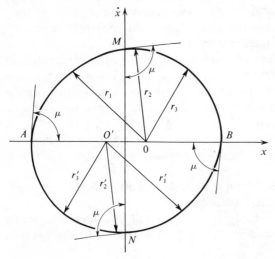

Fig. 1.8

proper normalization.   The interesting feature of this phenomenon occurs at the points A and B, as will be shown now (Minorsky [15]).

It is known that the logarithmic spiral is characterized by the constancy of the angle μ between the radius vector and the tangent. On the other hand, the two arcs AMB and BNA belong to the *same* spiral; these arcs are merely symmetrically situated with respect to the middle point between the two focal points O and O'.   In view of this the constant angle μ is maintained not only for all points of the arcs but also at the points A and B at which the two arcs join.   Thus the tangent (i.e., the first derivative) along the arcs is continuous everywhere including the points A and B.

Let us investigate now the situation in the second order, that is, in the *curvature* of these arcs.   It is recalled that the radius of curvature R for a logarithmic spiral is given by the formula $R = \sqrt{r^2 + r'^2}$, where $r' = dr/d\theta$, θ being the polar angle.   As for $h \ll 1$, and near the points A and B in which we are interested, r'^2 can be neglected in comparison with r^2, and the preceding formula becomes simply: $R \cong r$.

When the representative point moving along the arcs crosses the point B (the same argument holds obviously for A), shortly *before* the point B the radius of curvature is $r_1 = OB$, and, shortly after it, it is $O'B$. Thus, on traversing the point B, the radius of curvature undergoes a discontinuity: $\Delta R = O'B - OB$; this, at the same time, is a discontinuity in the radius vector r (since $r \cong R$ at this point). Since Δr means at the same time the sudden jump in energy (an impulse), we reach thus the important conclusion that $\Delta R = \Delta r = \Delta \sqrt{E}$.

In other words, the phenomenon will occur in the way in which it is represented in Fig. 1.8 (that is, with a continuously varying tangent) if, and only if, at the nonanalytic points A and B there are provided discontinuous inputs of energy $\Delta E = (\Delta R)^2$ adequate for closing the curve $AMBNA$. We use the term "nonanalytic points" A and B in the sense that although the first derivative (the tangent) is continuous, the second derivative (the curvature, or the radius of curvature) is discontinuous.

This establishes the condition for *closing* the curve. However, the physical phenomenon occurs in a different order. That is, given two impulses of magnitude, say ΔE, acting on a system represented by a linear dissipative differential equation [the left-hand side of Eq. (1.15)] the phenomenon will start from small amplitudes (i.e., small distance AB) in its initial stage.

During this initial period the energy input by the impulses will be *greater* than the dissipation, since the arcs AMB and BNA are yet small; in this transient stage the above-described picture of what happens in the stationary state is not yet reached, and the discontinuity will exist not only in the second order but also in the first order. As the result of this the amplitude (that is, the semilength PB or PA) will grow until it reaches a value at which the dissipation of energy on larger arcs will be just equal to the impulsive energy inputs taking place during each half-period of the process.

When this equality between the integrated continuous dissipation and the impulsive energy inputs is reached, the steady-state condition will be established in the manner previously described; that is, the closed trajectory will have a continuous tangent everywhere (including the nonanalytic points A and B).

The discontinuities will take place only in the second order, that is, *in the curvature* of the trajectory at the points A and B at which the impulsive actions occur. The argument remains the same if one starts from larger arcs than those which correspond to the stationary state; in such a case the dissipation will be greater than the impulsive inputs, and the arcs will shrink until a value is reached for which the continuous dissipation will be just equal to the impulsive input of energy.

This phenomenon is of exactly the same nature as that taking place in a clock.   A clock is a mechanism consisting of two component parts: a torsional pendulum representing a dissipative system describable by the differential equation (1.15) and the escapement mechanism delivering properly timed impulses of a constant value.   The phase portrait of a clock is shown in Fig. 1.9.   Starting from a point A there is a logarithmic spiral AMB representing the trajectory of the torsional pendulum.   At the point B the escapement mechanism delivers an impulse BA which compensates for the energy lost in the dissipation.

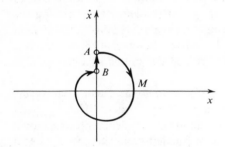

Fig. 1.9

If BA is just equal to the continuous loss of energy of the pendulum, the curve $AMBNA$ becomes closed and the phenomenon acquires a periodic character.

If, initially, the logarithmic arc is larger (smaller) than that corresponding to the stationary state, the arcs will shrink (grow) until the stationary arc is reached for which the continuous dissipation of energy is just exactly equal to the discontinuous energy input by the escapement mechanism.

The fact that in this case the energy input occurs only once per cycle does not change anything in the physical nature of the phenomenon; the only difference is that the discontinuity here occurs in the first order instead of the second order, as in the previously mentioned case (Fig. 1.8).

These phenomena are similar in all respects to the classical (analytical) limit cycles (Sec. 1.2); the only difference is that here they are *nonanalytic limit cycles*.

The idea of considering a limit cycle from the point of view of the balance of energies (dissipated and brought from outside) is apparently due to Liénard [14] in the analysis of his differential equation. However in Liénard's case this was merely an alternative (physical) interpretation of the results obtained analytically, since everything is analytical in his case.

In nonanalytic phenomena, which characterize the oscillatory behavior of nonlinear control systems, this approach—through the energy relations—is the only one available, since the analysis fails at the nonanalytic points.

We have considered this question in some detail, since in nonlinear control theory the understanding of these "nonanalytic" phenomena is of fundamental importance. As was mentioned already, modern control systems are full of "quasidiscontinuities" of this nature in their various links, and it is not surprising that even the most perfect linear control system (at least from the point of view of its designer) frequently exhibits a nonlinear feature—in the form of self-sustained oscillations. In accordance with our postulate, such systems are definitely *nonlinear*, but in this case the nonlinearities are of a *nonanalytic* nature.

1.6 CONCLUSIONS

We have attempted in this chapter to present a few fundamental points in the theory of nonlinear control systems before entering into their detailed study. The simplest way to do this is through a comparative study of what is known from the classical nonlinear theory of oscillations and what appears in the new approaches dealing with nonlinear control systems.

Although there are a number of points in common between the two theories, the differences are probably not less important than these similarities. In fact, in spite of the full knowledge of the nonlinear theory of oscillations, one feels somewhat "lost" when confronted with apparent paradoxes, such as the one which we have tried to analyze in the preceding section.

However, once the essence of these new extensions is understood, the matter does not present any further difficulty.

The problem of stability does not present any difficulty either, since it makes use of a mathematical tool—the second method of Liapounov—which was known for many years (1892) but was adapted for use in solving problems in nonlinear control theory only recently (around 1945).

REFERENCES

Theory of differential equations

1. Bieberbach, L.: "Differenzialgleichungen," Springer-Verlag OHG, Berlin; E. L. Ince, "Ordinary Differential Equations," Longmans, Green, & Co., Inc., New York, 1927.
2. Coddington, E. A., and N. Levinson: "Theory of Ordinary Differential Equations," McGraw-Hill Book Company, New York, 1955.
3. Lefschetz, S.: "Differential Equations (Geometric Theory)," Interscience Publishers, Inc., New York, 1957.
4. Poincaré, H.: "Oeuvres," vol. 1, Gauthier-Villars, Paris, 1928; Sur les courbes définies par une équation différentielle, *J. Math.*, Paris, vol. 7, 1881, and vol. 8, 1882.
5. *a)* Sansone, G., and R. Conti: "Nonlinear Differential Equations," Pergamon Press, New York, 1964.
b) Reissig, R., Sansone, G., Conti, R.: "Nichtlineare Differential gleichingen Höherer Ordnung," Gremonese, Roma, 1969.

Theory of oscillations

6. Andronov, A. A., and S. E. Chaikin: "Theory of Oscillations," U.S.S.R., 1937 (in Russian); English translation by S. Lefschetz, Princeton University Press, Princeton, N.J., 1949.
7. Cesari, L.: "Asymptotic Behavior and Stability," Springer-Verlag OHG, Berlin, 1959.
8. Den Hartog, J. P.: "Mechanical Vibrations," McGraw-Hill Book Company, New York, 1940.
9. Minorsky, N.: "Introduction to Non-linear Mechanics," J. W. Edwards, Publishers, Incorporated, Ann Arbor, Michigan, 1947; 2d ed. called "Nonlinear Oscillations," D. Van Nostrand Company, Inc., Princeton, N.J., 1962.
10. Stoker, I. I.: "Nonlinear Vibration Theory," Interscience Publishers, Inc., New York, 1950.
11. "Studies in Non-linear Vibrations," New York University Institute of Mathematics, 1946.

Theory of approximations

12. Bogoliubov, N. N., and Y. A. Mitropolsky: "Asymptotic Methods in the Theory of Non-Linear Differential Equations," Moscow, 1958.
13. Krylov, N. M., and N. N. Bogoliubov: "Introduction to Nonlinear Mechanics," Kiev, 1937 (in Russian); free English translation by S. Lefschetz, Princeton University Press, Princeton, N.J., 1943.

General

14. Liénard, A.: *Rev. Gen. Elec.*, vol. 23, 1928.
15. Minorsky, N.: *Compt. Rend. Acad. Sci. Paris*, page 1347, Sept. 10, 1962.
16. Poincaré, H.: *Acta Math.*, vol 7.
17. Poincaré, H.: "Les Methodes Nouvelles de la Mécanique Céleste," vol. 1, Gauthier-Villars, Paris, 1892.

CHAPTER TWO
NONLINEARITIES
IN CONTROL SYSTEMS

2.1 IDEALIZATIONS

In Chap. 1 we investigated the fundamental differences between the nonlinear theory of oscillations and nonlinear control theory. In the former the functions involved are continuous with at least two continuous derivatives; in the latter some of the derivatives are discontinuous. This is primarily true of the second derivative, as was shown in Sec. 1.5, but is also often true of the first derivative.

These assumptions result from the *idealizations* used in the representation of nonlinear characteristics. Consider, for instance, the simplest possible case of a contact shunting a resistor carrying current (Fig. 2.1). If a relay is closed at $t = t_0$ and thus shunts the resistor,

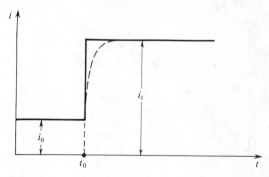

Fig. 2.1

the current will jump from the value i_0 to a large value i_1. This is obviously an idealization, since the closing is not instantaneous (on the scale of milliseconds, or possibly, microseconds). Further, even in a perfect inductionless circuit there is always a small residual inductance, which accounts for the form of the broken-line current shown in Fig. 2.1. (The idealized case is represented by the solid line.) It is, however, convenient to use such idealizations in speaking about isolated parts of a system (in this case a relay), that is, when no other associated circuit is being considered.

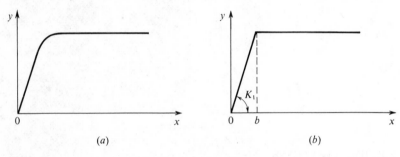

(a)   (b)

Fig. 2.2

Idealization can be used in all similar problems. Thus, for instance, the nonlinear characteristic shown in Fig. 2.2a by the solid line is idealized by the corresponding idealized characteristic of Fig. 2.2b, and so on.

This amounts to replacing the real nonlinear characteristic by a polygon of "broken lines." For each of these linear segments (Fig. 2.3), such as OB, BC, etc., a simple linear differential equation holds, but this introduces particular points such as $B, C, \ldots$ in Fig. 2.3,

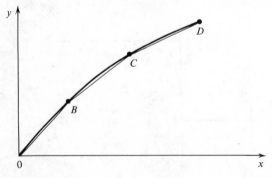

Fig. 2.3

which accounts for the difficulties of interpretation discussed in Sec. 1.5.

Although idealizations of this kind are used for *local* interpretations of the process under study, they can also be used over a period of time. For instance, if the real phenomenon being studied is *periodic*, an idealized description can still be used to establish the feature discussed above.

The advantage of using such idealizations lies in the simplification thus afforded. If one avoids using idealizations, the problem becomes more difficult, and the results are no more significant.

A classical example of the successful use of idealization is offered by the van der Pol equation

$$\ddot{x} + \mu(x^2 - 1)\dot{x} + x = 0$$

when the parameter μ is not small. There are two methods of approaching this equation. In one of them idealization is used; this leads to a simple picture of the *discontinuous theory of relaxation oscillations*. In the other, where no idealization is used, and a small arc (an arc with a large curvature, that is, with a small radius of curvature) is treated as an analytic arc, calculations become exceedingly complicated. It becomes necessary to use the asymptotic expansions, and the difficulty lies in "joining" these expansions with the regular analytic expansions (Taylor's series) in the neighboring regions (Minorsky [1, Chap. 30]).

Thus, it seems to be much simpler to treat a *bad analyticity* as no analyticity at all (assuming discontinuous derivatives) than to stick to an analytical treatment of such a problem. It is necessary, however, to keep in mind that a sequence of linear stretches in this approach always results *in the nonlinearization of the process as a whole*.

The above is an outline of some methods which have been particularly successful in the theory of nonlinear controls. These methods are known today under the generic name of *piecewise linear methods* and are discussed in detail in Chap. 8.

2.2 SOME TYPICAL NONLINEARITIES

The most frequently encountered nonlinearities are those involved in relays; Fig. 2.4 shows some examples: Fig. 2.4*a* shows an *ideal relay;* Fig. 2.4*b* shows a relay that has a *dead zone* (between $-b$ and $+b$) but does not have any hysteresis; 2.4*d* depicts a typical nonlinearity in which both hysteresis (between b and mb; $0 \leqslant m \leqslant 1$) and a dead zone (between $-mb$ and $+mb$) are present; 2.4a is a rather special form in which the hysteresis is symmetrical with respect to the origin.   The various characteristics may be considered as certain nonlinear functions of the variable x (e.g., current in the relay coil).

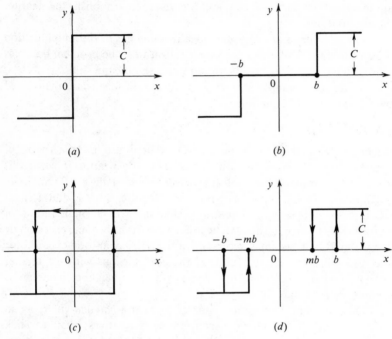

Fig. 2.4

One can imagine a number of other nonlinear characteristics (we shall encounter some of them later), but the concept of the idealization is always the same.   It consists of replacing the actual nonlinear characteristics (with "sharp corners") around the points shown by small circles in Fig. 2.4a and by broken lines in Fig. 2.4b.

The idealized effect of the saturation is indicated in Fig. 2.2; this particular characteristic can be supplemented by a "dead spot" (zone of unsensitivity), such as that shown in Fig. 2.4b and 2.4d.   In the saturation process an additional parameter generally occurs.   This measures the *slope* of the characteristic (see Fig. 2.5b).   It has the physical significance of an *amplification factor*.   Finally, one can also use an idealized representation of the hysteresis characteristic shown in Fig. 2.5.   Here part (a) shows the actual characteristic and (b) shows the idealized one.

In all these examples an additional parameter c—the magnitude of the discontinuous jump—is encountered.

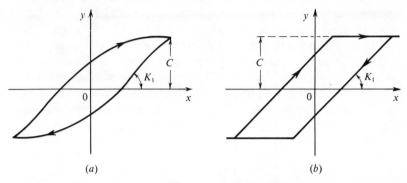

(a)   (b)

Fig. 2.5

The various cases described above can be represented by a nonlinear function which has the following forms:[1]

1. Ideal characteristic (Fig. 2.4a)

$$y = \Phi_1(x) = k_p \operatorname{sign} x \tag{2.1a}$$

2. Hysteresis (no dead zone) (Fig. 2.4c)

$$y = \Phi_2(x) = \begin{cases} k_p \operatorname{sign}(x - b) & \text{for } \dot{x} > 0 \\ k_p \operatorname{sign}(x + b) & \text{for } \dot{x} < 0 \end{cases} \tag{2.1b}$$

3. Dead zone only (Fig. 2.4b)

$$y = \Phi_3(x) = \frac{k_p}{2} [\operatorname{sign}(x - b) + \operatorname{sign}(x + b)] \tag{2.1c}$$

4. Hysteresis and dead zone (Fig. 2.4d)

$$y = \Phi_4(x) = \begin{cases} \dfrac{k_p}{2} [\operatorname{sign}(x - b) + \operatorname{sign}(x + mb)] & \text{for } \dot{x} > 0 \\[2mm] \dfrac{k_p}{2} [\operatorname{sign}(x - b) + \operatorname{sign}(x - mb)] & \text{for } \dot{x} < 0 \\[2mm] & 0 < m < 1 \end{cases} \tag{2.1d}$$

where $\dot{x} > 0$ ($\dot{x} < 0$) means motion to the right (left) on the diagram.

[1] For more details see Chap. 6. In formulas (2.1), taken from Tsypkin's book [3], the symbol k_p stands for C used in Figs. 2.4 and 2.5.

As is well known, a relay releases its action (closing or opening) when the corresponding critical threshold is reached; these thresholds are satisfied by expressions (2.1).   Since the output k_p is the same, the difference among the four cases lies in the determination of the instants at which these actions are released; this depends on x; $\dot{x}$ appears as a parameter which merely specifies the *direction* in which the process varies and is of importance only for the hysteresis feature; for characteristics with dead zones only, the *direction* of the process is not significant.

Another nonlinearity frequently encountered in control systems is "backlash" or "lost motion" (Fig. 2.6).   There are two distinct stages

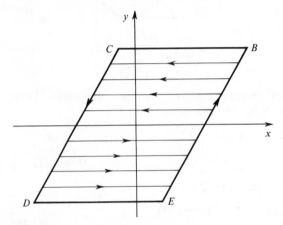

Fig. 2.6

of this phenomenon: the first occurs when the lost motion is traversed; and the second occurs after it has been traversed.   It is clear that during the first phase the load on the prime mover (e.g., servo-mechanism) is smaller than it is during the second phase.

Here we have the same situation as that described above; the process is described by *two differential equations*, one specifying the first phase and the other, the second phase.

The nonlinear characteristic of backlash is shown in Fig. 2.6. Two parallel straight lines DC and EB are separated by the distance $2b$ along the x axis, b being the half-width of the lost motion.   It is seen that when the backlash has been taken out (for $\dot{x} > 0$) and the representative point is at E, the motion continues along EB; if at a certain point B the sign of $\dot{x}$ reverses, the differential equation changes. The no-load trajectory BC will occur until the backlash is taken out again at C, after which another differential equation of motion (corresponding to the load) will begin along CD.   In this way the differential equations replace each other at all points of the straight lines EB and CD, which may be regarded as loci of nonanalytic points in the above-defined sense.

This nonlinear function $y = F(x)$ can be specified in this case by the following relations:

$$y = x - b \quad \text{for } \dot{y} > 0$$

$$y = x + b \quad \text{for } \dot{y} < 0 \tag{2.2}$$

$$\dot{y} = 0 \quad \text{and} \quad y = \text{const} \quad \text{for } |x - y| < b$$

There are a number of other typical nonlinearities which we shall encounter later; some of them consist of combinations of such simple nonlinearities as those which have been just described.

Finally, at times *several* nonlinearities may exist in a control system, and it is necessary to investigate their resultant effect on the system.

Not all these problems have been explored, but the material that has been investigated so far is sufficiently important to be significant for a large number of control systems.

2.3 PRESENCE OF NONLINEARITIES IN VARIOUS LINKS OF CONTROL SYSTEMS

The next question is: What is the behavior of a link (or "block") of a control system under the effect of some nonlinearity? It is well known from elementary linear theory that there are three important types of such links, which at the same time characterize the *transfer functions*. The latter can be defined as the solution of the differential equation of the link when a unit voltage (or force) is applied to the input of the link at rest. The three principal types are: (1) aperiodic link; (2) oscillatory link; and (3) integrating link.

1. The *aperiodic link* characterizes a differential equation of the first order and may be characterized, for instance, by the behavior of an electric relay-control circuit to which one applies suddenly a constant input voltage. Omitting this elementary calculation, this reduces to the differential equation of the form

$$T\dot{x}_2 + x_2 = kx_1 \tag{2.3}$$

in which x_1 is the constant unit input voltage and x_2 is the output voltage. If $\dot{x}_2$ is replaced by px, $p = d/dt$, the preceding equation is usually written as

$$Tpx_2 + x_2 = Kx_1 \qquad (2.3a)$$

T being the time constant, which gives the transfer function

$$W(p) = \frac{k}{Tp+1} = \frac{x_2}{x_1} \qquad (2.4)$$

2. In a similar manner one determines the transfer function of the *oscillatory link:*

$$W(p) = \frac{k}{T^2p^2 + 2\xi Tp + 1} = \frac{x_2}{x_1} \qquad (2.5)$$

ξ being the damping coefficient.

3. Finally, the *integrating link* always appears when the *speed* is controlled (instead of the angle, for instance); this corresponds to the basic relation

$$\dot{x}_2 = px_2 = kx_1 \qquad (2.6)$$

or, written differently,

$$x_2 = k \int_0^t x_1 \, dt \qquad (2.6a)$$

For the unit function at the input, $x_1 = 1$. This gives

$$x_2 = h(t) = kt \qquad (2.7)$$

From (2.6) it follows that the transfer function of the integrating link is

$$W(p) = \frac{k}{p} \qquad (2.8)$$

To summarize, if one calls the *characteristic operator* $d(p)$ the denominator of the transfer function $W(p)$ for these three typical cases, one has

1. $d(p) = Tp + 1$

2. $d(p) = T^2p^2 + 2\xi Tp + 1 \qquad (2.9)$

3. $d(p) = p$

These fundamentals having been recalled, we shall consider a few examples with reference to Fig. 2.7, in which $f_1(t)$ is the control signal which is reproduced as x_4 at the output of the system. $f_2(t)$ may be some additional external action (e.g., a certain vibration which is used for some purpose), and $f_3(t)$ may be, for example, a reaction caused by the load.

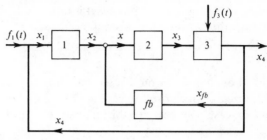

Fig. 2.7

Assuming that case 1 is an aperiodic link (or block), one gets, from the transfer function expression,

$$(T_1 p + 1)x_2 = k_1 x_1 \tag{2.10}$$

The "error" signal at the input will be

$$x_1 = f_1(t) - x_4 \tag{2.11}$$

We assume that link 2 is a nonlinear one, and

$$x_3 = F(x) \tag{2.12}$$

Link 3 is linear (e.g., a servomotor), and the equation for it is

$$(T_2 p + 1)p x_4 = k_2 x_3 + f_3(t) \tag{2.13}$$

Finally if the feedback connection is "rigid," the equation is

$$x_{fb} = k_{fb} x_4 \tag{2.14}$$

where k_{fb} is a constant.

The essential nonlinear element in this scheme is link 2. If it is a relay, it controls the voltage between $+c$ and $-c$ which, in turn, changes the direction of current in servomotor 3.

It is seen that the input x to the relay has three components:

$$x = x_2 - x_{fb} + f_2(t) \tag{2.15}$$

If one assumes that the relay has an ideal characteristic (Fig. 2.4a), the expression

$$F(x) = c \text{ sign } x \tag{2.16}$$

is the explicit form of this nonlinear feature.

We are thus able to set up the equations of the control system; for the time being, however, there is a difficulty presented by the form of the nonlinear element in case 2. Assume that in addition to the situation described above in link 1, we must take into account the effect of saturation. If this effect is idealized by the nonlinear function $F_1(x_1)$, the equation for this link becomes

$$(T_1 p + 1)x_2 = F_1(x_1) \tag{2.17}$$

For this function $F_1(x_1)$ one has to take the corresponding idealized characteristic (e.g., Fig. 2.8 with or without the dead zone, as the case may be). In this manner the linear relations are replaced

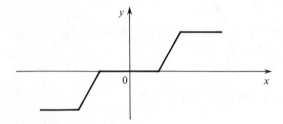

Fig. 2.8

by the corresponding nonlinear relations in the blocks in which these nonlinearities occur.

It should be recalled that each time one introduces an idealized nonlinear function $F(x)$, $F_1(x_1)$, ..., one introduces the *piecewise linear representation;* and there will be one differential equation for one segment of the "broken line," another for a different segment, and so on.

So far we have outlined the usual (linear) procedure for writing equations of subsequent links, treating the nonlinear terms in a formal manner. In order to be able to proceed further it will be necessary to *linearize* these nonlinear links. This process is discussed in detail in Chaps. 3 and 7.

Before leaving the question of different forms of nonlinearities, it is useful to mention some others that are occasionally encountered. For instance, the nonlinearity of the form shown in Fig. 2.2a can be approximated by the following function

$$F_1 = \begin{cases} k_1(1 - kx_1{}^2)x_1 & \text{for } |x_1| \leqslant b \\ c \text{ sign } x_1 & \text{for } |x_1| \geqslant b \end{cases} \tag{2.18}$$

where b and c are (approximately) the coordinates of the beginning of saturation. From the conditions $F_1 = c$ and $dF_1/dx_1 = 0$, for $x_1 = b$, one obtains the approximate relations [2]

$$k_1 = \frac{3c}{2b} \qquad k = \frac{1}{3b^2} \tag{2.19}$$

If the same nonlinearity is idealized by broken lines (Fig. 2.2b), one has:

$$F_1 = k_1 x_1 \qquad \text{for } |x_1| \leqslant b$$

and

$$F_1 = c \operatorname{sign} x \qquad \text{for } |x_1| \geqslant b, \ k = \frac{c}{b}$$

There is thus a difference in the determination of constants according to the idealization used.

If the input to block 1 in Fig. 2.7 is represented by a nonlinear function $F_1(x_1, px_1)$ of the variable x_1, as well as its derivative, instead of the linear relation

$$(T_1 p + 1)x_2 = k_1(1 + kp)x_1 \tag{2.20}$$

we have the nonlinear relation

$$(T_1 p + 1)x_2 = F_1(x_1, px_1) \tag{2.21}$$

One can also consider the case in which the time constant T_1, instead of being constant, is variable with either the input x_1 or the output x_2, that is:

$$T_1 = F_2(x_1) \qquad \text{or} \qquad T_1 = F_3(x_2) \tag{2.22}$$

In such cases, the equation for link 1 will be

$$F_2(x_1)px_2 + x_2 = k_1 x_1$$

or

$$F_3(x_2)px_2 + x_2 = k_1 x_1$$

instead of (2.10), which represents a linear link 1.

A nonlinearity may also be present in the output of the system. This often happens in certain followup systems, such as automatic pilots and similar servosystems, in which case link 3 (Fig. 2.7) is nonlinear; for instance

$$px_4 = F(x_3) \tag{2.23}$$

In such servomotors x_4 may be regarded as the angle of the servo (e.g., that displacing the rudder or a similar control element) and x_3 as the controlling factor (e.g., control voltage or displacement of an oil valve, etc.).   In such cases x_3 usually has a characteristic of the form shown in Fig. 2.8; this is true particularly for small values of x_3.   In the same link 3 there may be a time lag; in this case instead of (2.23) one would have

$$px_4 = F_r(x_3) = e^{(-\tau p)E(x)} \tag{2.24}$$

In such cases, in addition to being nonlinear, the problem becomes *transcendental*, since the system is governed by a *difference differential equation* instead of a differential equation (Minorsky [1, Chap. 21]).

To summarize, there is no end to complications if one tries to introduce more and more details into the original, relatively simple, idealization.

In view of this, with our present limited knowledge of these nonlinear effects in control systems, the practice is to consider the *principal* nonlinearities only and to omit a number of *secondary* ones by assuming the corresponding links in which they are located as linear.   We shall see that even with this simplified program, the matter is far from simple.

2.4   METHODS OF INVESTIGATION; STRUCTURAL SCHEMES

In Secs. 2.2 and 2.3 we have tried to introduce the necessary concepts gradually.   In Sec. 2.2 some nonlinearities encountered in control systems under the commonly used idealization (Sec. 2.1) were discussed.   In Sec. 2.3 we investigated the local effect of these nonlinearities in terms of the link in which they appear.   We shall now broaden this investigation by considering the whole control system. The primary object at this stage is to try and *lump* all that is linear together and to leave the essential nonlinear link separate in order to have, ultimately, a *reduced* linear link and a *nonlinear* one.

Much depends on the way in which this separation of what is linear from what is nonlinear is achieved; this means that a few somewhat arbitrary assumptions are unavoidable.   In the first place, a link which at first appears linear may, in reality, contain some nonlinearities.   Thus, in the expression

$$(T_1 p + 1)x_2 = F_1(x_1) \tag{2.25}$$

$(T_1 p + 1)$ is a linear operator, although the link itself is nonlinear because of the right-hand term $F_1(x_1)$; the same holds, of course, for all similar situations.   In view of this, the usual practice is to replace the essentially nonlinear terms, like $F_1(x_1)$, by another symbol, say y; thus (2.25) will be written as

$$(T_1p + 1)x_2 = y \tag{2.26}$$

In this form we can treat (2.26) formally as linear, on the condition that we later take into account that

$$y = F_1(x_1) \tag{2.27}$$

which ultimately makes it nonlinear.

This seemingly paradoxical process of assuming formally that something is linear which in reality is *not* linear is necessitated by the desire to find a result in more complicated situations in which *several* nonlinearities are involved.   Consider, for example, the following:

1. We say that nonlinear systems are of the *first class* if the *argument of the nonlinear function* contains only one variable (together with its derivative).   On the basis of this definition

$$y = F(x,px) \qquad \text{or} \qquad y = F(x) \tag{2.28}$$

is of the *first* class.

2. Nonlinear systems are of the *second class* if in the argument of the nonlinear function there are two (or more) variables connected to each other by *linear* differential equations.   Thus, for instance, if the nonlinear link is of the form

$$F_2(x_1)px_2 + x_2 = k_1x_1 \tag{2.29}$$

such a system belongs to the second class, even if there are no other nonlinearities involved, since $F_2(x_1)px_2$ is of the form

$$y = F(x_1,px_2) \tag{2.30}$$

This belongs to the second class according to the above classification, since x_1 and px_2 are related by the linear part of the system

$$Q_i(p)x_1 = R_i(p)x_2 + S_2(p)f_1(t) + S_2(p)f_2(t) \tag{2.31}$$

3. A nonlinear system is of the third class if the argument of the nonlinear function contains two (or more) variables related to each other by *nonlinear* differential equations.

The above classification (Popov and Pal'tov [2]) is tentative, and practically all that we know at present relates to nonlinearities of the first class.   On this basis nonlinear systems of the second class are those in which two variables connected to each other by a linear differential equation appear under the sign of a nonlinear function. Thus, for instance, if the system has a nonlinear link

$$F_3(x_2)px_2 + x_2 = k_1x_1 \tag{2.32}$$

and there are no other nonlinearities, it belongs to the first class, since the product $F_3(x_2)px_2$ is a nonlinear expression of the form $y = F(x,px)$ or $y = F(x)$. If, however, the nonlinear link is of the form

$$F_2(x_1)px_2 + x_2 = k_1x_1 \tag{2.33}$$

the system belongs to the second class, since the product $F_2(x_1)px_2$ is a nonlinear expression of the form

$$y = F(x_1,px_2) \tag{2.34}$$

in which x_1 and px_2 are connected by a linear differential equation, namely, by the differential equation of the linear part of the system. A nonlinear system

$$(T_1p + 1)x + bu^2x = k_1u \tag{2.35}$$

where

$$T_1 = \frac{2Jr\omega_0{}^2}{2c_2r\omega_0{}^2 + U_0{}^2} \qquad b = \frac{1}{2c_2r\omega_0{}^2 + U_0{}^2} \qquad k_1 = \frac{2U_0\omega_0}{2c_2r\omega_0{}^2 + U_0{}^2}$$

$$\tag{2.36}$$

is of the second class on the above basis. This system represents the differential equation of a two-phase induction motor written in the form

$$Ir\ddot{x} + (c_2r + \psi_1{}^2 + \psi_2{}^2)x = \psi_1\dot{\psi}_2 - \psi_2\dot{\psi}_1 \tag{2.37}$$

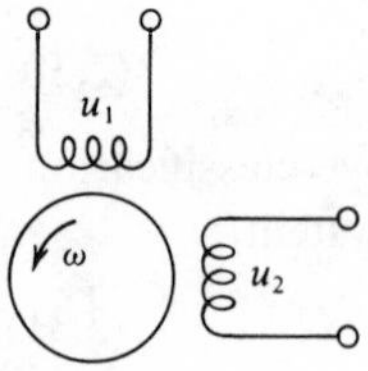

in which

$$\psi_1 = \int u_1 \, dt \qquad \psi_2 = \int u_2 \, dt$$

Fig. 2.9

where u_1, u_2 = voltages across each phase
r = ohmic resistance of rotor
c_2 = coefficient of linear friction
x = angular velocity of rotor

If one replaces $u_1 = U_0 \cos \omega_0 t$ and $u_2 = U_0 t \sin \omega_0 t$, after some simplifications of the results so obtained, one obtains expressions (2.35) and (2.36). In this case one has a nonlinearity u^2x in which the input (u) and the output (x) variables do not separate. In the presence of a linear and a dry friction of the form shown in Fig. 2.10 and of a linear restoring force, the differential equation of an oscillatory link has the form

$$mp^2x_2 + kpx_2 + c \operatorname{sign} px_2 + k_2x_2 = k_1x_1 \tag{2.38}$$

as long as

$$|k_1x_1 - k_2x_2 - mp^2x_2| \geqslant c \qquad \text{for } px_2 = 0 \tag{2.39}$$

If, however, for $px_2 = 0$ one has

$$|k_1x_1 - k_2x_2 - mp^2x_2| < c \tag{2.40}$$

(2.38) is correct only for $px_2 \neq 0$; if $px_2 = 0$, there is no motion.   It is noted that the equation of a nonlinear oscillation link with a dry

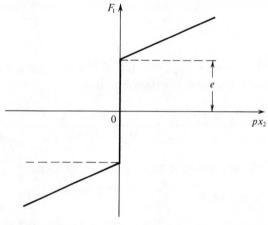

Fig. 2.10

friction F_1 is rather complicated in the general case.   In particular cases the matter is simplified.   Thus, for instance, if the mass is small (and can be neglected) the differential equation (2.38) with the same form of friction and the condition

$$-c \leqslant F_1 \leqslant +c \tag{2.41}$$

acquires the form

$$kpx_2 + c \operatorname{sign} px_2 = k_1x_1 \qquad \text{for } px_2 \neq 0 \tag{2.42}$$

$$-c < k_1x_1 < +c \qquad \text{for } px_2 = 0 \tag{2.43}$$

This is equivalent to the nonlinear function

$$px_2 = F_2(x_1) \tag{2.44}$$

shown in Fig. 2.11. This shows that the dry friction in this case manifests itself as a dead zone for the variables shown in Fig. 2.11.

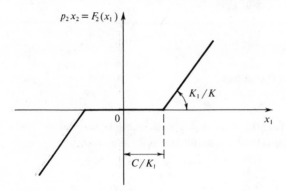

$p_2 x_2 = F_2(x_1)$

K_1/K

x_1

C/K_1

Fig. 2.11

If the mass is negligible but dry friction and restoring force are present, the differential equation becomes

$$c \operatorname{sign} px_2 + k_2 x_2 = k_1 x_1 \qquad \text{for } px_2 \neq 0 \tag{2.45}$$

$$(k_2 x_m - c) < k_1 x_1 < (k_2 x_m + c) \qquad \text{for } px_2 = 0 \tag{2.46}$$

This is equivalent to a nonlinear function

$$x_2 = F_3(x_1) \tag{2.47}$$

corresponding to the diagram of the lost motion (Fig. 2.6). To summarize, the complicated phenomenon of the dry friction can be simplified in the above particular cases (ideal relay characteristic, dead zone, and lost motion) and then analyzed without much difficulty.

2.5 DIFFERENTIAL EQUATIONS

Dealing with structural schemes, which was done in the preceding section, permits exploring local conditions of a control system only. Whenever it is desired to investigate the behavior of the system as a whole, one has to deal with differential equations which generally appear in the form

$$\dot{x}_i = X_i(x_1, \ldots, x_n) \qquad i = 1, \ldots, n \tag{2.48}$$

For linear systems it is more advantageous to write the differential system in the operational form

$$D_{i1}(p)x_1 + D_{i2}(p)x_2 + \cdots + D_{im}(p)x_m = f_i(t) \qquad i = 1, \ldots, m$$

$$(2.49)$$

where $D_{ij}(p)$ are operational polynomials and m is the number of links. Some of $D_{ij}(p)$ may be zeros. For instance, for control of an aircraft setting where $\psi = x_1$; $\beta = x_2$; $\delta = x_3$; $x = x_4$ [where ψ is the angle of deviation of aircraft from its course; β is the banking angle; δ is the rudder angle; and $x = (k_4 + k_5p + k_ep^2)\psi - k_{fb}\delta$] the operational polynomials are

$$D_{11}(p) = (T_1p + 1)p \qquad D_{12}(p) = k_2 \qquad D_{13}(p) = k_1 \qquad D_{14}(p) = 0$$

$$D_{21}(p) = -T_2p \qquad D_{22}(p) = T_2p + 1 \qquad D_{23}(p) = 0 \qquad D_{24}(p) = 0$$

$$D_{31}(p) = -(k_4 + k_5p + k_ep^2) \qquad D_{32}(p) = 0 \qquad D_{33}(p) = k_{fb}$$

$$D_{34}(p) = 1 \tag{2.50}$$

The differential system becomes

$$D_{11}(p)x_1 + \cdots + D_{1l}(p)x_l + \cdots + D_{1m}(p)x_m = f_1(t)$$

$$\cdots \cdots \cdots \cdots \cdots \cdots \cdots \cdots \cdots \cdots \cdots \cdots \cdots$$

$$D_{k1}(p)x_1 + \cdots + D_{kl}(p)x_l + F(x_l, px_l) + \cdots + D_{km}(p)x_m = f_k(t)$$

$$\cdots \cdots \cdots \cdots \cdots \cdots \cdots \cdots \cdots \cdots \cdots \cdots \cdots$$

$$D_{m1}(p)x_1 + \cdots + D_{ml}(p)x_l + \cdots + D_{mm}(p)x_m = f_m(t) \tag{2.51}$$

If the aircraft is controlled, to the above three linear equations is added

$$(T_3p + 1)p\delta = F(x) \tag{2.52}$$

for which (with the previous notations) one has

$$D_{41}(p) = 0 \qquad D_{42}(p) = 0 \qquad D_{43}(p) = (T_3p + 1)p \qquad D_{44}(p) = 0$$

$$f_4(t) = 0 \qquad f_3(t) = 0 \tag{2.53}$$

This equation is of the form:

$$y = F(px, x) \tag{2.54}$$

System (2.51) corresponds to the system $y = F(x, px)$ if one designates $x_l = x$ and $F(x_l, px_l) = y$, and has

$$Q(p) = \begin{vmatrix} D_{11}(p) & \cdots & D_{1l}(p) & \cdots & D_{1m}(p) \\ \cdots & \cdots & \cdots & \cdots & \cdots \\ D_{m1}(p) & \cdots & D_{ml}(p) & \cdots & D_{mm}(p) \end{vmatrix} \tag{2.55}$$

and $R(p)$ is the algebraic complement to the element (k,l) of this determinant; $S_1(p)$ and $S_2(p)$ are similar complements for the $(1,l)$ and $(2,l)$ elements if $f_1(t)$ and $f_2(t)$ are in the first and in the second lines.

2.6 NONLINEAR ELEMENTS; REDUCTION OF NONLINEARITIES

It is customary in investigations of nonlinear control systems to reduce the differential equation to the simplest possible form consisting of linear and nonlinear elements, as shown in Fig. 2.12. We shall frequently encounter systems reduced to this form. The process of such a reduction depends on the particular problem involved. Thus, for instance, in the case in which a control system's only nonlinearity is in the form of a relay, there is no difficulty in reducing the system to its component parts: L (linear) and NL (nonlinear). In more complicated cases the separation of linear and nonlinear parts may be less obvious. For example, certain linear elements such as $(T_1 p + 1)x_2$ in the equation $(T_1 p + 1)x_2 = F_1(x_1)$ or px_4 in the equation $px_4 = F(x_3)$, etc., may be present in the nonlinear link itself. Hence it seems logical to lump all linear parts of nonlinear elements together and to designate them as the *reduced linear part*.

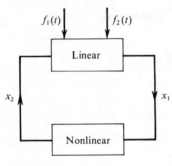

Fig. 2.12

This process is necessary when the nonlinearities enter in a rather complicated form. In what follows we shall not be concerned with this question, since in all problems treated below we shall consider a pure form of nonlinearity (Fig. 2.4a), which has no" linear residue," so to speak. In engineering problems involving quantitative relations the above-mentioned reduction may be of importance.

2.7 CONCLUDING REMARKS

In this chapter we have presented not only a description of different nonlinearities encountered in control systems, but have also touched the question of their classification. The latter subject is still somewhat unsettled, and, in fact, all examples given in Chap. 7 are concerned with the nonlinearities of the first class. We know hardly anything at all about the other forms. Further, it is probable that the nature of nonlinearities and their mutual relations are less important than the ultimate differential system in which they appear. One can argue that for that purpose one has to be able to simplify the differential system in order to have *only one nonlinearity in one of the equations.* (This situation is discussed in Chap. 8, in which even for nonlinearities of the first class calculations are long.) Thus the classification of nonlinearities discussed in Sec. 2.4 is, at least for the time being, provisional, since it is impossible to tell at present what the significance of it will be for the ultimate differential system and its solution.

Attempts have been made so far toward achievement of (1) approximate solutions and (2) exact solutions. The former are studied in Chap. 7 and the latter in Chap. 8. In neither case do we try to enlarge the concept of nonlinearities beyond the "first class," since even in the simplest possible case of an ideal relay characteristic (Fig. 2.4*a*), the problems are still too complicated if one tries to obtain quantitative relations. In fact, when dealing with approximate solutions, one can achieve certain results (in the engineering sense) only by simplifying some aspects of the mathematical procedure. This occasionally requires further justifications. When dealing with the exact solutions, one is faced with certain difficulties, transcendental by their nature, in the computational part of these problems. In spite of these difficulties, however, the progress made so far in these two directions has been considerable.

The most important feature of nonlinear characteristics reviewed in this chapter is their effect on the production of self-excited oscillations; this is, indeed, why nonlinear problems appeared in control theory. It is well known that in linear control systems self-excited oscillations are impossible (see Chap. 1) and, conversely, that the appearance of such oscillations always indicates that the system in question is nonlinear. This point will be emphasized in what follows.

REFERENCES

1. Minorsky, N.: "Nonlinear Oscillations," D. Van Nostrand Company, Inc., Princeton, N.J., 1962.

2. Popov, E. P., and I. P. Pal'tov: "Methods of Approximations in the Theory of Non-linear Control Systems," Fizmatgiz, Moscow, 1960.

3. Tsypkin, J. Z.: "Theory of Relay Control Systems," Gostehizdat, Moscow, 1955.

CHAPTER THREE
LINEARIZATION

3.1 INTRODUCTORY REMARKS

The terms "averaging" and "linearization" have generally the same meaning, although the second term is more frequently used.

The method of linearization originated more than a century ago, although in recent years the term has acquired special significance because of the requirements of the theory of oscillations.

In control theory, in which many types of nonlinearities occur, one must be careful in defining the process. In fact, the term "linearization" is somewhat indefinite, and for each new class of problems one has to select a definition which will answer the requirements of the particular case. For this reason it is useful to investigate the question of linearization thoroughly before attempting to outline its requirements in connection with control theory.

One of the early attempts to introduce the concept of linearization occured in mechanics and, in particular, in the theory of small motions. It is well known that given a certain nonlinear function $f(x)$, which might represent, for example, the potential energy of a system, one develops this function in Taylor's series about a certain value $x = x_0$ (generally, the position of equilibrium). If one assumes further that $f(x_0) = 0$, one obtains the expression

$$f(x) = (x - x_0)f'(x_0) \tag{3.1}$$

If oscillations are small and one assumes that $x_0 = 0$, the higher-order terms are negligible, and one can write

$$f(x) = k_0 x \tag{3.2}$$

In this fashion the nonlinear function $f(x)$ is "linearized" by the linear relation (3.2), in which $k_0 = \left(\dfrac{df}{dx}\right)_{x=0}$. This is permissible so long as x remains small; because of this, the method is called "the method of small motions." In this particular case the linearization is very simple and merely consists in replacing the curve $f(x)$ by the tangent at the origin. Clearly, however, the same problem can be linearized in different ways; for example, one can linearize either the nonlinear characteristic or the differential equation itself.

In electrical engineering, particularly in problems of energy dissipation, it is customary to introduce the so-called "root–mean–square" values. For an ohmic circuit, the loss of energy is ri^2, where r is constant. It is convenient therefore to use as a measure of an average heat dissipation per cycle the quantity $(1/T)\displaystyle\int_0^{2\pi} i^2 \, dt$, and the square root of this quantity is precisely the root mean square of the current.

If the question of the heat dissipation only is involved, one can deal with the root–mean-square value on the same basis that one uses it in dealing with direct current; this simplifies engineering calculations.

If the problem is nonlinear, resistance r is a certain function of i, and the problem becomes more complicated, since one has to calculate the average value $(1/T)\displaystyle\int_0^{2\pi} r(i)i^2 \, dt$, and so on.

These questions acquired considerable importance in the theory of nonlinear oscillations. In his early work van der Pol often used the method of averaging; however, only recently (around 1937) was the problem investigated in its generality (N. Krylov and N. Bogoliubov [3]).

The early theory of linearization developed by Krylov and Bogoliubov (1934) had no connection with the theory of control systems; only later were such connections perceived. In a later publication (1937) Krylov and Bogoliubov developed a method known as *equivalent linearization* (Sec. 3.3), which gave a convenient algorithm which was used in later studies of these questions; again, however, problems of control were not considered.

In the meantime there was a considerable amount of activity both in the United States and England on the "describing-function method," which became firmly entrenched in Anglo-American technical literature.

A very clear and extensive exposition of this method can be found in a treatise by J. G. Truxall [6], in which it is stated that

THE DESCRIBING FUNCTION ANALYSIS OF NONLINEAR SYSTEMS IS BASED ON THREE ASSUMPTIONS: (1) THERE IS ONLY ONE NONLINEAR ELEMENT; (2) THE OUTPUT OF THE NONLINEAR ELEMENT DEPENDS ONLY ON THE PRESENT VALUE AND PAST HISTORY OF THE INPUT; (3) IF THE INPUT TO THE NONLINEAR ELEMENT IS SINUSOIDAL, ONLY THE FUNDAMENTAL COMPONENT OF THE OUTPUT OF THIS ELEMENT CONTRIBUTES TO THE INPUT.

For the development of linearization in this chapter, point 3 is more important than the first two, since it led to the establishment of the present-day theory (describing-function method), which is based directly on the analytical foundation of the nonlinear theory. We shall not describe the existing describing-function methods, but shall outline an alternative method of a similar nature developed recently by Popov and Pal'tov [5]. The method is based on a unique operational algorithm of the first order, which leads to a systematic determination of the linearized parameters and in this manner permits attacking practically all existing problems—both analytical and nonanalytical (that is, those involving relays and similar discontinuous devices). The method is derived from the theory of equivalent linearization (Sec. 3.2), but its originality lies in the application of the abovementioned operational algorithm (Sec. 3.5) for obtaining the coefficients of linearization. This method has been applied to a great number of engineering problems (Sec. 3.6) and is probably the most developed method at present so far as applied problems are concerned.

One can state with little exaggeration that in this treatise (780 pages) the codification of nonlinear (and nonanalytic) control theory has been practically accomplished. It must be noted, however, that the progress that has resulted from use of this particular theory of linearization has been hindered somewhat by complications in the theory of stability (Sec. 3.7); unfortunately this is unavoidable, since, once linearization has been accomplished, the problem *formally becomes linear*. This necessitates the use of the Hurwitz criteria (valid only in linear problems). As a result, the *formal* treatment of stability on this basis does not eliminate what is *physically* nonlinear in the problem, and rather delicate readjustments must be made in the Hurwitzian criteria in order to adopt them for a process for which they were not originally intended. Apart from this difficulty connected with the question of stability, however, the "harmonic linearization" method turned out to be eminently successful and must be considered to be a very promising member of the family of methods that developed from the early work of Krylov and Bogoliubov.

One further method of linearization (Sec. 2.4) is due to Aiserman [1]; its purpose is somewhat different from that of the abovementioned theories of linearization (equivalent, describing-function, and harmonic), which deal mainly with the problem of synthesis, that is, the problem of expressing the ultimate problem in terms of its parameters in order to be able to modify the results according to the appropriate changes in the parameters.   The problem dealt with by Aiserman is almost the opposite of this; his method is to dispose of these parameters in order to make an essentially nonlinear problem (assuming, of course, *near-linearity*, as in all such problems) behave *as if it were linear*.   In other words, it is desired to construct a *linear model* of a given nonlinear system; that is, Aiserman's idea concerns a somewhat theoretical point: the investigation of the behavior of a nonlinear system by its linearized model.

In all problems of linearization the important feature is *its limits*. As long as one operates within the limits for which the linearized procedure has been established, conclusions remain correct; if this condition is disregarded, however, errors are inevitable.

To summarize, the procedure of linearization in all these studies is not something which is set up once and is therefore applicable under all conditions.   On the contrary, it is a tool which requires a good deal of common sense in selecting *what* is to be linearized and *how* it is to be linearized.   Once a definite policy has been adopted, it is necessary to comply with the accepted conditions; inconsistencies in procedure can introduce errors.

3.2 EQUIVALENT LINEARIZATION OF THE KRYLOV-BOGOLIUBOV THEORY

Although this subject is adequately covered in many textbooks (see for example, Bogoliubov and Mitropolsky [2]), we shall review here some essential points which will be needed later.   Consider a differential equation of the form

$$\ddot{x} + \omega^2 x + \mu f(x,\dot{x}) = 0 \qquad (3.3)$$

in which $f(x,\dot{x})$ is a continuous, generally nonlinear, function of x and $\dot{x}$ admitting at least two derivatives and μ is a small parameter.   From the general theory (of Poincaré) it is known that the solution of (3.3) is given in the form of a series

$$x(t) = x_0(t) + \mu x_1(t) + \cdots \qquad (3.4)$$

in which the nonwritten terms relate to the approximation of higher orders. We are interested only in the first approximation, for which the written terms in (3.4) are sufficient.

If $\mu = 0$, (3.3) reduces to a simple linear differential equation whose solution is

$$x = a \sin (\omega t + \varphi) \qquad \dot{x} = a\omega \cos (\omega t + \varphi) \qquad (3.5)$$

where a and φ are constants determined by the initial conditions.

The idea of this theory is to take (3.5) as the solution of (3.3) when $\mu \neq 0$ but is small. This means that a and φ must be considered as certain *unknown functions of t*, and conditions by which the solution (3.5) can be "fitted" to represent the solution of (3.3) must be introduced.

Since $a = a(t)$ and $\varphi = \varphi(t)$, it is clear that expression (3.5) for $\dot{x}$ can subsist if one has an additional condition

$$\dot{a} \sin (\omega t + \varphi) + a\dot{\varphi} \cos (\omega t + \varphi) = 0 \qquad (3.6)$$

Differentiating the second equation (3.5), taking into account the fact $a = a(t)$, $\varphi = \varphi(t)$, and substituting $x, \dot{x}$, and $\ddot{x}$ by these values into (3.3), one obtains

$$\dot{a}\omega \cos (\omega t + \varphi) - a\omega\dot{\varphi} \sin (\omega t + \varphi)$$
$$+ \mu f[a \sin (\omega t + \varphi), a\omega \cos (\omega t + \varphi)] = 0 \quad (3.7)$$

Solving (3.6) and (3.7) with respect to $\dot{a}$ and $\dot{\varphi}$, one gets

$$\dot{a} = - \frac{\mu}{\omega} f[a \sin (\omega t + \varphi), a\omega \cos (\omega t + \varphi)] \cos (\omega t + \varphi)$$

$$\qquad (3.8)$$

$$\dot{\varphi} = \frac{\mu}{a\omega} f[a \sin (\omega t + \varphi), a\omega \cos (\omega t + \varphi)] \sin (\omega t + \varphi)$$

Thus the original differential equation (3.3) has been replaced by system (3.8) of two first-order differential equations in terms of $a(t)$ and $\varphi(t)$. Since μ is a small parameter and the function f is finite, clearly $a(t)$ and $\varphi(t)$ are *slowly varying functions of t*.

On the other hand, the functions

$$f[a \sin (\omega t + \varphi), a\omega \cos (\omega t + \varphi)] \cos (\omega t + \varphi)$$

and

$$f[a \sin (\omega t + \varphi), a\omega \cos (\omega t + \varphi)] \sin (\omega t + \varphi)$$

(we write γ instead of $\omega t + \varphi$) can be expanded in Fourier series:

$$f(a \sin \gamma, a\omega \cos \gamma) \cos \gamma = K_0(a) + \sum_{n=1}^{\infty} [K_n(a) \cos n\gamma + L_n(a) \sin n\gamma]$$

$$(3.9)$$

$$f(a \sin \gamma, a\omega \cos \gamma) \sin \gamma = P_0(a) + \sum_{n=1}^{\infty} [P_n(a) \cos n\gamma + Q_n(a) \sin n\gamma]$$

where

$$K_0 = \frac{1}{2\pi} \int_0^{2\pi} f[a \sin (\omega t + \varphi), a\omega \cos (\omega t + \varphi)] \cos \gamma \, d\gamma$$

$$P_0 = \frac{1}{2\pi} \int_0^{2\pi} f[a \sin (\omega t + \varphi), a\omega \cos (\omega t + \varphi)] \sin \gamma \, d\gamma$$

$$K_n(a) = \frac{1}{\pi} \int_0^{2\pi} f[a \sin (\omega t + \varphi), a\omega \cos (\omega t + \varphi)] \cos \gamma \cos n\gamma \, d\gamma$$

$$L_n(a) = \frac{1}{\pi} \int_0^{2\pi} f[a \sin (\omega t + \varphi), a\omega \cos (\omega t + \varphi)] \cos \gamma \sin n\gamma \, d\gamma$$

$$P_n(a) = \frac{1}{\pi} \int_0^{2\pi} f[a \sin (\omega t + \varphi), a\omega \cos (\omega t + \varphi)] \sin \gamma \cos n\gamma \, d\gamma$$

$$Q_n(a) = \frac{1}{\pi} \int_0^{2\pi} f[a \sin (\omega t + \varphi), a\omega \cos (\omega t + \varphi)] \sin \gamma \sin n\gamma \, d\gamma$$

$$(3.10)$$

Equation (3.8) becomes then:

$$\dot{a} = -\frac{\mu}{\omega} K_0(a) - \frac{\mu}{\omega} \sum_{n=1}^{\infty} [K_n(a) \cos n\gamma + L_n(a) \sin n\gamma]$$

$$(3.11)$$

$$\dot{\varphi} = \frac{\mu}{a\omega} P_0(a) + \frac{\mu}{a\omega} \sum_{n=1}^{\infty} [P_n(a) \cos n\gamma + Q_n(a) \sin n\gamma]$$

It should be noted that the above trigonometric expansions *are not Fourier series* properly speaking because the coefficients K, L, P and Q are functions of $a(t)$. An important simplification is, however, evident at this point; that is, if the duration of the process is sufficiently long in comparison with the longest period T of the trigonometric functions, one can assume that during T the trigonometric functions remain *approximately constant*. In such a case, for each time interval the series becomes the ordinary Fourier series, and the integration between 0 and T wipes out all trigonometric terms except $K_0(a)$ and

$P_0(a)$, and (3.11) reduces to

$$\frac{a(t+T)-a(t)}{T} = -\frac{\mu}{\omega}K_0[a(t)] \qquad \frac{\varphi(t+T)-\varphi(t)}{T} = \frac{\mu}{a\omega}P_0[a(t)]$$

$$(3.12)$$

In view of the above remark concerning the duration of the process, we can change the time scale and consider T as ΔT and, ultimately, as dt at the limit. Passing to the continuous variable, (3.12) can be written as:

$$\dot{a} = -\frac{\mu}{\omega}K_0(a) \qquad \dot{\varphi} = \frac{\mu}{a\omega}P_0(a) \qquad (3.13)$$

Since, under the above assumption, we are now dealing with the Fourier series, one can determine $K_0(a)$ and $P_0(a)$ by the Fourier procedure. In this manner one obtains the famous Krylov-Bogoliubov formulas for the first approximation

$$\dot{a} = -\frac{\mu}{\omega}\frac{1}{2\pi}\int_0^{2\pi} f(a\sin\gamma, a\omega\cos\gamma)\cos\gamma\,d\gamma = \Phi(a)$$

$$(3.14)$$

$$\dot{\psi} = \Omega(a) = \omega + \frac{\mu}{a\omega}\frac{1}{2\pi}\int_0^{2\pi} f(a\sin\gamma, a\omega\cos\gamma)\sin\gamma\,d\gamma$$

A slight dissymmetry in the second equation of (3.14) is due to the desire of the authors to introduce the *linear* frequency ω so that the second term on the right of the second equation of (3.14) represents the nonlinear frequency correction $\Delta\omega$. In such a case $\dot{\psi} = \Omega(a) = \omega + \Delta\omega$ is the *nonlinear frequency*.

We note in passing that the smallness of μ in this theory is required for a different reason than in the theory of Poincaré; in the latter it is required merely by the consideration of convergence of the series (3.4). In the Krylov-Bogoliubov theory μ must be small, since only in such a case are a and φ *slowly varying* functions of t [Eqs. (3.8)], and this fact permits replacing the complicated equations (3.11) by the simpler ones (3.13).

3.3   EQUIVALENT LINEARIZATION

This question appears in the general theory of Krylov-Bogoliubov as a side issue, but, as it turns out, it is of importance for control theory. We shall follow the notations of the Krylov-Bogoliubov exposition, which generalizes a little the differential equation (3.1) in order to take into account physical problems; instead of (3.3), we shall consider the differential equation

$$m\ddot{x} + k\dot{x} + \mu f(x,\dot{x}) = 0 \tag{3.15}$$

which has obvious physical significance. The fundamental idea remains the same, only the harmonic solution is now taken as[1]

$$x = a \cos \psi \tag{3.15a}$$

The amplitude $a(t)$ and the "total phase" $\psi(t)$ satisfy the differential equation (3.14) of the first approximation. A slight change in the notations: $v^2 = k/m$, as well as (3.15), yields

$$\dot{a} = \frac{\mu}{2\pi v m} \int_0^{2\pi} f(a \cos \varphi, -av \sin \varphi) \sin \varphi \, d\varphi$$

and
$$\tag{3.16}$$

$$\dot{\psi} = \omega(a)$$

where $\omega(a)$, the nonlinear frequency, is obtained from an auxiliary equation

$$\Omega^2(a) = \gamma^2 + \frac{\mu}{\pi m a} \int_0^{2\pi} f(a \cos \varphi, -av \sin \varphi) \cos \varphi \, d\varphi \tag{3.17}$$

The idea of these changes is to be able to discuss the results from a physical point of view.

If one introduces two functions $\bar{\lambda}(a)$ and $\bar{k}(a)$ defined by the relations

$$\bar{\lambda}(a) = -\frac{\mu}{\pi a v} \int_0^{2\pi} f(a \cos \varphi, -av \sin \varphi) \sin \varphi \, d\varphi$$

$$\tag{3.18}$$

$$\bar{k}(a) = k + \frac{\mu}{\pi a} \int_0^{2\pi} f(a \cos \varphi, -av \sin \varphi) \cos \varphi \, d\varphi$$

Eqs. (3.16) become

$$\dot{a} = -\frac{\bar{\lambda}}{2m} a \qquad \dot{\psi} = \omega \qquad \omega = \sqrt{\frac{\bar{k}}{m}} \tag{3.19}$$

Differentiating (3.15a) and taking into account (3.19), one gets

$$\dot{x} = -a\omega \sin \psi - \frac{\bar{\lambda}}{2m} a \cos \psi \tag{3.20}$$

---

[1] The change from the form $x = a \sin \psi$ to $x = a \cos \psi$ is of no importance, but with (3.15) it will be more convenient to follow the Krylov-Bogoliubov exposition.

Differentiating once more, one obtains after some transformations

$$\ddot{x} = -\frac{\bar{k}}{m}x - \frac{\bar{\lambda}}{m}\dot{x} - \left(\frac{\bar{\lambda}}{m}\right)^2\frac{a}{2}\cos\psi + \frac{\bar{\lambda}}{2m}a^2\frac{\partial\omega}{\partial a}\sin\psi - \frac{1}{2m}a\frac{\partial\bar{\lambda}}{\partial a}\frac{\bar{\lambda}}{2m}x$$

$$(3.21)$$

If one takes into account (3.18), after some further transformations one obtains ultimately (Bogoliubov and Mitropolsky [2, Chap. 1])

$$m\ddot{x} + \bar{\lambda}\dot{x} + \bar{k}x \cong O(\mu^2) \qquad (3.22)$$

This shows that if one defines the *equivalent parameters* $\bar{\lambda}(a)$ and $\bar{k}(a)$ by (3.18), the *linearized* differential equation (3.22) will have *practically* [more correctly, up to the order $O(\mu^2)$] the same solution as the original nonlinear differential equation (3.15). Equation (3.22) holds for the first order only. From that point of view $O(\mu^2) \cong 0$. For higher-order approximations, see the Krylov-Bogoliubov treatise.

It may not be clear at first why an a priori definition of $\bar{\lambda}$ and $\bar{k}$ should lead to the result (3.22) or why this result is needed. The authors of this method explain the first question by showing that if these parameters $\bar{\lambda}$ and $\bar{k}$ are so defined, the two following physical principles are fulfilled: (1) the principle of the equivalent balance of energy; and (2) the principle of the harmonic balance. We shall see later that the second principle plays an important role in the elaboration of a new method of *harmonic linearization* (see Sec. 2.5).

There remains the second question: why is this procedure needed? We have replaced the nonlinear differential equation (3.15) by a "linearized" one (3.22). Yet there is no special difficulty in solving the nonlinear differential equation by approximations; moreover, the linearized equation (3.22) is not simpler than (3.15), since it also involves integrations [Eq. (3.18)]. Thus it is difficult at first to see why the linearized equation is preferable to the initial nonlinear one. In fact, the real advantage of the method of linearization appears in connection with control problems. In fact, in control systems most of the links (blocks) are linear. One, or possibly two, are nonlinear. Hence, if the nonlinear links are linearized, the *whole system can be treated as linear*; this is of considerable importance. We shall discuss these questions in more detail later, and shall mention here only the two "principles" illustrating definitions (3.18).

In the principle of the *equivalent balance of energy* one replaces the nonlinear force $F = \mu f(x,\dot{x})$ by the equivalent linear $F_L = \bar{k}_1 x + \bar{\lambda}\dot{x}$, $\bar{\lambda}$ and $\bar{k}$ being defined by (3.18). The physical argument runs as follows. If the two systems—the nonlinear and the linearized one—are equivalent, this means that the work of F and that of F_L per cycle must be the same; this results in the equation

$$\mu \int_0^T f(x,\dot{x})\dot{x}\, dt = \bar{\lambda} \int_0^T \dot{x}^2\, dt \qquad (3.23)$$

It is observed that the coefficient $\bar{k}$ does not enter into this expression, since the work of a conservative force per cycle is zero. Since the integrals are finite, $\bar{\lambda}$ must clearly be of the same order as μ, that is, small. On the other hand, in the first approximation $x = a \cos \psi$, $\dot{x} = -a\omega \sin \psi$ (where $\psi = \omega t + \psi_0$); one considers a and ψ as constant during one period $2\pi/\omega$. Substituting in the left side of (3.23) this "generating" (or zero-order) solution, one has

$$-\mu \int_0^{2\pi} f(a \cos \psi, -a\omega \sin \psi)a \sin \psi\, d\psi \qquad (3.24)$$

On the right-hand side one has

$$\bar{\lambda} = -\frac{\mu}{\pi a \omega} \int_0^{2\pi/\omega} a^2\omega^2 \sin^2 \psi\, d\psi = \bar{\lambda}a^2\omega \int_0^{2\pi} \sin^2 \psi\, d\psi = +\bar{\lambda}a^2\omega\pi$$
$$(3.25)$$

so that from (3.23) one obtains

$$\bar{\lambda} = -\frac{\mu}{\pi a \omega} \int_0^{2\pi} f(a \cos \psi, -a\omega \sin \psi) \sin \psi\, d\psi \qquad (3.26)$$

and this is precisely (3.18).

The second equivalent parameter $\bar{k}$ can be interpreted in a similar way by introducing the concept of "wattless power," but we shall not discuss this interpretation, since it is more or less obvious.

The second principle—that of the *harmonic balance*—is more important, and we shall encounter it later in connection with the method of *harmonic linearization* (Sec. 3.5). The beginning of the argument is the same as in the principle of the balance of energy. One has two forces: the nonlinear $F = \mu f(x,\dot{x})$ and the equivalent linear: $F_L = \bar{\lambda}\dot{x} + \bar{k}x$. We consider the harmonic oscillation: $x = a \cos \psi$, $\psi = \omega t + \theta$, which corresponds to the zero-order approximation (i.e., the so-called "generating solution"). With F_L this approximation will be: $F_L = F_{L0} \cos (\omega t + \theta_L)$. On the other hand, the nonlinear F is given by a Fourier series whose fundamental harmonic is $F = F_0 \cos (\omega t + \theta)$. If one *admits* the validity of the harmonic balance one has:

$$F_0 = F_{L0} \qquad \theta = \theta_L$$

By writing explicitly these relations, one can again establish the principle of linearization.   In fact

$$F_L = \bar{k}_1 a \cos (\omega t + \theta_L) - \omega \bar{\lambda} a \sin (\omega t + \theta_L) \tag{3.27}$$

On the other hand the fundamental harmonic of F is

$$F = \frac{\mu}{\pi} \left[\int_0^{2\pi} f(a \cos \tau, -a \sin \tau) \cos \tau \, d\tau \right] \cos (\omega t + \theta)$$

$$+ \frac{\mu}{\pi} \left[\int_0^{2\pi} f(a \cos \tau, -a \sin \tau) \sin \tau \, d\tau \right] \sin (\omega t + \theta) \tag{3.28}$$

If one equates the coefficients of $\cos (\omega t + \theta)$ and $\sin (\omega t + \theta)$ in (3.27) and (3.28), one again obtains expressions for $\bar{k}_1$ and $\bar{\lambda}$ in (3.18), since $\theta = \theta_L$.

It is seen that the two "principles"—that of equivalent balance of energy and that of harmonic balance—amount to the same thing, since the work done by higher harmonics during one cycle is zero.

It is worth noting that there are two different logical procedures in the contents of this section.   If Eqs. (3.18) are established by mathematical reasoning, one does not need any "principles" but only the *physical interpretations* of this reasoning. If, however, one is guided by a plausible physical reasoning (a "principle"), then (3.18) is merely a mathematical expression of this reasoning.

3.4   LINEARIZATION ACCORDING TO AISERMAN

The term "linearization" is considerably overtaxed.   In the preceding and in the following sections this term is used in the sense of the Krylov-Bogoliubov theory, that is, ultimately in the sense of differential equations.

In this section we shall indicate briefly another formulation of this concept suggested by Aiserman [1], which has rather a purely engineering significance and may be of interest in connection with interpretation of experimental data.

The argument develops as follows.   Suppose we have a control system of which we can obtain a number of characteristics.   Is it possible to assert that the system is *sufficiently linear*?   In fact, if one succeeds in demonstrating this, the matter is much simpler, since one can follow the standard linear theory without the complications arising from nonlinearities.   In fact, the analysis of this section permits establishing conditions for such an assertion.

One can argue of course (see Sec. 1.6) that if the system in question exhibits self-oscillations, then it is certainly nonlinear. To this argument one can clearly set up a counterargument by saying something like the following. The system may be nonlinear, but conditions may be such that self-excited oscillations have no chance to develop. One can thus be lost in arguments and counterarguments of this nature.

Aiserman tries to show that under *certain additional conditions* it is possible to give a criterion of linearity. This criterion is connected with experimental data which can be easily obtained, but it does not seem to be an easy matter to modify such data if the criterion is *not* fulfilled. For that reason the whole argument—namely, how to obtain a truly linear model of a given system—seems to have primarily an academic interest.

To summarize, the theory discussed above is to some extent going in the *opposite direction* from that we are trying to follow here. In other words, instead of studying the behavior of nonlinear systems, Aiserman tries to follow an argument which will produce linearity, and calls this *linearization*. His definition of this term is clearly different from that which we have just learned from the Krylov-Bogoliubov theory.

The starting point for our argument is the observation that in many elementary links of which control systems are composed, the laws are simple and reduce to differential equations of the form[1]

$$\dot{\Delta y} = \frac{d \, \Delta y}{dt} = F(\Delta x, \Delta y) \tag{3.29}$$

or

$$\ddot{\Delta y} = \frac{d^2 \, \Delta y}{dt^2} = F(\Delta x, \Delta y, \dot{\Delta y}) \tag{3.30}$$

In these notations x stands for input and y for output; that is, Δx is an increment of the input quantity and Δy an increment of the output quantity. For the time being we do not need to specify what these quantities are. The departures of Δ may be conveniently counted from the state of equilibrium of the system. One can also express these relations in a dimensionless form by dividing them by some reference values X^* and Y^*, but this is of no importance at present.

Aiserman gives a number of examples illustrating the form of the general relations (3.29) and (3.30). We shall discuss a few of these.

---

[1] We maintain the notations of Aiserman.

Case 1: equations of a motor   One can take $\Delta\omega$ as the generalized output coordinate—the departure of the angular speed from its set value.   Thus we assume here that $\Delta y = \Delta\omega$.   For the input coordinate one can take the position α of a regulating member.   In other words, we assume that $\Delta x = \Delta\alpha$ for Eqs. (3.29) and (3.30).

The equation of the motor will then be

$$I\,\dot{\Delta\omega} = \Delta M \qquad\qquad\qquad (3.31)$$

where $\dot{\Delta\omega} = d\,\Delta\omega/dt$

  I = reduced moment of inertia

  ΔM = difference between driving and resisting moments

Clearly, one can set $\Delta M = F(\Delta\omega,\Delta\alpha)$ and write (3.31) as

$$I\,\dot{\Delta y} = F(\Delta x,\Delta y) \qquad\qquad\qquad (3.32)$$

with $\dot{\Delta y} = d/dt\,\Delta y$.   The form of $F(\Delta y,\Delta x)$ depends on a number of parameters: the characteristic of the motor; that of the load; and perhaps some others.   In general, the function F is nonlinear.

Case 2: capacity phenomena   Many questions of physics reduce to differential equations of the first order, in which case they characterize what is called a "capacity phenomenon."   This has three properties: (1) that it maintains the state of equilibrium as the result of a balance between incoming and outgoing fluid of some kind; (2) there is only one "container" in which this fluid either increases or decreases; and finally (3) the increase or the decrease of the fluid depends on the input or output coordinate or on both.   Depending on the nature of the "fluid," the phenomena may be either of hydraulic, pneumatic, or thermal nature, etc., but what is essential is the fact that they always reduce to the same differential equation of the first order.   For instance, consider first the *thermal capacity*.   If θ is the temperature of a body, M its mass, C, the specific thermal capacity of a unit mass, and Q_1 and Q_2, the quantities of heat communicated to, or removed from, in unit time, one can write

$$Q_1 = Q_{10} + \Delta Q_1 \qquad Q_2 = Q_{20} + \Delta Q_2$$

where $Q_{10} = Q_{20}$ is the quantity of heat in the state of equilibrium; it is clear that

$$\Delta Q_1 - \Delta Q_2 = \Delta Q \qquad\qquad\qquad (3.33)$$

is the quantity of heat communicated to the body that serves for changing its temperature; we thus have, from the well-known theory,

$$MC\,d\theta = \Delta Q\,dt \qquad\qquad\qquad (3.34)$$

or, differentiating,

$$MC\dot{\theta} = \Delta Q \qquad (3.35)$$

or, finally,

$$\dot{\theta} = \frac{1}{MC}\Delta Q = \frac{1}{MC}F(\Delta x, \Delta y) \qquad (3.36)$$

in the notation of Eq. (3.32).

Exactly similar relations are obtained if the fluid is either air or liquid; in such cases the representation of pneumatic or hydraulic phenomena is the same as that done in connection with the thermal "fluid."

Case 3: fourpole Consider the scheme shown in Fig. 3.1. As the input coordinate one can take the voltage $U(t)$ and as output, the voltage $U_c(t)$ across the condenser C.

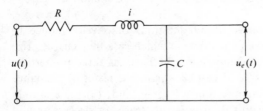

Fig. 3.1

In the transient state the voltage drops across the elements R, L, and C are, respectively, $R\,(dq/dt)$, $L\,(d^2q/dt^2)$, and $(1/c)q$, q being the quantity of electricity flowing through the circuit per unit time. Clearly,

$$q = CU_c \qquad (3.37)$$

so that the corresponding voltages will be: $RC\dot{U}_c$, $LC\ddot{U}_c$, and U_c, and since this must be equal to the output $U(t)$, one has the differential equation

$$LC\ddot{U}_c + RC\dot{U}_c + U_c = U(t) \qquad (3.38)$$

Considering U_c as Y (output) and $U(t)$ as X (input), (3.38) becomes

$$CL\ddot{Y} + CR\dot{Y} + Y = X \qquad (3.39)$$

These examples show that all such processes characterizing a perturbed equilibrium can be expressed in terms of the input-output relations.

There is, however, a difference between case 3 and the group of phenomena in cases 1 and 2. In fact, in case 3 all parameters are linear, so that the ultimate equation is also linear. In the phenomena indicated in cases 1 and 2 one is not certain about this; in fact all parameters have been lumped under the sign of the function F and one does not know a priori whether it is linear or not.

The argument begins at this point and consists in showing that F *is linear*. Take, for example, the general form (3.29) of the differential equation. One can write it as

$$\dot{Y} = b \, \Delta X - a_1 \, \Delta Y \tag{3.40}$$

This differential equation will be linear if

$$b = \left[\frac{\partial F}{\partial \Delta x} \right] \qquad -a_1 = \left[\frac{\partial F}{\partial \Delta y} \right]_0 \tag{3.41}$$

In a similar manner, for (3.30) we shall have

$$\ddot{\Delta Y} = b \, \Delta X - a_1 \, \Delta Y - a_2 \, \dot{\Delta Y} \tag{3.42}$$

in which b and $-a_1$ have the values (4.13) and a_2 is given by

$$-a_2 = \left[\frac{\partial F}{\partial \dot{\Delta Y}} \right]_0 \tag{3.43}$$

The subscript 0 in Eqs. (3.41) and (3.43) indicates that the derivatives are taken at the origin of coordinates, that is, after the differentiations, the quantities X_0 and Y_0 are replaced for X and Y. This origin may be taken at any point from which the increments Δ are counted. This presupposes that the derivatives (3.41) and (3.43) *exist*. If these derivatives do not exist, the element is called *nonlinearizable*.

In order to determine the numerical values of coefficients a and b, one must not only know the function F but be able to calculate X and Y from the experimental data. The calculation can be conducted as follows. Suppose that we have the nonlinear differential equation

$$\dot{\Delta Y} = \frac{1}{D} F(X, Y) \tag{3.44}$$

representing a control process. If the function F is known analytically, formula (3.41) permits calculating the coefficients b and $-a_1$ directly. If however F is given as a family of curves, the coefficients are calculated from the graphical procedure in the planes $[F(\Delta X, \Delta Y), \Delta Y]$ and $[F(\Delta x, \Delta Y), \Delta x]$. That is, for the chosen point (for which one wishes to know the behavior of the system) one draws tangents which give the necessary data for the determination of these coefficients.

We shall not enter into further details of this method of linearization, which is treated extensively in Aiserman [1]. As was mentioned
in the beginning of this section this method does not deal with the
linearization of *existing nonlinearities* (as do the methods of Secs. 3.3
and 3.5) but is directed toward a somewhat different end: given a
nonlinear differential equation, Aiserman wishes to modify its coefficients in such a manner that it *becomes linear* after the introduction of
these new coefficients. The author calls this particular procedure:
*the reduction of a given nonlinear differential equation to the corre-
sponding linear model.* Once such a model is calculated, one can
proceed further with purely linear methods of analysis.

3.5 HARMONIC LINEARIZATION

In a recent publication Popov and Pal'tov [5] developed a form of
linearization that they designate by the term "harmonic." This form
of linearization is similar to that of the Krylov-Bogoliubov theory
(Sec. 3.2) but has a different form. In the Krylov-Bogoliubov theory,
from which this method is derived, one always remains in the analytic
domain. The concept of linearization in that theory is defined through
the introduction of a certain linear (or, better, *linearized*) differential
equation whose solution differs from the solution of the given nonlinear differential equation by a quantity of a predetermined order of
smallness [Eq. (3.22)].

The Popov-Pal'tov (PP) theory considers a purely harmonic
signal acting on an essentially nonlinear element. In the initial argument a relay is used as representative of such an element, but later on
the argument is generalized for many other nonlinearities, such as
those mentioned in Chaps. 1 and 7.

This raises the question: what is the significance of the linearization
when the discontinuities are encountered? Let us consider first the
usual linearization that occurs when the phenomenon develops continuously, as is shown in Fig. 3.2. Here 3.2*a* and 3.2*b* differ only in
the form of the nonlinear characteristic; for (*a*) the concavity is turned
toward the *y* axis, and for (*b*) it is turned toward the *x* axis.

If the characteristic *F* is traversed back and forth between *O* and
C during, for instance, a periodic process, one will obviously have a
kind of "variable linearization" if we still wish to retain formula (3.2)
for each position of the representative point on the curve *F*. The
averaging will ultimately give a certain intermediate value for k
contained in the interval $k < k_{av} < k_m$ for the curve (*a*) and in the

interval $k > k_{av} > k_m$ for the curve (b), where k_{av} is a certain average value of k resulting from the variation of the variable x between the points O and C in Fig. 3.2.

From this remark it follows that the law of motion of the representative point R on the characteristic F and, in particular, the range of

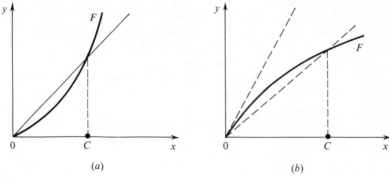

(a) (b)

Fig. 3.2

this motion, will have an effect on the determination of the coefficient entering into formula (3.2).

If, however, we wish to consider a discontinuous jump between O and C corresponding to some fixed abscissa $x = A$, the form of the curve between OC will obviously not play any role, and, if we wish to retain our previous definition, in this case we shall have simply

$$k = \frac{F(A)}{A} \tag{3.45}$$

since there is no averaging to be done and the point R jumps directly into the point C, for which the ordinate is $F(A)$ and the abscissa is simply $x = A$. This will be, therefore, the tangent of the angle between OC and the abscissa axis.

Assume now that x varies as a harmonic function of time

$$x = A \sin \Omega t \tag{3.46}$$

To this variation of x will correspond a more complicated variation of $y = F(x)$. If there were a linear relation between x and y, clearly in this case y would vary also in a simple manner and would be

$$y = A_e \sin \Omega t \tag{3.47}$$

where the subscript e designates this linear relation.

We introduce now the following definition. We shall call *equivalent linearization* a coefficient k_0 for which

$$k_0 = \frac{A_e}{A} \tag{3.48}$$

That is, the oscillations of the variable y for the linear case (3.47) must correspond *exactly to the first harmonic* of the nonlinear variable $y = F(x)$ when x varies harmonically. Clearly this idea is nothing but the *principle of harmonic balance* of the Krylov-Bogoliubov theory (Sec. 3.2) represented in a geometrical form.

Since x varies harmonically by our assumption, the nonlinear oscillation will be then $y = F(x) = F(A \sin \Omega t)$, which may be considered as a Fourier series. Since the characteristic is odd, there will be no terms with cosines, so that the first harmonic in which we are interested will be

$$y_1 = A_F \sin \Omega t = A_F \sin \psi \qquad \psi = \Omega t \tag{3.49}$$

where

$$A_F = \frac{1}{\pi} \int_0^{2\pi} F(A \sin \psi) \sin \psi \, d\psi \tag{3.50}$$

Since we wish to determine the equivalent linearization by the relation $A_e = A_F$, this yields the following expression for k_0:

$$k_0 = \frac{1}{\pi A} \int_0^{2\pi} F(A \sin \psi) \sin \psi \, d\psi \tag{3.51}$$

This is the fundamental formula in the theory of harmonic linearization.

As an example consider that the nonlinear characteristic $y = F(x)$ is of the form: $y = k_1 x + k_2 x^3$. Using (3.51), one obtains

$$k_0 = \frac{k_1}{\pi A} \int_0^{2\pi} A \sin^2 \psi \, d\psi + \frac{k_2}{\pi A} \int_0^{2\pi} A^3 \sin^4 \psi \, d\psi = k_1 + \tfrac{3}{4} k_2 A^2 \tag{3.52}$$

Hence the coefficient of linearization will be

$$y = k_0 x = (k_1 + \tfrac{3}{4} k_2 A^2) x \tag{3.53}$$

In this case the first harmonic of the nonlinear oscillation will be

$$y_1 = (k_1 + \tfrac{3}{4} k_2 A^2) A \sin \Omega t \tag{3.54}$$

The authors of this method use the term *harmonic linearization*. It should be emphasized once more that in this form the term *linearization* guarantees the *equality between the amplitudes of oscillation in the linear case and that of the first harmonic of the nonlinear case.*

The fact that one can represent, by this form of linearization, the quasidiscontinuous functions is its principal feature.   In order to show

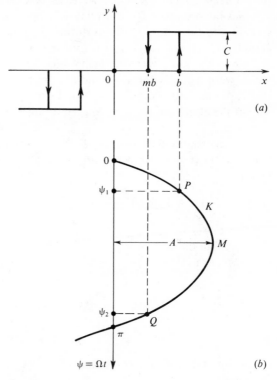

Fig. 3.3

this, we assume that the nonlinearity in question is a relay, whose characteristics are shown in Fig. 3.3*a*.

It is recalled that if x increases from zero ($\dot{x} > 0$), the relay remains open until the point $x = \bar{b}$ is reached, at which point the relay closes the contact, which gives rise to a discontinuous action $+C$ which remains constant for a further increase of x.   If, however, x decreases ($\dot{x} < 0$), the signal $+C$ remains until the variable x reaches the value $x = mb$ (where m is a fraction: $0 \leqslant m \leqslant 1$), at which point the relay opens the circuit; the signal $+C$ disappears at this point.   For $x < 0$ the phenomenon is symmetrical with respect to the origin O.

Suppose now that x varies harmonically ($x = A \sin \Omega t = A \sin \psi$; $\psi = \Omega t$), as shown in Fig. 3.3b. The time axis is directed downward as shown; it is assumed that the amplitude $A > b$. It is clear that the point b (Fig. 3.3a) is reached when the sinusoidal signal (3.3b) reaches the point P of the curve K, to which corresponds the instant ψ_1 (expressed in angular measure, since $\psi_1 = \Omega t_1$). After the maximum at the point M (when $x = A$), x decreases, and when it reaches the value $x = mb$ (at the point Q), the relay will open at the instant ψ_2 corresponding to the point Q. Thus during the interval $(0, \pi)$ the constant action $+C$ exists only during the time in which the representative point R follows the arc PMQ (the heavy line) of curve K, and this action will be zero when the arcs OP and $Q\pi$ are traversed.

It should be noted that if $A < b$, the relay will be open all the time, so that the above sequence of "on" and "off" of the signal occurs only if $A > b$.

In accordance with formula (3.51) the coefficient of the harmonic linearization (which, from now on, we shall designate by letter q) will be

$$q(A) = \frac{2}{\pi A} \int_{\psi_1}^{\psi_2} F(A \sin \psi) \sin \psi \, d\psi \qquad (3.55)$$

Since, in the case of a relay, $F(A \sin \psi) = c$, the preceding expression reduces to

$$q(A) = \frac{2}{\pi A} \int_{\psi_1}^{\psi_2} c \sin \psi \, d\psi = \frac{2c}{\pi A} (\cos \psi_1 - \cos \psi_2) \qquad (3.56)$$

If one takes into account the values of ψ_1 and ψ_2, this formula becomes

$$q(A) = \frac{2c}{\pi A} \left[\sqrt{1 - \frac{b^2}{A^2}} - \sqrt{1 - \frac{m^2 b^2}{A^2}} \right] \qquad A > b \qquad (3.57)$$

The coefficient $q(A)$ concerns the linearization of the nonlinear quantity associated with $\sin \psi$, but, as we shall see later, it is necessary to calculate also the linearized expression for the derivative term associated with $\cos \psi$. This expression [(cf. Eq. (3.55))] has the form

$$q'(A) = \frac{2}{\pi A} \int_{\psi}^{\psi_2} F(A \sin \psi) \cos \psi \, d\psi \qquad (3.58)$$

and a similar calculation yields

$$q'(A) = \frac{2}{\pi A} \int_{\psi_1}^{\psi_2} c \cos \psi \, d\psi = \frac{2c}{\pi A} \sin \psi \Big|_{\psi_1}^{\psi_2} = \frac{2c}{\pi A} (\sin \psi_2 - \sin \psi_1)$$

(3.59)

And again, with the explicit values of ψ_1 and ψ_2, one obtains

$$q'(A) = -\frac{2cb}{\pi A^2} (1 - m) \qquad A \geqslant b$$ (3.60)

The calculation of these coefficients $q(A)$ and $q'(A)$ will play an important role in Chap. 7.

As another more complicated example consider an idealized non-linear characteristic (Fig. 3.4) with a dead zone and saturation. Since

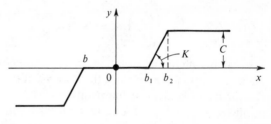

Fig. 3.4

the graphical construction [that is, the correlation of the (*a*) and the (*b*) parts of the diagram] is sufficiently clear from Fig. 3.3, we shall not reproduce it. The essential point is that for the averaging, one has to carry out three different integrations:

1. The dead zone in which $F = 0$ and which has the interval $(0,b_1)$ along the x axis
2. The linear characteristic with the slope k in the interval (b_1,b_2)
3. The constant value $F = c$ for $x > b_2$

We shall not reproduce this simple but long calculation; we write only the final result:

$$q(A) = \frac{2k}{\pi} (\psi_2 - \tfrac{1}{2} \sin 2\psi_2 - \psi_1 + \tfrac{1}{2} \sin 2\psi_2)$$

$$+ \frac{4kb_1}{\pi A} (\cos \psi_2 - \cos \psi_1) + \frac{4c}{\pi A} \cos \psi_2$$

A considerable number of coefficients $q(A)$ and $q'(A)$ for different nonlinear characteristics can be found in Popov and Pal'tov [5, Chap. 3].

3.6 FUNDAMENTALS OF THE METHOD OF HARMONIC LINEARIZATION

Once the linearizing coefficients q and q' are calculated, the nonlinear (and generally nonanalytic) function $F(x,\dot{x})$ can be written in the form

$$F(x,px) = qx + \frac{q'}{\Omega}px \qquad (3.61)$$

where $p = d/dt$. If there are some other linear expressions represented by differential polynomials $Q(p)$ and $R(p)$, the usual operational form of the differential equation is

$$\left[Q(p) + R(p)\left(q + \frac{q'}{\Omega}p \right) \right] x = 0 \qquad (3.62)$$

Many differential equations in control theory appear in this form. As was mentioned previously the Popov-Pal'tov theory is derived from the theory of equivalent linearization (Sec. 3.3). In view of this, the coefficients q and q' of this particular "harmonic" linearization are defined by the analogous formulas

$$q = \frac{1}{\pi A} \int_0^{2\pi} F(A \sin \psi, A\Omega \cos \psi) \sin \psi \, d\psi$$

$$\qquad (3.63)$$

$$q' = \frac{1}{\pi A} \int_0^{2\pi} F(A \sin \psi, A\Omega \cos \psi) \cos \psi \, d\psi$$

In the preceding section we gave a very simple example of the calculation of q and q', but many other forms of these coefficients are possible according to the different functions $F(x,px)$, and Eq. (3.63) gives the general algorithm for these calculations.

Note that the amplitude A and the frequency Ω generally enter into these calculations and may appear therefore in the expressions for q and q'. There are a number of procedures by which these problems can be solved; we shall discuss only two of them. The first method is convenient for investigations of a general character and is used for the great majority of problems. In it, the characteristic equation is first determined; in the operational form it is

$$Q(p) + R(p)\left(q + \frac{q'}{\Omega}p \right) = 0 \qquad (3.64)$$

Setting $p = j\Omega$ in (3.64) and separating the real and the imaginary parts, one can write it as

$$X(\Omega) + jY(\Omega) = 0 \tag{3.65}$$

where X and Y are polynomials in Ω; the coefficients of these polynomials may contain the amplitude. As the result of (3.65) one has two equations (algebraic or, possibly, transcendental)

$$X(A,\Omega) = 0 \qquad Y(A,\Omega) = 0 \tag{3.66}$$

Thus one has two equations for the determination of the two unknowns A and Ω. In general the amplitude A does not enter into these equations *directly* but appears only indirectly through $q(A)$ and $q'(A)$.

It is clear that the determination of amplitude and frequency is generally *possible*. However, assuming that this part of the problem is solved, it is necessary to show also that such a solution is *stable*, since only then can we say that such a solution exists *physically*.

The second method is based on the property of the Hurwitzian determinants that indicates a pair of purely imaginary roots if $\Delta_{n-1} = 0$. [See (3.72).] The remaining determinants are positive.

For instance, if one writes the characteristic equation as

$$a_0 p^n + a_1 p^{n-1} + \cdots + a_{n-1} p + a_n = 0 \tag{3.67}$$

and notes that the coefficients a_i may depend on A and Ω, then for the system of the fourth order ($n = 4$), $\Delta_{n-1} = 0$ in this case has the form

$$a_3(a_1 a_2 - a_0 a_3) - a_4 a_1^2 = 0 \tag{3.68}$$

whereas the second equation (3.66) yields

$$a_1 \Omega^2 = a_3 \tag{3.69}$$

For a system of the third order, instead of Eqs. (3.68) and (3.69) one has

$$a_1 a_2 - a_0 a_3 = 0 \qquad a_0 \Omega^2 = a_2 \tag{3.70}$$

This second method is useful when the coefficients a_i *do not depend on* Ω, that is, when the nonlinearity is of the form $F(x)$.

There are other methods by which one can determine the amplitude A and the frequency of the self-excited oscillation from the operational form (3.62). However, in all such problems the periodic solution established analytically *exists if it is stable*; it is necessary, therefore, to investigate how the question of stability can be studied in a linearized problem.

Before attempting to answer this question, it will be necessary to investigate first the significance of Hurwitz's criteria in linearized problems from the standpoint of stability.

3.7 SELF-EXCITATION IN TERMS OF THE HURWITZ CRITERIA

Once a differential equation (or a system of such equations) has been linearized, it is treated as linear so long as one remains within the limits for which the linearization holds. In view of this the question of stability must also be treated on the basis of Hurwitz's criteria applicable to linear differential equations.

We shall assume that Hurwitz's theorem and its applications are known and will limit ourselves only to its statement; our object is merely to show that in some special cases of linearization the use of this theorem results in certain difficulties.

Given a polynomial of degree

$$f(x) = a_0 + a_1 x + \cdots + a_n x^n \qquad \text{with } a_n \neq 0 \qquad (3.71)$$

with real coefficients, in many applications it is of interest to know the conditions under which all roots of (3.71) have negative real parts. Hurwitz's theorem states: *Eq.* (3.71) *has all roots with negative real parts if, and only if, the determinants*

$$\Delta_1 = a_1 \qquad \Delta_2 = \begin{vmatrix} a_1 & a_3 \\ a_0 & a_2 \end{vmatrix}$$

$$\Delta_3 = \begin{vmatrix} a_1 & a_3 & a_5 \\ a_0 & a_2 & a_4 \\ 0 & a_1 & a_3 \end{vmatrix} \cdots \Delta_n = \begin{vmatrix} a_1 & a_3 & \cdots & a_{2n-1} \\ a_0 & a_2 & \cdots & a_{2n-2} \\ \cdots & \cdots & \cdots & \cdots \\ 0 & 0 & \cdots & a_n \end{vmatrix} \qquad (3.72)$$

are positive, provided $a_0 > 0$. (The latter can always be done.)

If the polynomial (3.71) represents the characteristic equation of the corresponding differential equation, it is clear that the fulfillment of the Hurwitz condition means that the solution tends to zero as all exponentials vanish for $t \to \infty$, and this condition is called *stability*. If at least one Hurwitzian determinant is either negative or zero, the situation is different. Thus, for instance, if $f(x)$ has a pair of imaginary roots $+i\alpha$ and $-i\alpha$, one can write

$$f(x) = a_0 x^n + \cdots + a_n = (a_0 x^{n-2} + b_1 x^{n-3} + \cdots + b_{n-2})(x^2 + \alpha^2) \qquad (3.73)$$

with $a_0 > 0$; $\alpha \neq 0$ real; and $b_1, \ldots, b_{n-2}$ real.   If all roots

$$a_0 x^{n-2} + b_1 x^{n-3} + \cdots + b_{n-2} = 0 \tag{3.74}$$

have negative real parts, one has $\Delta_1 > 0$, $\Delta_{n-2} > 0$; since $f(x)$ has two imaginary roots ($+i\alpha$ and $-i\alpha$), it follows that $A_{n-1} = 0$ (K. Magnus [4]) and, therefore, $\Delta_n = 0$.

There is no difficulty in using Hurwitz's theorem in the linearized equations so long as the original differential equation does not have any feature of self-excitation.   However if there is self-excitation beginning with a certain value of parameter, this will manifest itself in that Δ_{n-1} will vanish; and if stability existed (on the basis of the Hurwitz theorem) when Δ_{n-1} was positive, this will not be the case after Δ_{n-1} becomes negative, having passed through the zero value.   In other words, using the terminology of linear differential equations (and particularly that of Hurwitz's theorem), the system is *stable* so long as all determinants (3.72) are positive and becomes *unstable* when Δ_{n-1} goes through zero and becomes negative thereafter.   This means that there appears a pair of purely imaginary roots which later becomes a pair of complex conjugate roots with *positive* real parts; this clearly represents the self-excitation of the system.

This brings us to a rather delicate point in the argument, which depends on whether this situation is interpreted from the point of view of the linear theory (i.e., the Hurwitz theorem) or from a nonlinear point of view.

If one analyzes more closely the statement of Hurwitz's theorem, one observes that the concept of stability (or instability) is identified with the decrease (or increase) of the solution.

It is known, however, from nonlinear theory that in the nonlinear domain there is an additional concept of *stationary motion* (of the *limit cycle* type).   But if a nonlinear differential equation has been linearized, it has to be treated as linear; that is, one has to use Hurwitz's theorem in connection with the analysis of stability.   If, in addition, the original nonlinear differential equation (the one which has been linearized) contains the feature of self-excitation, this feature is lost in the process of linearization.   One finds oneself thus in a vicious circle which is perhaps best illustrated by the picture of a dialog between two men, one of whom does not know the nonlinear theory and the other of whom does.

Let us consider the situation from the viewpoint of the former; in that case, if Δ_{n-1} (in Hurwitz's theorem) vanishes and becomes negative, we would say that the motion becomes *unstable* and the theorem does not give anything more.

However, from the standpoint of the man knowing the nonlinear theory, this initial instability is merely the *instability of the singular point*; and if besides this there is a stable *limit cycle* (with a sufficiently small amplitude), the system will still be "stable" but *at that limit cycle* instead of at the singular point (the state of rest).

Thus our imaginary dialog leads nowhere, since the "linear point of view" does not permit grasping a *purely nonlinear* manifestation, and, conversely, the nonlinear argument cannot be brought into play within a purely linear theoretical framework. Unfortunately, this complicated situation is an unavoidable side issue that results from linearization.

Attempts have been made, however, to find a way out of this deadlock, and the reasoning involved goes something like this. Suppose we have a limit cycle and try to think about what happens in terms of the

linear theory (which, as we know, is utterly inadequate in this case). Refer now to Fig. 3.5, in which C is a stable limit cycle and C' and C'' are two nonperiodic trajectories, C' unwinding itself from an unstable singular point and winding itself onto C from the *inside*, and C'' being a similar nonperiodic external trajectory (see Chap. 1).

Let us try to think "in a linear fashion." Clearly, if one considers only the external trajectories C'', their amplitudes *decrease*; hence, if this circumstance is to be analyzed in terms of Hurwitz's theorem, this theorem must be used in its *original* formulation. That is, all Hurwitzian determinants must be positive, since only in that case does one have a *decaying motion*, as it is wished to have for trajectories C''.

Fig. 3.5

The inner trajectories C', on the other hand, are *increasing* with time; this can also be accounted for if we agree that for this inner region the Hurwitzian theorem *does not hold*. It can however be "adjusted" assuming that for the inner trajectories $\Delta_{n-1} < 0$ (that is, zero for the cycle C itself).

We thus reach the following conclusions:

1. Once a nonlinear system has been linearized, the question of stability must be taken care of by the *linear criterion* (the Hurwitz theorem).

2. If, in addition, the system is of a self-excited type (i.e., it has a stable limit cycle), one has to express also that the Hurwitz theorem holds for the *external* trajectories and conversely *does not hold* for the internal ones.[1]

3.8 STABILITY IN LINEARIZED PROBLEMS

The explanation in the preceding section permits formulating the problem more precisely. If a pair of purely imaginary roots appears in the characteristic equation, the degree of the remaining part $L_1(p)$ will be less than the original characteristic equation $L(p)$ by two units, since

$$L_1(p) = \frac{L(p)}{(p^2 + \Omega^2)}$$

With respect to $L_1(p)$ the Hurwitz criteria will still be fulfilled.

It follows therefore that there will be a pair of roots either exactly on the imaginary axis (if $p = \pm i\Omega$) or very near it, so that the damping will also be very near the zero value.

With this physical argument one can attempt to formulate more precisely what was said in connection with Fig. 3.5.

If A is the amplitude of the periodic solution (for which $\Delta_{n-1} = 0$), a perturbation Δa in the amplitude must be related to the perturbation in Δ_{n-1} in the following manner.

For $\Delta a > 0$ all Hurwitzian determinants must be positive.

For $\Delta a < 0$ these determinants must continue to be positive except Δ_{n-1}, which becomes negative.

With this modification of the criterion, it will give exactly what is needed according to what was said in connection with Fig. 3.5.   One can present this conclusion in a more compact form, as follows.

For a stable periodic solution two conditions are required.

1.

$$\left(\frac{\partial \Delta_{n-1}}{\partial a}\right)^* > 0 \qquad \text{otherwise} \qquad \left(\frac{\partial \Delta_{n-1}}{\partial q}\frac{dq}{da} + \frac{\partial \Delta_{n-1}}{\partial q'}\frac{dq'}{da}\right)^* > 0 \quad (3.75)$$

where the asterisk means that the partial derivatives are to be taken at the point $a = A$.

---

[1] It is obvious that for an *unstable* cycle an opposite conclusion holds, namely that the Hurwitz theorem *holds for the internal* trajectories and does not hold for the external ones.

The sign of these expressions *must not change* when the cycle is crossed, since both Δ_{n-1} and a change their signs simultaneously when the limit cycle is crossed (i.e, when $\Delta_{n-1} = 0$).

2. All remaining Δ_i (with the exception of Δ_{n-1}) must remain positive. The only change in the physical condition of the system (the passage from energy absorption to the energy dissipation, or vice versa) is effected through the next-to-last Hurwitzian determinant Δ_{n-1}.

One can imagine that the adaptation of the Hurwitz criterion to the case of a hard self-excitation (Chap. 1) would be even more difficult, since in that case one would have to impose still more requirements on these criteria. As far as we know this has not been done to date, although conditions of a hard self-excitation in nonlinear control systems have been definitely ascertained in some cases.

To summarize, the simplification of the problem resulting from linearization is unfortunately accompanied by a complication that results from the necessity of using Hurwitz's linear criteria in a problem which by its very nature is nonlinear.

It must be remembered that all this applies only when there are autooscillations; if they are absent, these difficulties disappear.

3.9   EXAMPLE

Consider the scheme in Fig. 3.6 in which (2) is a nonlinear element, the other blocks being linear.   *FB* is feedback.   We have the following relations:

$$(T_1 p + 1)x_2 = -k_1 x_1 \qquad x_3 = F(x)$$
$$x = x_2 - k_{fb} x_1 \qquad (T_2 p + 1)p x_1 = k_2 x_3 \tag{3.76}$$

The nonlinear element can be linearized so that

$$F(x) = qx \tag{3.77}$$

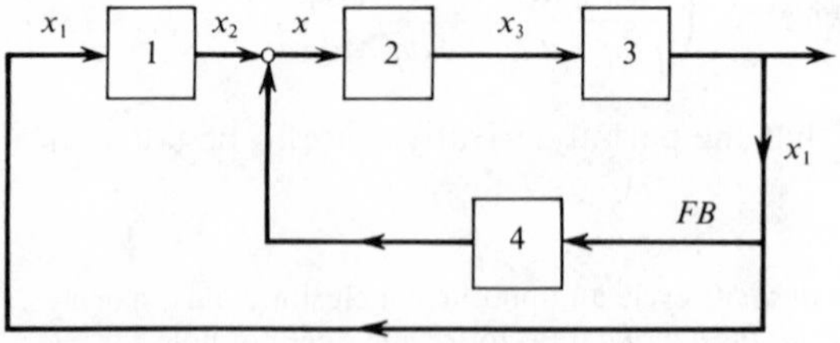

Fig. 3.6

q being the coefficient of linearization.   The characteristic equation obtains the following form

$$T_1 T_2 p^3 + (T_1 + T_2)p^2 + (1 + T_1 k_2 k_{fb} q)p + (k_1 + k_{fb})k_2 q = 0 \quad (3.78)$$

The characteristic equation of the open linear part is obtained for $q = 0$; that is:

$$T_1 T_2 p^3 + (T_1 + T_2)p^2 + p = 0 \tag{3.79}$$

It has a zero root but no imaginary roots, since by taking p as a factor in (3.78), one has a quadratic equation with positive coefficients. The Hurwitzian determinant Δ_{n-1} for (3.78) is

$$\Delta_{n-1} = (T_1 + T_2)(1 + T_1 k_2 k_{fb} q) - T_1 T_2 (k_1 + k_{fb})k_2 q \tag{3.80}$$

We note from the preceding theory that the limit of the zone of stability of the system is obtained when the minimum value of Δ_{n-1} (when q varies) is equated with zero, and, conversely, the limit of the zone of instability is given by equating with zero the maximum value of Δ_{n-1}. These extremal values are obtained from the formula

$$\frac{\partial \Delta_{n-1}}{\partial q} = 0 \tag{3.81}$$

If one applies this formula to (3.80) (after some intermediate calculations), one obtains

$$\frac{\partial \Delta_{n-1}}{\partial q} = T_1 k_2 (T_1 k_{fb} - T_2 k_1) = 0 \tag{3.82}$$

which gives the relation

$$k_{fb} = \frac{k_1 T_2}{T_1} \tag{3.83}$$

Thus the limit of stability is reached when the coefficient k_{fb} (of the feedback action) is in a definite relation with respect to other parameters.

We have insisted on this point in order to emphasize once more that, although owing to the linearization the differential equation has been reduced to a simple linear form easy to discuss, the question of stability, on the contrary, has been considerably complicated.

As will be seen in Chap. 4, the question of stability on a purely nonlinear basis is a relatively simple matter, since it reduces to ascertaining the sign of a derivative.   When one tries to do that in a *linearized* equation, the determination of zones (of stability or instability) always leads to long and tedious calculations such as those discussed here.

We have selected the simplest possible example that will illustrate this approach; a great variety of other examples can be found in Popov and Pal'tov [5].

3.10   ASYMMETRICAL OSCILLATIONS

The theory of harmonic linearization (Secs. 3.5 to 3.8) would not be complete if we did not explain its principal feature—the transmission of control action.   Previously we have been talking about the possibility of stable self-excited oscillations, in systems with discontinuous actions, such as those yielded by a relay inserted in an otherwise linear system.

All who have had experience with relay followup systems know that such systems always oscillate or "hunt" about their position of equilibrium.   It is clear that if there is no signal, these oscillations are *symmetrical* with respect to the point of equilibrium and that the coefficients of linearization [Eq. (3.63)] reflect this fact by their form.

Clearly, a more interesting question would be to investigate the way in which a *control action* can be realized in such a system.   The simplest example of this is that of a followup system, since we have just used this concept in explaining the equilibrium point when the control action is absent.

Consider, for example, a followup system intended for maintaining an auxiliary system in azimuthal alignment with a sensitive element G. The latter may be a gyro, and the auxiliary system may be the so-called "phantom system" F of a gyro compass.

In the past this was accomplished by means of a relay, which started the followup motor in opposite directions so as to obtain the average azimuthal alignment between the F and G elements.   Since, in reality, G is fixed in space, F has to be operated so that it will keep its alignment if the ship turns (in the *relative motion* it will appear that the gyro G turns and F has to follow it).   This may be accomplished by means of three contacts, two of them, say A and B, on the phantom system F and the third C, on the G element (the gyro).   If there is no ship's motion, the "hunting" is symmetrical; in fact, as soon as C comes in contact with A, the servomotor moves the system so that C comes in contact with B; from there it is thrown back on A, etc.   This results in a *symmetrical* oscillation (or hunt).

Suppose now that the ship is turning in the direction $A \rightarrow B$. Clearly to follow contact B, which is "running away," so to speak, contact C must remain on A a little longer than on B (because on B the impulse does not need to be so great, since the whole reference system has already moved from $A \rightarrow B$).

Thus *during the control action* the oscillation (which was symmetrical at no control) becomes *asymmetrical* with the control, and the amount of this asymmetry characterizes the transmission of the control signal.

The first conclusion is that the old coefficients q and q' of linearization are not sufficient to define the problem in this case. In fact, if one

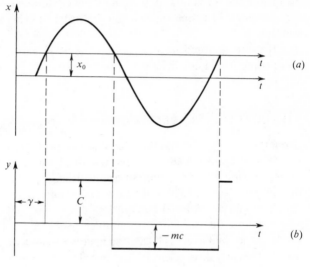

Fig. 3.7

wishes to use the procedure explained in connection with Fig. 3.3 for asymmetrical oscillations, it is necessary to displace the curve K by the amount x^0 which accounts for asymmetry (Fig. 3.7).

The oscillations x in the asymmetrical case will thus be of the form:

$$x = x^0 + x^* \tag{3.84}$$

where x^0 is the abovementioned shift of the abscissa axis (in the diagram) and x^* is the symmetrical component of oscillation which exists in all cases (whether x^0 exists or not).

By making an analogy with phenomena observed with regard to electrical oscillations, one can consider x^* as a "carrier oscillation" (of a relatively high frequency) and x^0 as a slowly varying signal accounting for the control action.

In view of this, in addition to Eqs. (3.63), which determine q and q' for the symmetrical oscillation x^*, it is necessary to add a third equation for the asymmetrical case:

$$F^0 = \frac{1}{2\pi} \int_0^{2\pi} F(x^0 + A \sin \psi,\ A\Omega \cos \psi)\ d\psi \tag{3.85}$$

which means that there is a constant term in the Fourier series represented by the function $F(x^0 + A \sin \psi, A\Omega \cos \psi)$. One thus has three equations

$$F^0 = F^0(x^0, A, \Omega) \qquad q = q(x^0, A, \Omega) \qquad q' = q'(x^0, A, \Omega) \qquad (3.86)$$

for the determination of the three quantities x^0, A, and Ω. The problem however is not simple, since the equations are nonlinear, and certain approximations are necessary in order to bring the problem to a solution.

It must be noted in passing that the asymmetrical problems have more complicated coefficients of linearization.

3.11 CONCLUDING REMARKS

From this survey it is seen that the object of linearization (or averaging) is not to establish a definite mathematical theorem but to indicate, rather, a wide range of different applications which can be carried out in different ways. These linearizations are used so that difficult problems can be replaced by simpler ones.

But how do we define a "simpler problem"? Here there is no definite rule, and everyone can use his own judgment.

In the early days of electricity, people were interested in the heating effects of a current in conductors, and after the discovery of Ohm's law, it was natural to think about "quadratic linearization." In this fashion the concept of the "root–mean-square value" appeared.

The method of "small motions" is another example of a kind of linearization; it works well if motions are, of course, "small."

However, all such pursuits acquired particular importance with the advent of nonlinear problems, and the contribution of Krylov and Bogoliubov was of great importance for modern trends. In fact, to linearize a nonlinear differential equation, according to the Krylov-Bogoliubov point of view, is to find a *linear* differential equation whose solution differs from that of the corresponding *nonlinear* differential equation by the prescribed amount of smallness. If this can be accomplished, then one can say (up to this approximation) that the two equations—the original nonlinear and the "linearized" (that is, linear) one—have (practically) the *same solution*. This in turn is considered to be the definition of linearization. However, on closer analysis, the situation is not so simple as it seems. Although the (practical) identity of solutions is a very strong mathematical argument, in some special cases there may be situations in which this is not yet sufficient. For example, in Secs. 3.7 and 3.8 it was shown that although the determination of the periodic solution is greatly facilitated by linearization, the question of the stability of this solution is rendered considerably more complicated.

There is another delicate point in all these questions, and that concerns the *range* for which linearization is effective; clearly, if one tries to go beyond a certain range, errors are inevitable. The method of harmonic linearization (Popov-Pal'tov) analyzed in Sec. 3.5 stresses this point particularly. This is illustrated in Fig. 3.3, in which part (*b*) provides the intervals (ψ_1,ψ_2), (ψ_2,ψ_3), . . . , in which the averaging is to be performed; if one of these intervals is "empty," it is simply omitted.

Unfortunately all that is gained by the accuracy with which the periodic solution is established is lost when stability is considered. In fact, instead of the straightforward procedure of determining the sign of the Eulerian derivative that will decide the question (Chap. 4), here one has to *force* the Hurwitzian criteria to do something which normally they are unable to do. This results in painstaking determination of zones of stability or instability by studying extrema of the next-to-last Hurwitzian determinant Δ_{n-1} (see Secs. 3.7 and 3.8).

All this indicates that linearization is not a panacea and must be used with a great deal of caution. At present, however, linearization has been used increasingly frequently in nonlinear problems in control theory. It is difficult to say at present whether this trend will persist or not. Much will depend on the progress of modern *discontinuous* theories (Chaps. 7 and 8); if these theories overcome their present difficulties, it is possible that linearization will lose its importance, at least to some extent, since these methods do not make use of it.

REFERENCES

1. Aiserman, M. A.: "Lectures of the Theory of Automatic Regulation," Fizmatgiz, Moscow, 1960.

2. Bogoliubov, N. N., and Y. A. Mitropolsky: "Asymptotic Methods in the Theory of Non-linear Oscillations," Moscow, 1958.

3. Krylov, N. M., and N. N. Bogoliubov: "Introduction to Non-linear Mechanics," Moscow, 1937.

4. Magnus, K.: *VDI-Forschungsh.*, no. 451, 1955; *Ingenieur Archiv.*, no. 5, 1956.

5. Popov, E. P., and I. P. Pal'tov: "Approximation Methods in the Theory of Non-linear Control Systems," Fizmatgiz, Moscow, 1960.

6. Truxall, J. G.: "Automatic Feedback Control System Synthesis," McGraw-Hill Book Company, New York, 1955.

CHAPTER FOUR
STABILITY
IN THE SENSE
OF LIAPOUNOV

4.1 INTRODUCTORY REMARKS: DEFINITION OF STABILITY

In Sec. 1.3 the method of the variational equations for the investigation of stability was outlined. This method was discovered independently by Poincaré [14] and by Liapounov [8], but since Poincaré's work was published a little earlier, the method is generally associated with the name of Poincaré. In Liapounov's work, the method is designated as the *first method*. Later on, Liapounov developed another method, which he called the *second method*; this forms the subject of this chapter and of Chap. 5.

The advantages of Liapounov's second method are: (1) it does not require any integration of the variational equations (generally a difficult and often impossible task); and (2) it gives the stability *in the large*, that is, either in a finite, or sometimes in the whole, region of the phase space. In the latter case stability is called *absolute* (or global) if it is asymptotic at the same time. The two basic advantages of Liapounov's second method make it particularly attractive for studies of stability in nonlinear control systems.

The second method has been known since 1892, but its application for control problems was not discovered until relatively recently (about 1944); this was because the difficulties in studies of stability in control problems were not understood until recently and because the work of Lur'e and Letov (Chap. 5) on this subject prepared the ground for systematic studies of these questions.

The material concerning this subject (particularly that from the U.S.S.R.) is so voluminous (Tsypkin [18]) that it is impossible to try to give a general picture of the efforts which have been made so far and which are still in progress. For that reason we give in this chapter only a few of the basic concepts of Liapounov's second method—those that are used in Chap. 5 in connection with control theory.

Quite recently the theory of stability was advanced by V. M. Popov [15] and [16]; he showed that certain concepts of linear theory (such as the so-called frequency characteristics) can be also used in nonlinear theory under certain conditions which are frequently encountered in applications. The most interesting feature of his discovery is the fact that this new concept of stability is closely related to Liapounov's second method. This was the situation toward the end of 1963, and for that reason, the subject cannot be considered closed; it is to be expected that these methods will come to the forefront in the near future. In this section we shall discuss Liapounov's basic definition of stability, and in Secs. 4.2 and 4.3, we shall outline a few fundamentals that we shall need to understand a more recent extension of these questions.

The formulation of Liapounov's theorem is given in Sec. 4.4, which covers the basic definition only and omits a number of ramifications which are particularly numerous in theorems concerning instability. In Sec. 4.5 some methods for the determination of Liapounov's function V are discussed, and Sec. 4.6 outlines some methods of approximations. Section 4.7 begins an outline of more recent trends, which concern the concept of *absolute stability*. Strictly speaking, this trend began with Lur'e's work [11], but a somewhat different approach was formulated later in the so-called "problem of Aiserman" [11]. It was shown that although for linear systems the method of Liapounov is straightforward (Sec. 4.7), for nonlinear problems the determination of the Liapounov function $V(x)$ is possible only under certain limitations (Sec. 4.8). Sections 4.9 and 4.10 concern the method of determining the V functions for linear systems by means of the so-called Liapounov operator Λ. For nonlinear functions (of the Lur'e-Aiserman class), synthetic determination of such functions is more difficult and requires the application of the so-called S procedure, which is discussed in Secs. 4.11 and 4.12.

Let us consider a dynamic system that is specified by the following system of differential equations

$$\dot{x}_i = X_i(x_1, \ldots, x_n) \qquad i = 1, \ldots, n \tag{4.1}$$

which can be conveniently written in the form

$$\dot{x} = X(x) \tag{4.2}$$

where $X(x)$ is a vector function of $x = (x_1, \ldots, x_n)$.

To integrate (4.1) or (4.2) means to determine the motion of the representative point R in the n space: $(x_1, \ldots, x_n) = (x)$.

The concept of the n space is purely formal but is convenient because most of the results of the two space (the phase plane) can be extended for the n space. It will be assumed that the functions X_i are continuous twice-differentiable functions of the indicated variables and that the fundamental theorems of existence and uniqueness of the solution hold. In this manner through each point x, that is $(x_1, \cdots, x_n)$, belonging to a certain domain Ω in which (4.1) or (4.2) holds, one and only one trajectory passes.

To integrate (4.1) or (4.2) means to determine the trajectory if certain initial conditions x_0 (or $x_{10}, \ldots, x_{n0}$) are given. Clearly by analogy with the two-dimensional cases the state of equilibrium (or a singular point of (4.1) or (4.2) is specified by the system of algebraic equations

$$X(x^*) = 0 \tag{4.3}$$

where x^* is a point of the n space. If one selects the origin at the point x^*, the preceding equation can be written as

$$X(0) = 0 \tag{4.4}$$

Very often $x^* = 0$ is referred to as the *trivial* (or zero) solution, and associated with the corresponding dynamics equation (4.4) [or rather *system* of equations (1.4)], it may be regarded as an equation of the *unperturbed motion*.

If we consider now a *perturbed motion*, clearly, instead of

$$x^* = 0 \qquad \text{or} \qquad x_{10}^* = x_{20}^* = \cdots = x_{n0}^* = 0$$

one must consider the differential equation, but the significance of x in that case will be different from the x in (4.1) and (4.2). More specifically, the new differential equation

$$\dot{x} = X(x) \tag{4.5}$$

will be the *variational equation*, since $(x) = (x_1, \ldots, x_n)$ are now the perturbations with this new choice of the origin:

$$x^* = 0$$

Starting from this point, one can give the following criteria of stability (Liapounov).

1. The unperturbed motion $X(0) = 0$ is called *stable* for $t = t_0$ with respect to the perturbations x if, for any positive number ϵ however small, one can determine another positive number $\eta(\epsilon)$ such that for all initial perturbations x_0 satisfying the set of conditions $|x_0| \leqslant \eta$ (where x_0 stands for $x_{10}, \ldots, x_{n0}$), the perturbed motion (4.5) satisfies the inequality

$$\|x(x_0,t_0,t)\| < \epsilon \qquad \text{for } t \geqslant t_0$$

2. The unperturbed motion $X(0) = 0$ is called *unstable* if there exists an ϵ such that for any η, however small, one can find x_0 satisfying the condition $|x_0| \leqslant \eta$, for which at least one inequality $|x(t)| < \epsilon$ is not fulfilled when $0 < t_1 < t$.

These conditions are nothing but the precise mathematical definition of a simple fact; that is, *stability exists if for a small initial motion the subsequent motion is also small. The instability is defined by the negation of this property.*

Very often it is preferable to use an alternative definition of a more dynamic character. The unperturbed motion (4.4) is called stable with respect to perturbations x if for any positive number A, however small, one can determine another number $\lambda(A)$ such that for all initial perturbations satisfying the condition

$$\sum_{k=1}^{n} x_{k0}^{2} \leqslant \lambda \tag{4.6}$$

the perturbed motion (1.5) satisfies the inequality

$$\sum_{k=1}^{n} x_{k}^{2}(t) < A \rightarrow \epsilon \tag{4.7}$$

for any $t > 0$.

The set of points satisfying (4.7) may be called "the A neighborhood" and that satisfying (4.6), "the ϵ neighborhood" (of the trivial solution).

The set (4.6) limits all initial conditions and the set (4.7) limits the development of the perturbed motion in the course of time.

A particular case in which

$$\lim_{t \to \infty} x_k = 0 \qquad k = 1, \ldots, n \tag{4.8}$$

gives the *asymptotic stability* of the perturbed motion.

4.2 LIAPOUNOV'S SECOND METHOD

The fundamental idea of Liapounov's second method is as follows. Instead of attacking the problem of stability on the basis of the variational equations, one tries to transform the differential equation to a form from which one can see directly (that is, without integration) whether its trajectory approaches the state of rest (the trivial solution) or not.

If one succeeds in showing that the trajectories enter a certain region Ω surrounding the position of equilibrium and never leave it, one can assert that the equilibrium (i.e., the unperturbed solution) is *stable*. If, moreover, one can show that the trajectory approaches the position of equilibrium for $t \to \infty$, the unperturbed solution is *asymptotically stable*.

The underlying idea of Liapounov's second method is an obvious, and simple, fact. If the initial motion is small and the subsequent motion is also small, the system is *stable*; if for small initial conditions the later motion is not small, the motion is *unstable*.

The factor that was introduced in the problem in order to obtain the abovementioned simple criterion of stability is a certain scalar function $V(x)$, where x, as previously, stands for $(x_1, x_2, \ldots, x_n)$. The function $V(x)$ has the following properties:

1. $V(x)$ is continuous together with its first derivatives in a certain open region Ω around the origin.
2. $V(0) = 0$.
3. Outside the origin (but always in Ω) $V(x)$ is positive.

This means that $V(x)$ is nonnegative and vanishes only at the origin, which is thus an isolated minimum. This defines $V(x)$ as a *positive definite function*. For instance, $V(x) = V(x_1,x_2,x_3) = x_1{}^2 + x_2{}^2 + x_3{}^2$ is a positive definite function, whereas the function $(x_1 + x_2)^2 + x_3{}^2$ is not, since apart from condition 2, it also vanishes when $x_1 = -x_2$, $x_3 = 0$.

It is useful to elaborate some geometrical concepts for the space of n dimensions in order to be able to use a geometrical language (LaSalle-Lefschetz [7]).

By analogy with the two-dimensional space E^2, in which a circle of center a, b and radius r is given by the equation

$$(x - a)^2 + (y - b)^2 = r^2 \tag{4.9}$$

one can extend the definition for the n space by defining the expression

$$(x_1 - a_1)^2 + (x_2 - a_2)^2 + \cdots + (x_n - a_n)^2 = r^2 \qquad (4.10)$$

as the $(n-1)$ sphere.

If $x - a$ is considered as a vector, Eq. (4.10) may be replaced by

$$\|x - a\| < r \qquad (4.11)$$

where a is the center of the spherical region and r is its radius. The spherical region will be denoted as $S(a,r)$; a set contained in $S(a,r)$ is bounded. The following are some definitions which permit specifying a certain number of basic sets in E^n.

1. REGION OF n SPACE is a point set U with two properties: (1) if C is a point of U, then $S(C,r)$ is entirely in U; (2) any two points C, D of U may be joined by an arc which is entirely in U.
2. SET U IS AN OPEN SET with the property that if a point C is in U, then a whole spherical region $S(C,r)$ for some r is also in U (i.e., property (1) holds but not necessarily property 2). Thus the interior of a square or any polygon in E^2 (the plane) is an open set of E^2.
3. THE CLOSED SET F is simply the outside of some open set U. Thus a straight line in any E^n and a plane in E^n are closed sets.
4. THE BOUNDARY BU OF AN OPEN SET U is the totality of the points C which are not in U but are such that every $S(C,r)$ contains points of U. BU is a closed set.
5. A COMPACT SET is a closed and bounded set. Thus, any bounded set together with its boundary is a compact set; for instance $S(C,r)$ plus its boundary is a compact set (called a *solid sphere*). Compact sets have a number of important properties, the following of which is needed. Let A be a compact set and $f(x)$ be a continuous (scalar) function on A. There can be found two numbers α and β such that $\alpha \leqslant f(x) \leqslant \beta$ for every point x of A. If $f(x)$ is positive at every point of A, then one can select α and β positive.

The following notation is used: (1) $A \cup B$ is a *union of sets A* and B or a set of elements contained in one or the other; (2) $A \cap B$ is an *intersection of A and B* or a set of elements contained in both; (3) the closure $\bar{A}$ is the closed set, which is the intersection of all closed sets containing A; it is the *smallest* closed set containing A.

It is assumed that in a certain open spherical region $\Omega: |x| < A$, the existence theorem for (4.2) holds (assuming the existence of continuous partial derivatives $\partial X_i/\partial x_j$). It is known from the general theory that in such a case through every point x of Ω one and only one trajectory passes. Designating by S^- the half-trajectory described by

$x(t)$ when $t \leqslant 0$, and by S^+ the other half-trajectory for $t \geqslant 0$, one can assert the following about the origin.

1. It is *stable* whenever for every $R < A$ there is an $r \leqslant R$ such that if a trajectory (motion) S^+ beginning at a point x^0 of $S(r)$ remains in $S(r)$ ever after [$S(r)$ being a sphere with its center at the origin and with radius r], a trajectory S^+ starting in $S(r)$ will never reach the boundary $H(R)$ of the sphere.

2. It is *asymptotically stable* if, in addition to being stable, the trajectory originating inside some $S(R_0)$, $R_0 > 0$, tends to the origin for $t \to \infty$.

3. It is *unstable* if (1) does not apply.

These definitions are easily interpreted in terms of the familiar properties of singular points; thus, for instance, stable foci or nodes belong to class 2; unstable ones, as well as saddle points, belong to class 3; and, finally, trajectories of conservative systems around centers belong to class 1.

4.3 EULERIAN DERIVATIVE, OR DERIVATIVE ALONG THE TRAJECTORY

In his studies of hydrodynamics Euler established a definition of a derivative that is particularly convenient for the study of conditions if one follows a line of flow. Consider a system

$$x_i(t) = X_i(x_1, x_2, \ldots, x_n) \tag{4.12}$$

in which X_i guarantees the existence and unicity of the solution; it is also assumed that the singular point exists at the origin. We also consider a positive definite function $V(x_1, \ldots, x_n)$. We call the Eulerian derivative of V the expression

$$\frac{dV}{dt} = \sum_{i=1}^{n} \frac{\partial V}{\partial x_i} \frac{dx_i}{dt} \tag{4.13}$$

in which $dx_i/dt = \dot{x}_i$ is substituted from (4.12), which gives

$$\dot{V} = \frac{dV}{dt} = \sum_{i=1}^{n} \frac{\partial V}{\partial x_i} X_i \tag{4.14}$$

Since the partial derivatives exist by assumption, (4.14) can also be written as

$$\dot{V} = \frac{dV}{dt} = X \operatorname{grad} V \tag{4.15}$$

The significance of $V(x_1, \ldots, x_n) = V(x)$ can be better understood in the two space (x,y) for $V(x,y)$ (see Fig. 4.1). Since V is positive definite, the surface $z = V(x,y)$ has the form shown, and it is clear that $V = z = c$, c being a positive constant, represents the section

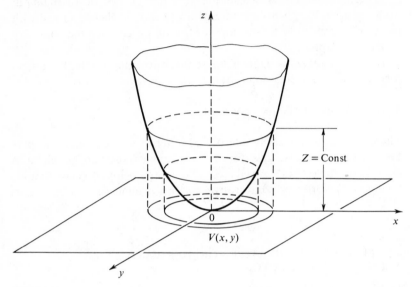

Fig. 4.1

of the surface V by the planes $z = c$. This gives in projection on the x, y plane a family of oval curves having c as parameter. The origin O is the innermost point of this family. The ovals represent at the same time certain levels on the V surface, and grad V has the significance of "steepness" (third dimension) between two adjoining ovals. If $\dot{V}$ is negative or zero in Ω neighborhood we call V *the function of Liapounov.*

4.4 LIAPOUNOV'S THEOREMS

Theorem 1 *Stability   If there exists in some neighborhood Ω of the origin a Liapounov function $V(x)$, the origin is stable.*

Theorem 2 *Asymptotic stability   If $-\dot{V}$ is also positive definite in Ω, then the stability is asymptotic.*

The geometrical idea of the proof for this theorem can be made in connection with Fig. 4.2, in which ovals $V(x,y)$ are shown by heavy lines and the spheres by dotted lines.   If $R < A$ and $H(R)$ is the sphere, one can find a constant c such that the oval $V(x,y) = c$ just comes inside $H(R)$.   One can also find a $r > 0$ such that $H(r)$ just comes inside $V(x,y) = c$.   Any trajectory S^+ originating at some point x^0 [the

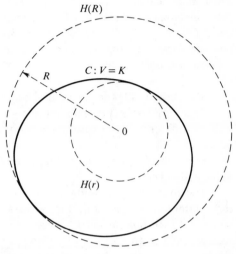

Fig. 4.2

interior of $H(r)$] has $V(x^0) < c$.   Since V is nonincreasing along trajectories x, the trajectory will never reach the oval c and, hence, will never reach $H(R)$.   Thus, any trajectory starting in $S(r)$ remains in $S(R)$, and this means *stability*.   Since V is positive and continuous in $H(R)$, it follows from the compactness of $H(R)$ that $V(x)$ has a positive minimum c on $H(R)$; that is, $V(x) \geqslant c$ on $H(R)$.   From the continuity of $V(x)$ and positive definiteness it follows that for r sufficiently small $V(x) < c$ in $S(r)$.   Thus Theorem 1 is proved.

Under Theorem 2, $V(x)$ decreases along S^+; since it cannot vanish anywhere except at the origin and since $-\dot{V}$ is also positive definite, the trajectory tends to the origin; this signifies *asymptotic stability*.

Theorem 3   *Instability   Let $V(x)$ be continuous, with continuous first partial derivatives in Ω, and let it vanish only at the origin.   If $\dot{V}$ is positive definite in Ω, then the origin is unstable.*

The argument for the proof is similar to that just given.

Theorem 4   *Under the same assumptions for V given in Theorem 2*

$$\dot{V} = \lambda V + V^*$$

where V^* is nonnegative in Ω and $\lambda > 0$; the origin is unstable.

Theorem 5   Četaev *theorem   If a region Ω_1 is inside Ω and V has the following properties: (1) $V(x)$ has continuous first partials in Ω; (2) $V(x)$ and $\dot{V}(x)$ are positive in Ω; (3) at the boundary points of Ω_1 inside Ω one has $V(x) = 0$; (4) the origin is a boundary point of Ω_1, then the origin is unstable.*

See Malkin [12] for proofs of Theorems 4 and 5.

There are somewhat different proofs of Liapounov's theorems, as well as different special cases, but for these details one must consult Krasovski [5].

From these few remarks, Liapounov's second method should be sufficiently clear.

The conditions imposed on $V(x)$ and on $\dot{V}(x)$ (in the case of stability) guarantee that the trajectory always crosses the "ovals" [i.e., the levels of $V(x)$] *from the outside toward the inside*; this in turn guarantees its approach to the origin.   If it only *approaches* and does not *reach* the origin, one simply has *stability*; if it actually reaches the origin (for $t \to \infty$) this means *asymptotic stability*.

A reversal of criteria (for example, say V and $\dot{V}$ were positive definite) leads to *instability*, but here the ramifications are more numerous.   Clearly if an appropriate Liapounov function is found, the question of stability versus instability is merely a matter of applying *definite criteria*, and one does not need to integrate the variational system.

4.5   DETERMINATION OF THE V FUNCTIONS

There are no definite rules for the determination of the V functions; in each case one has to analyze the individual function closely to determine whether it can be used as the V function.   Thus, if in the neighborhood of the origin, V may be represented as a power series in x_i, it can be written as

$$V = V_p(x) + V_{p+1}(x) + \cdots \tag{4.16}$$

in which $V_i(x)$ is a homogeneous polynomial in $x_1, \ldots, x_n$ of degree i; the first term $V_p(x)$ will be then an assembly of terms of the lowest degree of $V_p(x)$ of series $V(x)$. In a sufficiently small neighborhood around the origin the polynomials $V_{p+1}(x)$ are negligible as compared with $V_p(x)$, so that the terms $V_p(x)$ dominate all other terms, which can be then neglected. Another obvious requirement is that if p is odd, V cannot be a Liapounov function. In fact, each collection of terms in Eq. (4.16) is a homogeneous polynomial, and one can write, for instance, $x_1 = x_n u_1, \ldots, x_{n-1} = x_n u_{n-1}$, which expresses the $(n-1)$st variables in terms of the last; this gives

$$V_p(x) = x_n{}^p V_p(u)$$

Since u_i are fixed numbers, clearly the sign of V_p is that of $x_n{}^p$, and, for that reason, if p were odd, such a V could not be a Liapounov function, since the character of the positive definiteness would be lost. In the same manner, an assembly of terms with different signs, such as $x_1{}^2 - x_2{}^2$, etc., is to be ruled out.

The conditions of positive definiteness are fulfilled in the case of quadratic forms, i.e., when $V(x)$ is of the form

$$V(x) = \sum_{i,j=1}^{n} a_{ij} x_i x_j$$

4.6   ADDITIONAL STABILITY THEOREMS

The following theorems[1] involving stability on the basis of abridged equations are often useful. Given a nonlinear autonomous system

$$\dot{x}_i = \sum_{j=1}^{n} p_{ij} x_j + X_i(x_1, \ldots, x_n) \qquad i = 1, 2, \ldots, n \qquad (4.17)$$

in which p is a constant and $X_i(x_1, \ldots, x_n)$ are convergent power series in x_i beginning with terms of at least the second degree, one has the following theorem of Liapounov:

1. If all roots λ_i of the characteristic equation of the system $\dot{x}_i = \sum_{j=1}^{n} b_{ij} x_j$ have Re $(\lambda_i) < 0$, the equilibrium $(x_i = 0, i = 1, \ldots, n)$ is asymptotically stable whatever the terms X_i are.

---

[1] The theorems in 4.6 are stated only and *not proved* as this would require a considerable space; on the other hand, in what follows we do not use these theorems.

2. If among the roots of the characteristic equation of (4.20) there is at least one λ with Re $(\lambda) > 0$, the equilibrium is unstable whatever the terms X_i are.

3. If the characteristic equation does not have any roots λ with Re $(\lambda) > 0$ but has some roots λ with Re $(\lambda) = 0$, then the terms in X_i can be chosen such that they have either stability or instability.

Critical cases appear when: (1) the characteristic equation has one zero root, while others have negative real parts; and (2) when the characteristic equation has a pair of purely imaginary roots and the remaining roots have negative real parts.

In cases in which the function $V = V(x,t)$ contains the independent variable t explicitly, the following theorems of Liapounov hold.

1. If it is possible to find $V(t, x_1, \ldots , x_n)$ positive definite for which the Eulerian derivative

$$F = \frac{dV}{dt} = \frac{\partial V}{\partial t} + W$$

is of the sign opposite to that of V or is identically zero, the equilibrium is stable.

2. If condition 1 (critical cases) holds and, besides, F and V admit lim sup 0 uniformly, the equilibrium is asymptotically stable.

For instability, similar theorems exist:

3. If there exists a function $V(x,t)$ such that F and V reach the lim sup 0 uniformly, F being positive definite, and, for any arbitrary small x_i and $t \rightarrow \infty$, V has the same sign as F, the equilibrium is unstable (Četaev).

4. If for $t \rightarrow \infty$ and a sufficiently small Ω around the origin, the function V is positive and bounded and moreover, $F > 0$ for $V > \alpha$ and $F > L$, α and L being positive numbers $L = L(\alpha)$, then the equilibrium is unstable.

A number of other cases have been investigated recently, but for them, treatises on stability must be consulted (LaSalle [6]). Cases in which Liapounov's theorems hold are probably the ones most often encountered in applications; if these conditions are fulfilled, the problem is greatly simplified.

4.7 DIFFERENTIAL EQUATIONS OF CONTROL SYSTEMS[1]

In Chap. 5 we shall often encounter the differential equation of control systems in the form

$$\dot{x}_i = \sum_{j=1}^{n} a_{ij} x_j + b_i y \qquad i = 1, 2, \ldots, n$$

$$y = \varphi(\sigma) \qquad \sigma = \sum_{k=1}^{n} c_k x_k \qquad \varphi(0) = 0 \tag{4.18}$$

Although the physical significance of these equations is explained in Chap. 5, it is useful to mention that x is a generalized coordinate, y is a quantity measuring the control action, and σ is the signal.

In this form one recognizes that the only nonlinear function is $y = \varphi(\sigma)$, that is, the relation between the signal σ and the corresponding control action. In the absence of control, one obviously has a linear system

$$\dot{x}_i = \sum_{j=1}^{n} a_{ij} x_j \qquad i = 1, 2, \ldots, n \tag{4.19}$$

with the characteristic equation

$$\begin{vmatrix} a_{11} - \lambda & a_{12} & \cdots & a_{1n} \\ a_{21} & a_{22} - \lambda & \cdots & a_{2n} \\ \cdots\cdots\cdots\cdots\cdots\cdots\cdots\cdots \\ a_{n1} & a_{n2} & \cdots & a_{nn} - \lambda \end{vmatrix} = 0 \tag{4.20}$$

The form of Eq. (4.18) was inspired by the form of control systems, where practically all parameters may be considered as linear except one. That one is associated with the servomotor, and appears generally as a certain nonlinear function $y = \varphi(\sigma)$ of the signal σ.

The problem originated from a remark of Aiserman to the effect that generally in control systems one degree of freedom contains a nonlinear function $f(x_k)$, while the remaining $n - 1$ degrees are linear. That is,

$$\dot{x}_1 = p_{11} x_1 + \cdots + p_{1n} x_n + f(x_k) \qquad k \leqslant n \tag{4.21}$$

$$\dot{x}_i = p_{i1} x_1 + \cdots + p_{in} x_n \qquad i = 2, \ldots, n \tag{4.18}$$

Equations (4.18) and (4.21) are the same, but (4.21) is a particular case of y.

The study developed in this and the following sections of this chapter is possible if one basic limitation is taken into account. That

[1] See Aiserman and Gantmacher [2].

is, the condition of self-excitation (if the system is nonlinear) must be eliminated by requiring that the characteristic equations (4.20) corresponding to the linear matrix $\|a_{ij}\|$ have no roots with positive real parts. This property is designated below by the symbol (H), which means that this matrix is *Hurwitzian* (that is, its roots have negative real parts).

There is one other requirement, which concerns the choice of functions $\varphi(\sigma)$ for which the problem of absolute stability can be carried out; this is discussed in Sec. 4.8.

We complete this section with a remark concerning different equivalent forms of the system given in Eq. (4.18) [Aiserman and Gantmacher [2]]. Thus, for instance, if, instead of (4.18), the characteristic equation (4.20) has a zero root, one obtains the following system:

$$\dot{z}_i = \sum_{j=1}^{n-1} d_{ij}z_j + S_i y \qquad i = 1, 2, \ldots, n$$

$$y = \varphi(\sigma) \qquad \sigma = \sum_{j=1}^{n} c_i^* z_i \qquad (4.22)$$

And if in these transformed equations $c_n^* \neq 0$, one can use the variable σ instead of z_n. After some further transformations, one can write, instead of (4.22),

$$\dot{z}_i = \sum_{j=1}^{n-1} d_{ij}z_j + S_i y \qquad i = 1, 2, \ldots, n - 1 \qquad (4.23)$$

$$\dot{\sigma} = \sum_{k=1}^{n-1} l_k z_k - \rho y$$

Then, instead of (4.22), one deals with the system

$$\dot{u}_i = \sum_{k=1}^{n-1} d_{ij}u_j + S_i \xi \qquad i = 1, 2, \ldots, n - 1$$

$$\dot{\xi} = y \qquad y = \varphi(\sigma) \qquad \sigma = \sum_{k=1}^{n-1} l_k u_k - \rho \xi \qquad (4.24)$$

The system in Eq. (4.24) can be transformed into (4.23) if the variables $u_1, u_2, \ldots, u_{n-1}, \xi$ are replaced by the variables

$$z_i = \sum_{j=1}^{n-1} d_{ij}u_j + \rho_i \xi \qquad i = 1, \ldots, n - 1 \qquad \sigma = \sum_{k=1}^{n-1} l_k u_k - \rho \xi \quad (4.25)$$

There are some additional transformations possible, but we shall not dwell on this point; it is important to remember that all these equivalent systems have the same stability properties, but from the point of view of their control characteristics they are quite different. Thus, for instance, system (4.18) is a typical control system in which the control action y is obtained from the followup (or feedback) arrangement on the resultant control signal σ.

In the equivalent system (4.23) this followup or feedback action controls the *rate of change* $\dot{\sigma}$ of the signal (Minorsky [13]).

Obviously these interpretations become possible only *after* the identification of the equivalence of these various forms is done; a priori one cannot see this identity of control systems with entirely different constructional features.

4.8   FORMULATION OF THE PROBLEM

We are here interested in obtaining the conditions for the *absolute stability* of control systems.   By this term will be meant the fulfillment of the following two conditions:

1. The zero solution (Sec. 4.1) is asymptotically stable (α).
2. The zone of attraction of $x = 0$ (that is, $x_1 = x_2 = \cdots = x_n = 0$) is in the whole phase space (β).

Clearly this new definition of stability is stronger than condition α, for asymptotic stability, alone.   From the point of view of applications it is more valuable, since the "zone of attraction" has no limitations, and this permits us to be unconcerned with calculation of the "limit of the zone of stability" (see Sec. 7.8), which constitutes a rather painstaking problem in control engineering.   We have mentioned already the requirement that the matrix of the linear part of Eq. (4.18) should be (H).   The second requirement concerns the form of the allowable functions $\varphi(\sigma)$ for which the problem of absolute stability is possible.

The origin of the studies concerning the latter is, perhaps, a hypothesis made by Aiserman on the basis of certain heuristic reasoning (illustrated in Fig. 4.3).   Suppose we know that for the linear functions $\varphi_1 = h_1\sigma$ and $\varphi_2 = h_2\sigma$ (h_1 and h_2 being positive constants), a system is asymptotically stable.   It seems reasonable to expect that for a nonlinear function $\varphi(\sigma)$ contained in the "Aiserman angle" γ, the condition of stability will still exist.   In fact for $n = 2$ the Aiserman hypothesis was actually proved in a number of cases, but difficulties appeared in systems with a larger number of degrees of freedom.

It turned out later that Aiserman's suggestion was useful in defining the approach to the question of absolute stability, that is, asymptotic stability "in the large," the latter term being understood to mean "the whole phase space."

These new developments were initiated to some extent by the recent discovery of V. M. Popov [15] and [16] (Sec. 4.13), who showed that the problem of stability, particularly of *absolute stability*, can be treated by the well-known linear method of *frequency characteristics*, provided

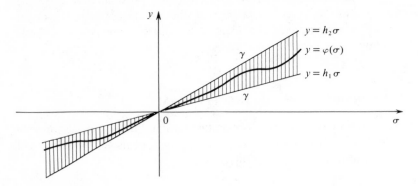

Fig. 4.3

that: (1) the nonlinear system is of a non-self-excited type; and (2) the nonlinearity is subject to the above restriction by the angle γ (Fig. 4.3).

This discovery aroused considerable interest because up to that time the stability of linear systems had been treated by linear criteria (Hurwitzian criteria, Nyquist diagram, etc.), and for the nonlinear systems the only criterion of stability available was Liapounov's second method.

In fact, ever since the appearance of nonlinear problems, their treatment has been in terms of the theory of real variables, whereas for linear systems, the theory of complex variables has been decidedly preferable. (This presupposes, of course, that one is interested in self-excited oscillations, in which case the theory of complex variables lacks a fundamental concept—that of the limit cycle.)

Popov's discovery—that linear methods could be used for nonlinear problems—was thus somewhat unusual, although the opportunity to use powerful methods of linear theory in the nonlinear domain was very attractive.   And, provided the condition of self-excitation is ruled out, there is no reason why Popov's method cannot be used.

It can be shown (Aiserman and Gantmacher [2]) that this study is greatly simplified owing to the fact that the form of functions $\varphi(\sigma)$ is immaterial so long as the condition

$$0 \leqslant \frac{\varphi(\sigma)}{\sigma} \leqslant k \qquad (4.26)$$

where k is either a finite positive number or infinity is fulfilled.   [In the latter case, Eq. (4.26), one has $0 \leqslant \varphi(\sigma)/\sigma$.]   This inequality is represented graphically in Fig. 4.4.   It should be noted that the geometrical form of condition (4.26) is analogous to that shown in Fig. 4.3,

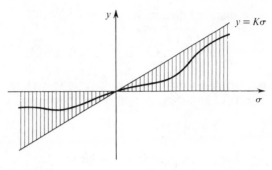

Fig. 4.4

but is different in the sense that the plane of this representation is the control plane (σ, y).

One can define the concept of absolute stability as follows:

If in a system of the form (4.18) *with any* $\varphi(\sigma)$ *satisfying* (4.26) *the zero solution is asymptotically stable, such a system is called absolutely stable.*

Before we discuss this problem in detail, we shall add a few remarks to what was said previously about Liapounov's theory.

4.9   LIAPOUNOV'S OPERATOR Λ

As we mentioned in Sec. 4.7, property (H) is to be introduced as one of the two limitations under which the problem of absolute stability is possible.   On physical grounds this is obvious; in fact, this condition rules out the question of self-excitation in the first place and also permits a more extensive use of Liapounov's second method.

We begin by investigating the uncontrolled system, (4.18), which reduces simply to

$$\dot{x}_i = \sum_{j=1}^{n} a_{ij} x_j \tag{4.27}$$

This case has been investigated by Liapounov himself, who showed that it is always possible to build a positive definite quadratic form

$$L(x) = \sum_{i,j}^{n} l_{ij}x_ix_j \qquad l_{ij} = l_{ji} \tag{4.28}$$

such that its Eulerian derivative

$$\dot{L}(x) = \sum_i \frac{dL(x)}{dx_i}\frac{dx_i}{dt} = \sum \left(2\sum_j l_{ij}x_j \sum_k a_{ik}x_k \right) \tag{4.29}$$

is a negative definite quadratic form (Sec. 4.4).

Take an arbitrary positive definite quadratic form

$$G(x) = \sum_{ij} g_{ij}x_ix_j \tag{4.30}$$

with fixed $g_{ij} = g_{ji}$. It is possible to select the coefficients l_{ij}, in (4.28), in a single-valued manner, so that the right-hand side in (4.29) should coincide with $-G(x)$, in which case $\dot{L}(x) = -G(x)$.

This operation for passing from an arbitrary $G(x)$ to $L(x)$ can be designated by Λ, the Liapounov operator; that is,

$$\Lambda[G(x)] = L(x) \tag{4.31}$$

From the identity

$$\sum_i \left(2\sum_j l_{ij}x_j \sum_k a_{ik}x_k \right) = -\sum_{ij} g_{ij}x_ix_j \tag{4.32}$$

it is seen that the coefficients g_{ij} of the quadratic form $G(x)$ are expressed in terms of l_{ij} of the quadratic form in a linear manner. Moreover the coefficients of these forms depend linearly on a_{ij}. This system of linear relations can be expressed in terms of l_{ij} of $L(x)$; the latter are (also linearly) expressible in terms of g_{ij} of $G(x)$. This latter operation (the inverse linear and homogeneous transformation) is precisely the analytic expression of the operator Λ, which thus is linear.

It depends on the coefficients a_{ij} of (4.18). If the system is stable, the operator Λ transforms any positive definite form $G(x)$ into the corresponding positive definite form $L(x)$. For example, for $n = 2$, take

$$L(x) = l_{11}x_1{}^2 + 2l_{12}x_1x_2 + l_{22}x_2{}^2$$

$$G(x) = g_{11}x_1{}^2 + 2g_{12}x_1x_2 + g_{22}x_2{}^2$$

Forming the identity (4.32) after some transformations and equating the coefficients of $x_1{}^2$, $x_2{}^2$, and x_1x_2 on both sides of the identity, one obtains the relations

$$a_{11}l_{11} + a_{21}l_{12} = -\tfrac{1}{2}g_{11} \qquad a_{12}l_{11} + (a_{11} + a_{22})l_{12} + a_{21}l_{22} = -g_{12}$$

$$a_{12}l_{12} + a_{22}l_{22} = -\tfrac{1}{2}g_{22} \tag{4.33}$$

Forming the determinant of the coefficients l_{11}, l_{12}, and l_{22}, one finds that it is different from zero, since the characteristic equation

$$\begin{vmatrix} a_{11} - \lambda & a_{12} \\ a_{21} & a_{22} - \lambda \end{vmatrix} = \lambda^2 - (a_{11} + a_{22})\lambda + (a_{11}a_{22} - a_{12}a_{21}) = 0$$

is (H), and the product of its roots $\lambda_1\lambda_2$ and their sum $\lambda_1 + \lambda_2$ are different from zero as one verifies it.

Solving the system (4.33) with respect to l_{11}, l_{12}, and l_{22}, one obtains the analytical expression

$$l_{11} = -\frac{1}{2D}\,[(a_{11}a_{12} - a_{12}a_{21} + a_{22}{}^2)g_{11} - 2a_{21}a_{22}g_{12} + a_{21}{}^2g_{22}]$$

and a similar expression for l_{12} and l_{22}.

4.10 ABSOLUTE STABILITY ON THE BASIS OF LIAPOUNOV'S SECOND METHOD

We consider again the system (4.18); we shall look for a continuous differentiable function $V(x_1, \ldots, x_n)$ having the following properties.

1. V is positive definite in the whole n space except at the origin, where it is zero:

$$V(0) = 0 \qquad x_1 = \cdots = x_n = 0$$

2. Its Eulerian derivative

$$\dot{V} = \sum_i \frac{\partial V}{\partial x_i}\left[\sum a_{ik}x_k + b_i\varphi(\sigma)\right] \tag{4.34}$$

is negative definite in the whole n space except at the origin, where $\dot{V}(0) = 0$.

3. $\lim_{x \to \infty} V = \infty$ (condition of Barbashin-Krasovski).

It can be shown that there exists the zero solution, and the existence of the function V guarantees the existence of absolute stability.

Consider now the Liapounov function of the form

$$V = L(x) + \beta \int_0^\sigma \varphi(\sigma)\, d\sigma \tag{4.35}$$

where $L(x) = \sum_{ij} l_{ij} x_i x_j$, $l_{ij} = l_{ji}$, and β is a real fixed number. As in the linear case, we determine the coefficients l_{ij} by means of the operator Λ, that is, $\Lambda[G(x)] = L(x)$, making use of Eq. (4.32).

Consider first $\beta \geqslant 0$. Then for any positive definite $G(x)$, V in Eq. (4.35) will also be positive definite since $L(x)$ is positive definite and $\beta \int_0^\sigma \varphi(\sigma)\, d\sigma$ is nonnegative for $\beta \geqslant 0$ in view of

$$\frac{\varphi(\sigma)}{\sigma} \geqslant 0 \tag{4.36}$$

In the case in which $\beta \geqslant 0$, one has $V \geqslant L(x) > 0$, and, since $\lim_{x \to \infty} L(x) = \infty$, one has also $\lim V(x) = \infty$. Thus conditions 1 and 3 are always fulfilled, and it is necessary to satisfy only condition 2. The Eulerian derivative here is

$$\dot{V} = \sum_i \frac{\partial V}{\partial x_i} \frac{dx_i}{dt} = \sum_j \left[2\sum_j l_{ij} x_j + \beta\varphi(\sigma)c_i \right]\left[\sum_j a_{ij} x_j + b_i\varphi(\sigma) \right] \tag{4.37}$$

and in view of (4.32) one has

$$\dot{V} = -\sum_{ij} g_{ij} x_i x_j + \varphi(\sigma) \sum_j \left[\sum_i (2l_{ij} b_i + \beta a_{ij} c_i) \right] x_j + \varphi^2(\sigma)\beta \sum b_i c_i \tag{4.38}$$

With regard to V, it is positive definite, but one cannot assert now that $\dot{V}$ is negative definite because of the nonlinear function for which $\varphi(\sigma)/\sigma \geqslant 0$.

The problem now is to guarantee the negative definiteness of (4.38) for any function $\varphi(\sigma)$ in the angle (4.26).

In fact (4.38) contains the nonlinear function $\varphi(\sigma)$ and *is not* a quadratic form of $x_1, \ldots, x_n$, so that there are no criteria which could guarantee that $\dot{V}$ be negative definite.

4.11 LUR'E'S TRANSFORMATION; THE S PROCEDURE

In order to establish sufficient conditions for $\dot{V} < 0$, A. I. Lur'e suggested that the expression $[\sigma - \varphi(\sigma)/k]\varphi(\sigma)$ be added or subtracted from the right-hand side of Eq. (4.38); this expression [in view of (4.26), the conditions of which we assume to be fulfilled] is always nonnegative for $\varphi(\sigma)$ in the angle $[0, k]$.   In this case one has

$$\dot{V} = -S[x, \varphi(\sigma)] - \left[\sigma - \frac{\varphi(\sigma)}{k}\right]\varphi(\sigma) \tag{4.39}$$

where

$$S[x,\varphi(\sigma)] = -\dot{V} - \left[\sigma - \frac{\varphi(\sigma)}{k}\right]\varphi(\sigma) = \sum_{ij} g_{ij}x_i x_j$$

$$- \varphi(\sigma) \sum_i \left[\sum_j (2l_{ji}b_j + \beta a_{ji}c_i) + c_i\right]x_i + \varphi^2(\sigma)\left(\frac{1}{k} - \beta \sum_i b_i c_i\right) \tag{4.40}$$

From Eq. (4.39) it is seen that $\dot{V}$ will be negative definite if $S(x,y)$ is positive definite.

For the function S the replacement of $\varphi(\sigma)$ by y and the requirement of positive definiteness of $S(x,y)$ as the quadratic form of $n + 1$ independent variables does not present any contradiction.

This leads to the so-called S *procedure*, which can be specified by the equations

$$S(x,y) = \sum_{ij} g_{ij}x_i x_j - 2y \sum_i d_i x_i + ry^2 \tag{4.41}$$

where

$$\alpha_i = \sum_j (l_{ij}b_j + \tfrac{1}{2}\beta a_{ij}c_j) + \tfrac{1}{2}c_i \tag{4.42}$$

$$r = \frac{1}{k} - \beta \sum_i b_i c_i \tag{4.43}$$

The problem can be reduced to show that the quadratic form $S(x,y)$ of $n + 1$ independent variables can be made positive definite; that is

$$S(x,y) > 0 \tag{4.44}$$

If one succeeds in doing this, it can be shown that Eq. (4.18) has absolute stability.   In fact, from Eqs. (4.44) and (4.39), it follows that $\dot{V} < 0$.

The three conditions outlined previously are also fulfilled.

The S procedure permits determining the Liapounov functions of the type of Eq. (4.35), but it is clear that there are some functions which escape detection by this method.   In fact, the procedure consists in treating $y = \varphi(\sigma)$ as the $(n + 1)$st independent variable (in addition to $x_1, \ldots, x_n$), but in reality there is a relation between y and x_k through the last two equations of (4.18).

4.12   APPLICATION OF THE S PROCEDURE

From the positive definiteness of $S(x,y)$ considered as a function of $n + 1$ independent variables it follows that r must be positive, since for the positive definite quadratic form all coefficients of the squares of the variables must be positive.   There remains, then, the case $r = 0$ which requires a further investigation.

Case when $r > 0$ In this (normal) case there are two possibilities:

1. We require that for $S(x,y)$, there must be fulfilled $n + 1$ inequalities of Silvester, which are the necessary and sufficient conditions for its positive definiteness.   However, the first n conditions of Silvester contain only the coefficients g_{ij}; these are certainly fulfilled, since the form $G(x) = \sum_{ij} g_{ij} x_i x_j$ has been chosen as positive definite.   Hence the last, the $(n + 1)$st inequality, is the only one to be considered; it is

$$\begin{vmatrix} g_{11} & \cdots & g_{1n} & \alpha_1 \\ \cdots & \cdots & \cdots & \cdots \\ g_{n1} & \cdots & g_{nn} & \alpha_n \\ \alpha_1 & \cdots & \alpha_n & r \end{vmatrix} > 0 \tag{4.45}$$

Developing this determinant, one gets

$$r\Delta - \sum_{ij} G_{ij}\alpha_i\alpha_j > 0 \tag{4.46}$$

where

$$\Delta = \begin{vmatrix} g_{11} & \cdots & g_{1n} \\ \cdots & \cdots & \cdots \\ g_{n1} & \cdots & g_{nn} \end{vmatrix}$$

and G_{ij} is the minor corresponding to g_{ij}.   The condition (4.46) is thus a sufficient condition for absolute stability.   One can write (4.46) differently if we have

$$g_{ij}^{(-1)} = \frac{G_{ij}}{\Delta} \tag{4.47}$$

In this case it becomes

$$\sum_{ij} g_{ij}^{(-1)}\alpha_i\alpha_j < r \tag{4.48}$$

Replacing r by the right-hand side of Eq. (4.43) and introducing the notation

$$\sum_{ij} g_{ij}^{(-1)} \alpha_i \alpha_j + \beta \sum_j b_j c_j = \Phi(b,c) \tag{4.49}$$

inequality (4.46) becomes

$$\Phi(b,c) < \frac{1}{k} \tag{4.50}$$

The quantity $\Phi(b,c)$ is a quadratic form of $2n$ variables b_i and c_i, so that the equation $\Phi(b,c) = 1/k$ determines a family of central hypersurfaces of the second order in the $2n$ space of the parameters b_i and c_i.

For each β the hypersurface divides the space into two regions; the inequality (4.50) corresponds to the region containing the origin.

2. The second procedure is to transform the expression (4.41) so as to have terms not containing y.   One has:

$$S(x,y) = r\left(y - \frac{1}{r}\sum_j d_j x_j\right)^2 + \sum_{ij} g_{ij} x_i x_j - \frac{1}{r}\left(\sum_j \alpha_j x_j\right)^2 \tag{4.51}$$

Since we have assumed that $r > 0$ in order to have (4.51) positive definite, it is necessary and sufficient that the quadratic form

$$Q(x) = \sum_{ij} q_{ij} x_i x_j = \sum_{ij} g_{ij} x_j x_j - \frac{1}{r}\left(\sum_j \alpha_j x_j\right)^2 \tag{4.52}$$

be positive definite.   It is noted that

$$q_{ij} = g_{ij} - \frac{1}{r}\alpha_i \alpha_j \tag{4.53}$$

It was shown previously that g_{ij} and α_j depend linearly on l_{ij} [of the quadratic form $L(x)$].   Thus the coefficients q_{ij} depend *quadratically* on l_{ij} in view of $\alpha_i \alpha_j$.

If one considers an arbitrary positive definite quadratic form $Q(x)$ (that is, chooses its coefficients q_{ij}) from Eq. (4.53), one obtains $\frac{1}{2}n(n+1)$ quadratic equations with respect to the same number of the unknown coefficients l_{ij}.

If this system of quadratic equations has a real solution, the quadratic form $L(x)$ in such a case is positive definite, because the quadratic form

$$G(x) = \sum_{ij} q_{ij} x_i x_j = Q(x) + \frac{1}{r}\left(\sum_j \alpha_j x_j\right)^2 \tag{4.54}$$

is positive definite, since $L(x)$ is obtained from $G(x)$ using the operator Λ.

It can be shown that the system of $\frac{1}{2}n(n + 1)$ quadratic equations can be reduced to a system of n quadratic equations with respect to n quantities α_i.

We omit a number of intermediate algebraic calculations and indicate the result. One obtains n quadratic equations with respect to the n unknown coefficients $\alpha_1, \ldots, \alpha_n$.

$$\frac{c_i}{2} + \sum_j p_{ij}b_j = \alpha_i - \frac{1}{2}\beta \sum_j a_{ij}c_j - \frac{1}{r}\sum_j m_{ij}(\alpha_1, \ldots, \alpha_n)b_j \qquad (4.55)$$

In these equations:

$$p_{ij} = l_{ij} - \frac{1}{r}m_{ij}(\alpha_1, \ldots, \alpha_n) \qquad (4.56)$$

Since the form $Q(x)$ is supposed to be given, one must also consider p_{ij} as given. The coefficients m_{ij} of the form $M(x)$ are quadratic functions of $\alpha_1, \ldots, \alpha_n$, and l_{ij} are connected with the unknowns $\alpha_1, \ldots, \alpha_3$ linearly by Eqs. (4.42) (Lur'e [9]).

If one can select the form Q so that the system (4.55) has real solutions $\alpha_1, \ldots, \alpha_n$, the form $G(x)$ is determined by (4.52) and $L(x) = \Lambda[G(x)]$.

In such a case Liapounov's function exists in the form

$$V = L(x) + \beta \int_0^\sigma \varphi(\sigma)\,d\sigma \qquad \beta > 0 \qquad (4.57)$$

and this establishes the condition for absolute stability.

Case when $r = 0$ In this case the quadratic form

$$S(x,y) = G(x) + \sum_i \alpha_i x_i y \qquad (4.58)$$

cannot be a positive definite form of $n + 1$ independent variables $x_1, \ldots, x_n, y$. However, it can be made equal to $G(x)$, and, therefore, V will be of a definite sign if, following Lur'e, one equates all α_i with zero; that is [see Eq. (4.42)],

$$\sum_j (l_{ij}b_j + \frac{1}{2}\beta a_{ij}c_j) + \frac{1}{2}c_i = 0 \qquad (4.59)$$

Let

$$G(x) = \left(\sum_i u_j x_j\right)^2 + Q(x)$$

be a function formed of an arbitrary positive definite quadratic form $Q(x)$ and $\left(\sum_j u_j x_j\right)^2$, where u_j are real numbers. One applies the operator Λ to (4.52):

$$\Lambda[Q(x)] = \Lambda[G(x)] - \frac{1}{r}\Lambda\left[\left(\sum_j \alpha_j x_j\right)^2\right] \tag{4.60}$$

which is otherwise written

$$\Lambda[G(x)] = L\left[\left(\sum_j u_j x_j\right)^2\right] + P(x) \tag{4.61}$$

where

$$\Lambda[G(x)] = L(x) = \sum_{ij} l_{ij}x_i x_j \qquad L[Q(x)] = P(x) = \sum_{ji} p_{ij}x_i x_j$$

Identifying the coefficients in (4.61), one has

$$l_{ij} = m_{ij}(u_1, \ldots, u_n) + p_{ij} \tag{4.62}$$

where

$$\Lambda\left[\left(\sum_j \alpha_j x_j\right)^2\right] = M(x) = \sum_{ij} m_{ij}x_i x_j \tag{4.63}$$

Replacing (4.62) in (4.59), one obtains another system of quadratic equations in terms of u_i:

$$\sum_j m_{ij}(u_1, \ldots, u_n)b_i + \tfrac{1}{2}\beta \sum_j a_{ij}l_j + \sum_j p_{ij}b_i + \tfrac{1}{2}c_i \tag{4.64}$$

If one sets $p_{ij} = 0$ in (4.55) and (4.64), one obtains the so-called *limit system* of quadratic equations. Therefore the system in which $p_{ij} \neq 0$ may be called a system of *prelimit equations*. We shall not continue this matter, since it leads to further complications. This theory is due to Lur'e [9]; it makes it possible to ascertain whether these limit equations (also called *resolving equations*) have real solutions; if they do, there exists absolute stability.

4.13 THE THEORY OF V. M. POPOV; GENERALITIES

In recent years a series of papers by a Roumanian mathematician, V. M. Popov, has opened entirely new vistas in the theory of stability and, indirectly, in methods of mathematical analysis. It is well known that early linear classical control theory was based on a number of propositions taken from the theory of differential equations in the *complex domain*. The theorems of Cauchy, concepts of zeros, and concepts of poles of analytic functions with various ramifications such as the Nyquist diagram, the methods of O. Heaviside, etc.,—all these belong to the theory of differential equations in the complex domain. This is very convenient for engineers because a number of graphical constructions (hodographs, etc.) often permit obtaining the desired results without involving the theory of differential equations.

The advent of nonlinear theory caused considerable changes in these familiar procedures. In fact, in the nonlinear methods, use is generally made of the *real variable*. The introduction of this variable in mathematical physics is largely due to H. Poincaré, whose fundamental contribution was the theory of *limit cycles*, which is outlined in Chap. 1.

Only the two-dimensional theory of these closed trajectories has been explored so far (Chap. 1). It should be noted that the concept of limit cycles exists only in the *real domain* and that there is nothing analogous to it in the complex domain. This is probably the principal reason that, beginning with Poincaré, the habit of using the real variable in all nonlinear problems was formed. The use of the real variable is largely based on the use of the solutions in the form of a series arranged according to the ascending powers of a certain parameter; although the various geometrical interpretations can still be used, they are not so simply related to the fundamentals of the theory as are the analogous concepts in the complex domain. Because of Popov's theory, this attitude toward nonlinear problems seems to be changing, since it has become possible to use a great many graphical methods (Sec. 6.15), although the latter appear in a form somewhat different from that in which they appear in the complex domain.

There is, however, one limitation; that is, the nonlinear systems which fall within the scope of Popov's method must be Hurwitzian (*H*); by this is meant those linear differential systems whose fundamental matrix has roots with negative real parts; in such systems self-excitation is ruled out. In fact, as we saw in Chap. 3 (this will be still more apparent in Chap. 7) self-excitation renders a linearized analysis very complicated. Conversely, if one rules out self-excitation by considering essentially only the (*H*) systems, one cannot a priori see any reason why the complex variable cannot be used in the nonlinear (*H*) problems; this is precisely the principal feature of the Popov theory.

Another interesting point is the possibility of defining more precisely the concept of *absolute stability* (sometimes called *global stability*). This concept is very convenient, since if absolute stability exists, there is no necessity for calculating the "zones of stability" (that is, the regions from which the system can approach the equilibrium point). We shall see in Sec. 7.8 that the determination of the zones of stability constitutes a rather complicated procedure in control engineering practice. If the stability is *absolute*, such procedure becomes unnecessary, since the dynamic system will reach the position of equilibrium no matter what its initial conditions are. Although the complete exposition of Popov's theory, particularly of its connection with the general theory of stability, cannot be attempted here, it is still useful to mention it briefly, since it seems likely that the impact of these new ideas on the nonlinear problems of control will be felt in the near future.

4.14   ABSOLUTE STABILITY

Anticipating somewhat the contents of the following chapter, it is useful to mention that, although the formulation of stability for linear systems on the basis of Liapounov's second method does not present any special difficulty, for nonlinear systems it is necessary to impose the condition (4.26), in which k is a fixed number. This means that in the (σ,y) plane the nonlinear characteristic $y = \varphi(\sigma)$ must be contained inside the Aiserman angle (the shaded area in Fig. 4.4); in this expression σ is the control signal, which is defined in Chap. 5. Whether the function y has common points with the sides of the angle or not depends on the circumstances of each problem, but, anticipating this possibility, we shall indicate this angle by the square brackets $[0,k]$ if y is inside the angle without touching its rectilinear limits. If, however, one limit is included, the notation will be either $(0,k]$ or $[0,k)$, according to whether the abscissa axis or the ray $y = k\sigma$ are included. Thus, for instance, the inequality

$$0 < \frac{\varphi(\sigma)}{\sigma} \leqslant k \qquad \sigma \neq 0 \tag{4.65}$$

means that the σ axis is excluded, but the $y = k\sigma$ ray is not. This permits us to define the concept of *absolute stability* in the following manner:

Given a system

$$\dot{x}_i = \sum_{j=1}^{n} a_{ij}x_j + b_i y \qquad i = 1, \ldots, n \tag{4.66}$$

$$y = \varphi(\sigma) \qquad \sigma = \sum_{k=1}^{n} c_k x_k$$

and a fixed k, the system will called absolutely stable for any $\varphi(\sigma)$ satisfying Eq. (4.65) if the zero (or trivial) solution is asymptotically stable in the whole phase plane.

There are several possible cases according to the nature of the roots of the matrix $\|a_{ij}\|$ of the linear part. For example: (1) $\|a_{ij}\|$ is $[H]$; and (2) some of the roots of $\|a_{ij}\|$ are on the imaginary axis, and the remaining ones are to the left of it. We cannot enter here into the various ramifications of the problem, and shall consider only the fundamental case in which the system (4.66) is $[H]$. (For details see Aiserman and Gantmacher [2].)

4.15 FREQUENCY CHARACTERISTICS

It was suspected long ago that the stability of a simple system $R + M$ (R = relay, M = linear system) depends on the characteristic of M. It is probable that this was the first stimulus for the studies of frequency characteristics. Equations (4.66) can be written as a system of algebraic equations if one introduces the operator $p = d/dt$ and writes (4.66) formally as a system

$$px_i - \sum_{j=1}^{n} a_{ij}x_j = b_i y \qquad \sum_{k=1}^{n} c_k x_k - \sigma = 0 \tag{4.67}$$

The quantity $-\sigma$ can be written (by Kramer's rule) as

$$-\sigma = \frac{K(p)y}{D(p)} \tag{4.68}$$

where

$$D(p) = \begin{vmatrix} p - a_{11} & -a_{12} & \cdots & -a_{1n} & 0 \\ -a_{21} & p - a_{22} & \cdots & -a_{2n} & 0 \\ \cdots & \cdots & \cdots & \cdots & \cdots \\ -a_{n1} & -a_{n2} & \cdots & p - a_{nn} & 0 \\ c_1 & c_2 & \cdots & c_n & 1 \end{vmatrix}$$

$$= \begin{vmatrix} p - a_{11} & -a_{12} & \cdots & -a_{1n} \\ -a_{21} & p - a_{22} & \cdots & -a_{2n} \\ \cdots & \cdots & \cdots & \cdots \\ -a_{n1} & -a_{n2} & \cdots & p - a_{nn} \end{vmatrix} \tag{4.69}$$

and $K(p)$ is

$$K(p) = \begin{vmatrix} p - a_{11} & -a_{12} & \cdots & -a_{1n} & b_1 \\ -a_{21} & p - a_{22} & \cdots & -a_{2n} & b_2 \\ \cdots & \cdots & \cdots & \cdots & \cdots \\ c_1 & c_2 & \cdots & c_n & 0 \end{vmatrix} \tag{4.70}$$

so that σ and y are connected by the equation

$$D(p)\sigma = -K(p)y \tag{4.71}$$

where $D(p)$ and $K(p)$ are polynomials in p:

$$\begin{aligned}D(p) &= p^n + A_1 p^{n-1} + \cdots + A_n \\ K(p) &= B_0 p^m + B_1 p^{m-1} + \cdots + B_m\end{aligned} \qquad n \geqslant m \tag{4.72}$$

If one sets

$$W(p) = \frac{K(p)}{D(p)} \tag{4.73}$$

Eq. (4.68) becomes

$$-\sigma = W(p)y \tag{4.74}$$

The quantity $W(p)$ is the *transfer function* of the linear theory. If one replaces the operator p by $i\omega$ in (4.73), $i = \sqrt{-1}$, one obtains the frequency characteristic of the linear part

$$W(i\omega) = \frac{K(i\omega)}{D(i\omega)} \tag{4.75}$$

from the input y to the output $-\sigma$.

As previously mentioned, the frequency characteristics are often used in linear control theory. ω is considered as a parameter, which permits tracing the curve—the *hodograph*—without the actual integration of the differential system; this is one of the advantages of the complex-variable treatment, which was mentioned in Sec. 4.13.

In addition to the hodograph (or characteristic) $W(i\omega)$, one can use sometimes the *modified hodograph* $W^*(\omega)$, which is defined by the relation

$$\text{Re } W^*(\omega) = \text{Re } W(i\omega) \qquad \text{Im } W^*(\omega) = \omega \text{ Im } W(i\omega) \tag{4.76}$$

The hodograph $W^*(\omega)$ differs from the hodograph $W(i\omega)$ merely in its extension along the imaginary axis. Besides this, since $W^*(\omega) = W^*(-\omega)$, it is sufficient to study the hodograph for $\omega > 0$, since the same hodograph corresponds to the negative ω. Since in the polynomials

$$\begin{aligned}D(p) &= p^n + A_1 p^{n-1} + \cdots + A_n \\ K(p) &= B_0 p^m + B_1 p^{m-1} + \cdots + B_m\end{aligned} \tag{4.77}$$

one has $n \geqslant m$, several cases must be considered:

1. If $n - m \geqslant 1$, one has the relation

$$\lim_{\omega \to \infty} W(i\omega) = 0 \tag{4.78}$$

Likewise, if $n - m > 1$, one has also the relation

$$\lim W^*(\omega) = 0 \qquad \text{for } \omega \to \infty \tag{4.78a}$$

2. If $n - m = 1$, one has

$$\operatorname*{Re\,}_{\lim \omega \to \infty} W^*(\omega) = 0 \qquad \operatorname*{Im\,}_{\lim \omega \to \infty} W^*(\omega) = -B_0^* \tag{4.79}$$

In this case the limit point on the hodograph is on the imaginary axis.

For $\omega = 0$ the initial point (for $n - m = 1$) is

$$W(0) = \frac{K(0)}{D(0)} = \frac{B_m}{A_n} \tag{4.80}$$

so that both hodographs begin ($\omega = 0$) at the same point of the real axis. It should be noted that both the initial and the final points of both hodographs are situated in a finite region of the complex plane if ω is finite. If, however, $\omega \to 0$ for the hodograph $W(i\omega)$, there is an exception to this rule, since the hodograph in this case extends to infinity if $K(0) \neq 0$.

4.16   ANALYSIS OF LINEAR PROBLEMS

In the case in which the relation $y = \varphi(\sigma)$ reduces to $y = h\sigma$, the problem is linear.

$$\dot{x}_i = \sum_{j=1}^{n} a_{ij} x_i + h b_i \sigma \qquad i = 1, \ldots, n \tag{4.81}$$

The characteristic operator in this case is

$$D(p) + hK(p) = 0 \tag{4.82}$$

and it is noted that the system is (H) if $0 \leqslant h \leqslant k$.

If the system is opened, the characteristic operator reduces to

$$D(p) = 0 \tag{4.83}$$

If the system is closed ($h \neq 0$), it is necessary that the hodograph of the vector

$$h_0 W(i\omega) = \frac{h_0 K(i\omega)}{D(i\omega)} \tag{4.84}$$

should not intersect the real axis between the points -1 and $-\infty$ and that negative intersection (say downward) should correspond to a positive intersection (say upward).

With respect to the hodograph $W(i\omega)$ the above statement is equivalent to the condition that no intersection with the real axis should take place in the interval $(-1/h_0, -\infty)$. If h_0 varies between 0 and k, the quantity $-1/h_0$ varies between $-1/k$ and $-\infty$. Hence the conclusion:

For the stability of (4.80) for any h in the interval $0 \leqslant h \leqslant k$ it is necessary and sufficient that the hodograph $W(i\omega)$ and hence also $W^*(\omega)$ (since their points of intersection with the real axis are the same) should not have any intersections with the real axis between $-\infty$ and $-1/k$, including the latter point.

In this manner the interval $(-1/k, -\infty)$ is a kind of *forbidden region* which the hodograph must not reach; this holds for any h. So far we are in agreement with the Nyquist diagram, since the problem is linear; Fig. 4.5 illustrates this case.

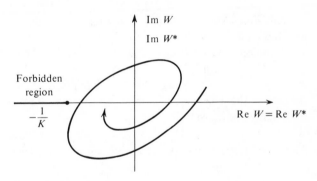

Fig. 4.5

4.17   ANALYSIS OF NONLINEAR PROBLEMS

In the nonlinear case $y = \varphi(\sigma)$ is a nonlinear function of σ. It is useful to mention (the details are in Chap. 5) that this formula characterizes the relation between the signal σ and the response $\varphi(\sigma)$ of the servomotor, and it is well known that such relations are nonlinear (dead zones, coulomb friction, saturation, etc.). As mentioned earlier, the condition

$$0 < \frac{\varphi(\sigma)}{\sigma} \leqslant k \qquad \sigma \neq 0 \tag{4.85}$$

has been introduced (Lur'e), in which k is a finite positive number which can even be infinity. This means that the nonlinear characteristic is contained entirely between $y = k\sigma$ and the abscissa axis. Since the sign of equality is also admitted, the curve $y = \varphi(\sigma)$ may have some points of intersection with the sides of the angle and can even coincide with them over finite intervals.

One can introduce now, on the basis of inequality (4.85), the following definition of absolute stability.

We call systems of the form (4.66) *absolutely stable if, for a given k and for any $\varphi(\sigma)$ satisfying inequality* (4.85), *the zero solution is asymptotically stable in the whole phase space.*

In general, the problem of absolute stability may be formulated in three different manners:

1. Knowing system (4.66) (i.e., knowing its coefficients), investigate the absolute stability in the angle $[0,k]$.
2. Knowing the coefficients of (4.66), determine the maximum value of k for which absolute stability exists.
3. Knowing k and being able to change some of the coefficients, determine them in such a manner as to have the maximum region G in which absolute stability exists.

The third problem has not yet been completely solved (1963).

4.18 POPOV'S THEOREM

It is useful to explain first the significance and scope of the theorem. The first question is: what additional requirements must be fulfilled in order to justify the existence of absolute stability in the nonlinear case? The answer to this question is given by the following theorem.

Theorem 1 *The sufficient condition for the absolute stability of system* (4.66) *in angle* $[0,k]$ *and in the normal case is that there be a finite real* *number q for which for any ω > 0 the inequality*

$$(P): \quad \text{Re} \, (1 + iq\omega)W(i\omega) + \frac{1}{k} > 0 \tag{4.86}$$

holds.

One can give the following geometrical interpretation to this theorem by writing

$$W^*(\omega) = X + iY \tag{4.87}$$

where

$$\text{Re} \, (1 + iq\omega)W(i\omega) = \text{Re} \, W(i\omega) - q\omega \, \text{Im} \, W(i\omega) = X - q^Y$$

Condition (4.86) then becomes

$$X - q^Y + \frac{1}{k} > 0 \qquad \text{for any } \omega > 0 \tag{4.88}$$

Equation

$$X - q^Y + \frac{1}{k} = 0 \tag{4.89}$$

represents a straight line P (the Popov line), which passes through the point $(-1/k,0)$ on the abscissa axis and has a slope equal to $1/q$. The line P divides the plane into two half-planes. Criterion (4.88) specifies the half-plane *to the right* of P. This permits formulating the theorem in a geometrical form.

Theorem 2   *For conditions specified in Theorem 1 it is sufficient to determine a straight line P passing through the point $(-1/k,0)$ such that the hodograph $W^*(\omega)$ be situated strictly to the right of P.*

Figure 4.6 illustrates this condition; in (a), (b), and (c) of that figure Popov's criterion is fulfilled and absolute stability exists. In (d) of that figure line P does not exist, although the hodograph does not intersect the abscissa axis in the "forbidden interval." Several remarks are noteworthy:

1. According to the theorem, the hodograph must be situated to the right of P; in such a case it cannot cut the abscissa axis to the left of $(-1/k,0)$ or at this point.
2. In the original formulation the criterion requires that the hodograph be situated to the right of P. It is clear that this condition can be

weakened to the extent of admitting some points of intersection of the hodograph and P.   In such a case absolute stability cannot be guaranteed for the angle $[0,k]$ but for a smaller angle $[0, k - \epsilon]$; $0 \leqslant \epsilon \leqslant k$. Geometrically this means that after the straight line P has been drawn

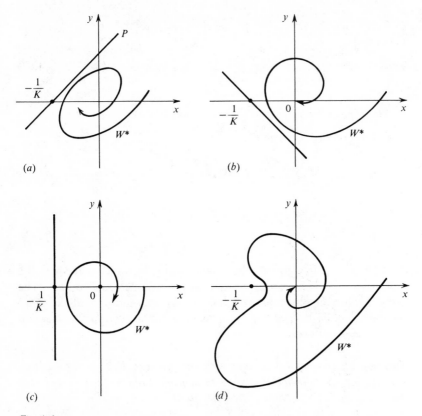

Fig. 4.6

through the point $(-1/k,0)$, one draws a parallel line P' (parallel to P) through the point $(-1/(k - \epsilon), 0]$; the theorem clearly holds with respect to the line P'.

3. Sometimes it is convenient to replace (4.86) with

$$(P_\delta): \quad \text{Re } (1 + iq\omega)W(i\omega) + \frac{1}{k} \geqslant \delta > 0 \qquad (4.90)$$

where δ is a positive number; in fact if the limit point $W^*(\infty)$ is not on P, then the shortest distance between the points on P and $W^*(\omega)$ is always a positive number.   In such a case any point (X, Y) of $W^*(\omega)$ satisfies the inequality

$$X - q^Y + \frac{1}{k} \geqslant \delta > 0 \tag{4.91}$$

which justifies the above assertion.   If the limit point $W^*(\infty)$ is on P, one can turn P around the point $(-1/k,0)$ [in fact this limit point cannot coincide with the point $(-1/k,0)$], so that all points of $W^*(\omega)$ will again be to the right of P', where P' is the new position of P after the rotation (Fig. 4.7).

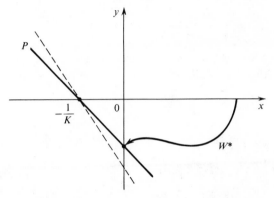

Fig. 4.7

4. For the proof of the theorem one can use the normal case, that is, the case corresponding to the angle $[0,k]$ (Fig. 4.4); special cases corresponding to $[\epsilon,k]$ (Fig. 4.3) can be reduced to the normal case by a linear transformation

$$y = k\sigma - \tilde{y} \tag{4.92}$$

which transforms the system (4.66) to a similar system but with different coefficients and a different nonlinear function: $\tilde{\varphi}(\sigma) = k\sigma - \varphi(\sigma)$.

If $\varphi(\sigma)$ satisfies the inequality

$$0 < \frac{\varphi(\sigma)}{\sigma} \leqslant k \qquad \sigma \neq 0 \tag{4.93}$$

$\tilde{\varphi}(\sigma)$ will likewise satisfy the inequality

$$0 \leqslant \frac{\tilde{\varphi}(\sigma)}{\sigma} < k \tag{4.94}$$

Hence transformation (4.92) transforms the characteristics of the angle $(0,k]$ into those of the angle $[0,k)$ and interchanges the sides of this angle; thus the characteristic $\varphi(\sigma) = 0$ becomes $\tilde{\varphi}(\sigma) = k\sigma$ and $\varphi(\sigma) = k\sigma$ becomes $\tilde{\varphi}(\sigma) = 0$. Hence, if the initial system was stable for $\varphi(\sigma) = k\sigma$, the transformed system will be stable for $\tilde{\varphi}(\sigma) = 0$. In this case transformation (4.92) transforms a special case into the fundamental, or "normal," one. Between $W(i\omega)$ and $\tilde{W}(i\omega)$ there exists a relation

$$-\sigma = W(i\omega)y = W(i\omega)(k\sigma - \tilde{y}) \tag{4.95}$$

From this

$$-\sigma = \frac{W(i\omega)}{1 + kW(i\omega)} = \tilde{W}(i\omega)\tilde{y} \tag{4.96}$$

which shows that between the new characteristic $\tilde{W}$ and the old one there is a relation

$$\tilde{W}(i\omega) = -\frac{W(i\omega)}{1 + kW(i\omega)} \tag{4.97}$$

In view of this

$$\operatorname{Re}(1 - iq\omega)\tilde{W} + \frac{1}{k} = \operatorname{Re}\left[(-1 + iq\omega)\frac{W}{1 + kW} + \frac{1}{k}\right]$$

$$= \operatorname{Re}\frac{iq\omega W + (1/k)}{1 + kW} = \frac{1}{|1 + kW|^2}\operatorname{Re}\left[\left(iq\omega W + \frac{1}{k}\right)(1 + k\overline{W})\right]$$

$$= \frac{1}{(1 + kW)^2}\operatorname{Re}\left[(1 + iq\omega W) + \frac{1}{k}\right] \tag{4.98}$$

This shows that for special cases inequality (4.86) for $W(i\omega)$ becomes

$$\operatorname{Re}(1 - iq\omega)\tilde{W}(i\omega) + \frac{1}{k - \epsilon} > 0 \tag{4.99}$$

Thus if Popov's theorem is proved for the normal case, the transformed system [in view of (4.99)] has absolute stability in the angle $[0, k - \epsilon]$ also. In such a case the initial system is stable in $[\epsilon,k]$, which proves the statement.

5. The discussion in (4) shows that the "special cases" can be reduced to the "normal" ones. In fact, instead of (4.86) one can use a weaker condition

$$\operatorname{Re}(1 + iq\omega)W(i\omega) + \frac{1}{k} > 0 \qquad 0 < \omega < \infty \tag{4.100}$$

since the inequality

$$\text{Re}\,(1 + iq\omega)W(i\omega) + \frac{1}{k} \geqslant 0 \qquad 0 \leqslant \omega < \infty \tag{4.101}$$

holds in view of (4.98). Inequality (4.100) does not preclude the existence of common points between $W^*(\omega)$ and the line P. Apart from (4.101) it is necessary that the initial system be stable for $\varphi(\sigma) = k\sigma$. In view of this $W^*(\omega)$ and hence $W(i\omega)$ must go through the point $(-1/k,0)$. In this manner condition (4.86) can be weakened still more, and

$$\text{Re}\,(1 + iq\omega)W(i\omega) + \frac{1}{k} \geqslant 0 \qquad W(i\omega) \neq -\frac{1}{k} \qquad \text{for } \omega \geqslant 0$$
$$\tag{4.102}$$

This means that in a special case the hodograph $W^*(\omega)$ can have any common point with P except the point $(-1/k,0)$.

6. In the preceding it was assumed that $q > 0$. In the case in which $q < 0$ one can again apply (4.92). Since the initial system is stable for $\varphi(\sigma) = k\sigma$, the transformed system will be a stable linear system for $\tilde{\varphi}(\sigma) = 0$. In this case the transformation transforms a special case into the normal one. Since $W(i\omega)$ is finite in the latter, from Eqs. (4.86) and (4.98) it follows that

$$\text{Re}\,(1 - iq\omega)\tilde{W}(i\omega) + \frac{1}{k} > 0 \tag{4.103}$$

This inequality differs from (4.86) only by the sign of q and the replacement of $W(i\omega)$ by $\tilde{W}(i\omega)$. Hence for the new (transformed) system Popov's condition is fulfilled for $q > 0$ in the normal case. Since, however, in this case the theorem is proved, the new system has absolute stability also. From this the absolute stability of the initial system follows also, since the two systems (the original and the transformed) are in reality the *same physical* system, and the difference between them is merely the matter of notations. This shows that the initial system has absolute stability for $q < 0$.

7. There remains the last case; that is, when $q = 0$. In such a case condition (4.86) reduces to the case in which $q > 0$ in (P). In fact, if $W^*(\omega)$ is to the right of the vertical through $(-1/k,0)$, it is also to the right with respect to the straight line through that point and has a sufficiently large slope. In view of these remarks it is sufficient to consider $q > 0$ in the proof of Popov's theorem. This proof (Aiserman and Gantmacher [2] and Popov [15] and [16]) is not reproduced here.

4.19   EXAMPLE

We propose to investigate system (4.66) in the following case:

$$\dot{x}_1 = a_{11}x_1 + a_{12}x_2 + b_1 y \qquad \dot{x}_2 = a_{21}x_1 + a_{22}x_2 + b_2 y$$
$$\sigma = c_1 x_1 + c_2 x_2 \qquad y = \varphi(\sigma) \tag{4.104}$$

In the normal case, in view of the assumed property [H] of the linear part of the system

$$A_1 = -a_{11} - a_{22} > 0 \qquad A_2 = a_{11}a_{22} - a_{12}^2 > 0 \tag{4.105}$$

Eliminating x_1 and x_2, one obtains the fundamental equation (4.71) in the form

$$D(p)(-\sigma) = K(p)y \tag{4.106}$$

where

$$D(p) = p^2 + A_1 p + A_2 \qquad K(p) = B_0 p + B_1$$

In these expressions

$$B_0 = -(b_1 c_1 + b_2 c_2) \qquad B_1 = a_{11}b_2 c_2 - a_{12}b_2 c_1 - a_{21}b_1 c_2 + a_{22}b_1 c_1$$

Hence the transfer function (from y to $-\sigma$) is

$$W(p) = \frac{B_0 p + B_1}{p^2 + A_1 p + A_2} \tag{4.107}$$

and the frequency characteristic is

$$W(i\omega) = \frac{iB_0\omega + B_1}{(A_2 - \omega^2) + iA_1\omega} = \frac{(iB_0\omega + B_1)[(A_2 - \omega^2)^2 - iA_1\omega]}{(A_2 - \omega^2) + A_1^2\omega^2} \tag{4.108}$$

The characteristic $W^*(\omega)$ (Sec. 4.15) has the following real and imaginary parts:

$$X = \frac{B_1(A_2 - u) + B_0 A_1 u}{(A_2 - u)^2 + A_1^2 u} \qquad Y = \frac{[B_0(A_2 - u) - B_1 A_1]u}{(A_2 - u)^2 + A_1^2 u} \tag{4.109}$$

where $u = \omega^2$.   The characteristic hodograph W^* always has a common point with the X axis ($Y = 0$) for $u = 0$; the abscissa of this point is

$$X_0 = \frac{B_1}{A_2} \tag{4.110}$$

It can have a second common point for

$$u = u_1 = A_2 - \frac{B_1 A_1}{B_0} \tag{4.111}$$

provided that $B_0 \neq 0$ and $u_1 \geqslant 0$. The abscissa of this second point of intersection with the X axis is given by the expression

$$X_1 = \frac{B_0(B_1{}^2 - B_0 B_1 A_1 + B_0{}^2 A_2)}{A_1(B_1{}^2 - B_0 B_1 A + B_0{}^2 A_2)} = \frac{B_0}{A_1} \tag{4.112}$$

We investigate the case in which $W^*(\omega)$ and the X axis have a common point with a negative abscissa. If there is such a point, its abscissa is designated by X^*. If, however, there are two points of intersection, with abscissas X_0 and X_1, we define

$$X^* = \min (X_0, X_1) \tag{4.113}$$

In such a case the angle (OK^*), $K^* = 1/|X^*|$, is the maximum angle in which stability exists for the linear characteristics $y = h\sigma; 0 \leqslant h < k^*$. It is possible to show that through the point $(X^*,0)$ one can draw a straight line (in the X, Y plane) so as to have $W^*(\omega)$ to the right of this line.

Consider first the case in which $W^*(\omega)$ has two common points with the X axis and take the tangent to $W^*(\omega)$ at the point $(X^*,0)$. Since $n = 2$, $W^*(\omega)$ cannot have more than two common points with any straight lines. However, any tangent to $W^*(\omega)$ has a double common point, so that in this case no other common points are possible. This means that the hodograph $W^*(\omega)$ is always situated on one side with respect to any of its tangents. This means that $W^*(\omega)$ is a convex curve. With respect to the tangent through $(X^*,0)$ the hodograph W^* is situated to the right, since its second common point (with the X axis) is also to the right.

If there is only one common point with the axis (i.e., for $u = 0$), then the whole hodograph W^* is situated on one side of the X axis; since W^* in the fundamental case is situated in the finite region, one can obtain the line P' by a small rotation of the X axis around the point $(X^*,0)$. The line P (the Popov line) can be obtained from P' by a small parallel shift to the left; it will go through the point of the X axis with the abscissa $- 1/(k^* - \epsilon); 0 \leqslant \epsilon \leqslant 1$. In such a case there will be absolute stability in the angle $[0, k^* - \epsilon]$.

If, however, $X_0 > 0$ and there is no second intersection of $W^*(\omega)$ with the X axis (or $X_1 > 0$), then the line P can go through the origin; in this case $k = \infty$ in the Popov criterion. If $X_0 > 0$, $X_1 > 0$ (or there is no second point of intersection), the line P can be traced through any point of the negative real axis; in such a case absolute stability exists in any angle $[0,k]$ where k is a finite number.

To summarize, if system (4.104) is stable for any linear characteristics $y = h\sigma$, $0 \leqslant h < k$, there is absolute stability in the angle $[0, k - \epsilon]$. This result was obtained by Erugin [4], Malkin [12], and Krasovski [5] by a different argument.

REFERENCES

1. Aiserman, M. A.: *Automatika i Tel.*, no. 223,1946 and no. 8, 1947; and *Vsp. Nauch. Foto.*, *Akad. Nauk. USSR*, vol. 4, 1949.
2. Aiserman, M. A., and F. R. Gantmacher: "Absolute Stability of Control Systems," U.S.S.R. Academy of Science, 1963.
3. Cesari, L.: "Asymptotic Behavior and Stability Problems," Springer-Verlag OHG, Berlin, 1959.
4. Erugin, N. P.: *Prikl. Mat. i Mekh.*, vol. 15, no. 2, 1951.
5. Krasovski, N. N.: Stability of Motion, Stanford University Press, Stanford, California, 1963.
6. LaSalle, J. P: *SIAM Rev.*, November, 1963.
7. LaSalle, J. P., and S. Lefschetz: "Stability of Liapounov's Direct Method with Applications," Academic Press, Inc., New York, 1961.
8. Liapounov, A. M.: "Probleme générale de la stabilité du mouvement," *Ann. Fac. Sci. Toulouse*, 1892.
9. Lur'e, A. I.: "Some Nonlinear Problems of Automatic Control," Goztehizdat, Moscow, 1957.
10. Lur'e, A. I.: *Prikl. Mat. i Mekh.*, vol. 9, no. 5, 1945; Direct Method of Liapounov, *Proc. 2d Pan Union Conf.*, 1955.
11. Lur'e, A. I. and U. N. Postnikeov: *Prikl. Mat. i Mekh.*, vol. 8, no. 3, 1944.
12. Malkin, I. G.: "Theory of Stability of Motion," Goztehizdat, Moscow, 1952.
13. Minorsky, J.: *Amer. Soc. Nav. Eng.*, May, 1922; Control Problems, *J. Fr. Inst.*, vol. 6, no. 232, 1941.
14. Poincaré, H.: "Les Méthodes Nouvelles de la Mécanique Céleste," vol. 1, Gauthiers-Villars, Paris, 1892.
15. Popov, V. M.: *Automatika i Tell.*, vol. 24, no. 1, 1963; vol. 23, no. 2, 1962; vol. 22, no. 8, 1961; vol. 19, no. 1, 1958.
16. Popov, V. M.: *Roumanian Akad. Sci.*, vol. 10, no. 1, 1960; vol. 9, no. 4, 1959; vol. 9, no. 1, 1959.
17. Silvester, J. J.: "Collected Mathematical Papers," vol. 1, p. 511, Cambridge, 1904.
18. Tsypkin, J. L.: *Dokl. Akad. Nauk. USSR*, vol. 145, no. 1, 1962.

CHAPTER FIVE
STABILITY
OF NONLINEAR
CONTROL SYSTEMS

5.1 INTRODUCTORY REMARKS

In this chapter we shall outline some applications of Liapounov's second method to problems of control. It should be noted that more than half a century elapsed between the formulation of this method by Liapounov and the time at which it began to be applied to problems of stability in control systems. This was mainly because of the difficulty of adopting this method to the differential systems which appear in control theory. A. I. Lur'e [2] and Lur'e and Postnikov [3] finally showed that if certain equations in control theory are reduced to a special *canonical form*, the application of Liapounov's second method is greatly facilitated and the problem of stability is solved in a relatively simple manner without the necessity of integrating the variational equations. Also, one can obtain directly the stability *in the large*, and this is of great importance in problems of control.

Lur'e's early work (around 1944) was closely followed by A. M. Letov [1], who systematically applied Lur'e's transformation to practically all known control problems; in this manner he established the problem of stability in nonlinear control systems on a new foundation.

In this chapter we shall attempt to give only a short review of this subject; for details refer to Letov [1]. The first seven sections of this chapter relate to a number of preliminary questions (such as Lur'e's transformation, the idealizations used, etc.). The application of

Lur'e's transformation to the problem of stability begins in Sec. 9, after its reduction to the canonical form has been explained.

Although the preliminaries may appear long and tedious (mainly because of the general form of equations written for a system with n degrees of freedom), the final result [see Eq. (5.63)] is so simple that the idea of the second method becomes almost obvious after one has gone through a long chain of these preliminary transformations.   From Eqs. (5.63) one can also see why the second method gives the *sufficient* criteria of stability and also why the stability so obtained is "in the large."

One should not, however, be overoptimistic about the method, since its difficulty lies in the *preliminary arrangement* of the problem to the form in which its application is simple.   The problem finally reduces to showing that the function V and its Eulerian derivative have opposite signs.   To reiterate, the reader must keep in mind that, although the second method is ultimately simple, the preparation of the ground for its application is, unfortunately, not simple, and it is precisely here that a physical grasp of the problem may help considerably in obtaining conditions under which a given problem can be simplified.

5.2   FORMULATION OF THE PROBLEM

The dynamic behavior of a linear system of m degrees of freedom can be expressed by a system of differential equations of the form

$$\dot{\eta}_k = \sum_{\alpha=1}^{m} b_{k\alpha}\eta_\alpha \qquad k = 1, \ldots, m \tag{5.1}$$

where η_k are some generalized coordinates and $b_{k\alpha}$ are constant parameters.   In this form the differential system (5.1) represents the *uncontrolled motion* of the corresponding dynamic (electrical, mechanical, etc.) system, and the problem of control consists precisely in influencing this uncontrolled motion by adding some terms characterizing the control action.

It is well known that the behavior of a system like this depends on the nature of the roots of its fundamental matrix.   This is usually expressed in the form of the "secular" or *characteristic* equation of the form

$$D(\rho) = |b_{\alpha k} + \rho\delta_{k\alpha}| = 0 \tag{5.2}$$

where ρ is a root and

$$\delta_{\alpha k} = \begin{cases} 0 & \text{for } k \neq \alpha \\ 1 & \text{for } k = \alpha \end{cases}$$

For simplicity of calculations ρ has been changed into $-\rho$ in Eq. (5.2).

In view of this all familiar criteria are just reversed in these notations (Letov's), and we shall preserve this arrangement in what follows.

System (5.1) is thus inherently stable, neutral, or unstable according to whether Re (ρ_k) is positive, zero, (at least for some coordinates), or negative, respectively.

We assume now that the uncontrolled system (5.1) is acted upon by some kind of controlling device whose action in different coordinates (or degrees of freedom) is indicated in the terms $n_k\mu$; $k = 1, \ldots, m$, μ being the coordinate of a control device of some kind, which, at the same time, measures the intensity of the control action.

Equations of a controlled system will then be

$$\dot{\eta}_k = \sum_{\alpha=1}^{m} b_{k\alpha}\eta_\alpha + n_k\mu \tag{5.3}$$

This is a very general, and a rather vague, formulation of the problem; we must introduce more definite information regarding the terms $n_k\mu$. The quantity μ measures the action of the regulating element in a particular degree of freedom, and the constant parameters n_k show how this action is felt in *other* degrees of freedom. There is a tacit assumption that μ itself is characterized by a differential equation in *its own* degree of freedom, such as:

$$V^2\ddot{\mu} + W\dot{\mu} + S\mu = f^*(\sigma) \tag{5.4}$$

where, in general, $V^2 =$ inertia
$$W = \text{velocity damping}$$
$$S = \text{restoring force}$$
This system is acted on by a force (or moment) $f^*(\sigma)$—a function of the signal σ. Very often some of these component actions may be negligible.

Thus, for instance, if V^2 and S are negligible, the differential equation (5.4) becomes

$$\dot{\mu} = \frac{1}{W} f^*(\sigma) = f(\sigma) \tag{5.4a}$$

Systems with such properties are often encountered when the control action is exerted by hydraulic mechanisms (e.g., variable-delivery pumps).

The signal σ remains to be analyzed; very often this signal (from control instruments) has the form (see Appendix)

$$\sigma = m\theta + n\dot{\theta} + p\ddot{\theta} \tag{5.5}$$

where θ is the departure of the system from its set equilibrium point $\theta = \theta_0 = 0$. In this form (5.5) it is apparent that the signal consists of a linear combination of the coordinate θ and its first and second derivatives, the coefficients m, n, and p being some proportionality factors.

In the general theory the variable η may be any quantity such that the same relation (5.5) can be written

$$\sigma = \sum_{\alpha=1}^{m} p_\alpha \eta_\alpha \qquad k = 1, \ldots, m \tag{5.6}$$

in which for the particular case (5.5) $\eta_1 = \theta$, $\eta_2 = \dot{\theta}$, and $\eta_3 = \ddot{\theta}$, the coefficients p_α being m, n, and p respectively of (5.5).

Some authors also specify the so-called "followup action" by writing (5.6) in the form

$$\sigma = \sum_{\alpha=1}^{m} p_\alpha \eta_\alpha - r\mu \tag{5.6a}$$

This form is a little more explicit than (5.6) and means that the action of the signal $\sum_{\alpha=1}^{m} p_\alpha \eta_\alpha$ is *reduced* owing to the followup (or feedback) of the control coordinate μ, which is affected by the feedback coefficient r. In this form [Eq. (5.6a)] one recognizes σ as the *error function* in control engineering terminology.

The nonlinear function $f(\sigma)$ representing the controlling force (or moment) may have different expressions according to the circumstances. For example, if one wishes to take into account the static (coulomb) friction, one can specify $f(\sigma)$ by the expressions

$$\begin{aligned} f(\sigma) &= 0 &&\text{for } |\sigma| \leqslant \sigma^* \\ \sigma f(\sigma) &> 0 &&\text{for } |\sigma| > \sigma^* \end{aligned} \tag{5.7}$$

where σ^* is a fixed positive number characterizing the "dead zone" of the static friction. For $|\sigma| > \sigma^*$ the signal will actually start the control action; for $|\sigma| < \sigma^*$, although the signal exists, the regulating element is blocked by the static friction.

Thus for $|\sigma| > \sigma^*$, the function $f(\sigma)$ is continuous, but for $\sigma = \pm \sigma^*$ it can become discontinuous.

In some cases, e.g., when the regulating element reacts rapidly on the signal, there may be the additional conditions

$$\sigma^* = 0 \qquad \left| \frac{df(\sigma)}{d\sigma} \right| \geqslant h > 0 \qquad \sigma \varphi(\sigma) > 0 \qquad \text{if } \sigma \neq 0 \tag{5.8}$$

where $\varphi(\sigma) = f(\sigma) - h\sigma$, and h is a fixed constant.

In what follows we shall refer to $f(\sigma)$, defined by Eq. (5.7), as belonging to class A, and to those functions which require the additional condition (5.8) as belonging to sublcass A'.

These terms (Letov's) emphasize that in case A' the regulating element has practically no dead zone.

Such conditions are sufficiently well fulfilled, as we mentioned in connection with modern variable-delivery pumps, in which the gradient of the driving force (or moment) is sufficiently high to be able to neglect the static friction even for small values of the signal σ. For that reason it is simpler to deal with the subclass A' only.

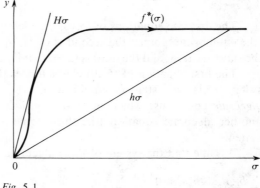

Fig. 5.1

In the case of the experimental curve giving $f(\sigma)$ (Fig. 5.1) it is sufficient to consider the characteristic in the region limited by two straight lines $H\sigma$ and $h\sigma$, $h > 0$ only. This classification is merely intended to characterize how closely a given characteristic approaches a purely discontinuous characteristic for which $H = \tan(\pi/2) = \infty$.

In such an ideal case, Eq. (5.6a) becomes

$$\sum_{\alpha=1}^{m} p_\alpha \eta_\alpha - r\mu = 0 \qquad (5.9)$$

In other words, the followup action $r\mu$ adjusts itself practically instantaneously to the value of the coordinate η, even for a small value of the signal σ. Clearly Eq. (5.9) represents an idealization of the regulating element devoid of any dead zone. One must keep in mind, however, that the fulfillment of condition (5.9) *is merely an idealization*; the nearer one comes to it, the more accurate is the predetermination of operation by Eq. (5.4).

5.3   EQUATIONS OF CONTROLLED SYSTEMS

With these preliminaries one can study in detail systems (5.1), (5.4), and (5.6a) of control equations.   The equilibrium point which a control system is supposed to maintain is then

$$\sum_{\alpha=1}^{m} b_{k\alpha}\eta_\alpha + n_k\mu = 0 \qquad k = 1, \ldots, m$$

$$S\mu = f^*(\sigma) \tag{5.10}$$

$$\sigma = \sum_{\alpha=1}^{m} p_\alpha\eta_\alpha - r\mu = 0$$

The first two equations of (5.10) are merely (5.3), in which $\dot{\eta}_k = 0$ (the equilibrium point); the second is (5.4), in which we conserve only the static friction; and the third is (5.6), that is, an ideal followup action.

The first equation of (5.10) characterizes the singular point of the system (5.1)—the state of equilibrium.   It is given by a system of *algebraic* equations, which must be considered in conjunction with another algebraic equation [the third equation of (5.10)] of control systems.

Assume that the system of these algebraic equations

$$\sum_{\alpha=1}^{m} b_{k\alpha}\eta_\alpha + n_k\mu = 0 \qquad \sum_{\alpha=1}^{m} p_\alpha\eta_\alpha - r\mu = \sigma \qquad k = 1, \ldots, m \tag{5.11}$$

has its determinant Δ different from zero:

$$\Delta = \begin{vmatrix} b_{11} & \cdots & b_{1m} & n_1 \\ \cdots\cdots\cdots\cdots\cdots\cdots \\ b_{m1} & \cdots & b_{mm} & n_m \\ p_1 & \cdots & p_m & -r \end{vmatrix} \neq 0 \tag{5.12}$$

In such a case (5.11) has a nontrivial solution of the form

$$\eta_k = A_k\sigma \qquad \mu = B\sigma \qquad k = 1, \ldots, m \tag{5.13}$$

where A_k and B can be determined, B being given by

$$B = \frac{\begin{vmatrix} b_{11} & \cdots & b_{1m} \\ \cdots\cdots\cdots\cdots \\ b_{n1} & \cdots & b_{mm} \end{vmatrix}}{\begin{vmatrix} b_{11} & \cdots & b_{1m} & n_1 \\ \cdots\cdots\cdots\cdots\cdots\cdots \\ b_{m1} & \cdots & b_{mm} & n_m \\ p_1 & \cdots & p_m & -r \end{vmatrix}} \tag{5.14}$$

There are clearly two possibilities according to whether $f^*(\sigma)$ belongs to class A or to subclass A'. If $f^*(\sigma)$ belongs to class A', it means that there is no static friction, and in this case the solution is trivial:

$$\eta_k^* = 0 \qquad k = 1, \ldots, m \qquad \mu^* = 0 \tag{5.15}$$

In case A, there is a "dead zone" of static friction, and any point in that zone may be regarded as an "equilibrium point." One has thus a continuum of solutions σ^* so long as $|\sigma^*| < \bar{\sigma}$, $\bar{\sigma}$ being the limit of the dead zone (of the coulomb friction).

5.4 THE NORMAL FORM OF DIFFERENTIAL EQUATIONS

Suppose that we are dealing with subclass A'; this will permit us to treat the problem more uniformly on the basis of differential equations.

Introducing a new variable

$$\xi = p\dot{\mu} + q\mu \tag{5.16}$$

in which the constants p and q are yet to be determined, we have first

$$\dot{\xi} = p\ddot{\mu} + q\dot{\mu} \tag{5.17}$$

Equations (5.16) and (5.17) permit determining $\dot{\mu}$ and $\ddot{\mu}$ in terms of μ, ξ and $\dot{\xi}$. The replacement of $\dot{\mu}$ and $\ddot{\mu}$ in (5.4) gives

$$\frac{V^2}{p}\dot{\xi} + \frac{1}{p}\left(W - \frac{q}{p}V^2\right)\xi + \left[S - W\frac{q}{p} + V^2\left(\frac{q}{p}\right)^2\right]\mu = f(\sigma)^* \tag{5.18}$$

If one determines $q/p = \lambda$ as the root of the square bracket in (5.18), one has

$$\lambda_1 = \rho_{m+1} \qquad \lambda_2 = \frac{S}{V^2}\frac{1}{\lambda_1} = \frac{1}{V^2}[W - \lambda_1 V^2] = \rho_{m+2} \tag{5.19}$$

Thus instead of (5.4) one has now a system

$$\dot{\mu} = -\mu\rho_{m+1} + \frac{1}{p}\xi$$

$$\dot{\xi} = -\xi\rho_{m+2} + \frac{p}{V^2}f^*(\sigma) \tag{5.20}$$

Since S, W, and V^2 are positive, the quadratic equation $V^2\lambda^2 - W\lambda + S = 0$ has roots with positive real parts.   With the notations

$$\mu = \eta_{m+1} \qquad \eta_k = b_{k,m+1} \qquad b_{m+1,k} = 0 \qquad b_{m+1,m+1} = -\rho_{m+1}$$

$$h_k = 0 \qquad k = 1, \ldots, m$$

$$h_{m+1} = \frac{1}{p} \quad \frac{p}{V^2} \, f^*(0) = f(\sigma) \qquad m + 1 = n \qquad p_{m+1} = -r_i \tag{5.21}$$

the equations take the form

$$\dot{\eta}_k = \sum_{\alpha=1}^{n} b_{k\alpha}\eta_\alpha + \eta_k\xi \qquad k = 1, \ldots, n \qquad \dot{\xi} = -\rho_{n+1}\xi + f(\sigma)$$

$$\sigma = \sum_{\alpha=1}^{n} p_\alpha\eta_\alpha \tag{5.22}$$

A number of particular cases can be discussed on this basis (Letov [1, pages 50–52]).

5.5 THE CANONICAL FORM OF DIFFERENTIAL EQUATIONS IN CONTROL THEORY

The principal purpose of the reduction of differential equations to the *canonical form* is to facilitate the application of Liapounov's second method.   It will be shown later that several forms of this reduction are possible according to whether the uncontrolled system is inherently stable or not.   In this section the reduction in which the system without control is already stable is outlined; this case is designated as the *first form* of the canonical transformation.

The canonical variables are defined as

$$x_s = \sum_{\alpha=1}^{n} C_\alpha^{(s)}\eta_\alpha + \xi \qquad s = 1, \ldots, n \tag{5.23}$$

Differentiating these equations and making use of (5.22) in order to eliminate the derivatives, one obtains

$$\dot{x}_s = \sum_{\alpha=1}^{n} C_\alpha^{(s)}\left(\sum_{\beta=1}^{n} b_{\alpha\beta}\eta_\beta + n_\alpha\xi \right) + [-\rho_{n+1}\xi + f(\sigma)] \tag{5.24}$$

If one wishes to transform the differential equation with new variables in order to present it in the canonical form defined by the differential equation

$$\dot{x}_s = -\rho_s x_s + f(\sigma) \qquad s = 1, \ldots, \eta \tag{5.25}$$

it is necessary to impose the following choice of constants:

$$-\rho_s C_\beta^{(s)} = \sum_{\alpha=1}^{n} b_{\alpha\beta} C_\alpha^{(s)} \qquad s, \beta = 1, \ldots, n \tag{5.26}$$

$$\rho_{n+1} - \rho_s = \sum_{\alpha=1}^{n} n_\alpha C_\alpha^{(s)} \qquad s = 1, \ldots, n \tag{5.27}$$

In these equations the quantities ρ are the parameters of the transformation; they are chosen as roots of the characteristic equation

$$\Delta(\rho) = \begin{vmatrix} b_{11} + \rho & b_{21} & \cdots & b_{n1} \\ \cdots\cdots\cdots\cdots\cdots\cdots\cdots\cdots \\ b_{1n} & b_{2n} & \cdots & b_{nn} + \rho \end{vmatrix} = 0 \tag{5.28}$$

In fact relations (5.25) can be obtained from relations (5.26) only in the case when ρ_s are determined from (5.28).

Let us assume that all roots of (5.28) are distinct and have

$$\text{Re } \rho_k > 0 \tag{5.29}$$

It should be recalled that in these notations ρ stands for $|\rho|$, so that the notations used here actually indicate the roots with *negative real parts* in commonly used notations; this, in turn, requires the fulfillment of the Hurwitzian criteria of stability:[1]

$$\Delta_1 > 0, \ldots, \Delta_n \geqslant 0 \tag{5.30}$$

They are obtained from (5.28) if one replaces ρ by $-\rho$. The $+$ sign in $\Delta_n = 0$ in Eq. (5.30) occurs if $\rho_1 = 0$.

The characteristic feature of the first form of canonical equations is that (5.28) does not contain any parameters of regulation; it contains only those of the uncontrolled system. This is because the latter is supposed to be inherently stable.

If all roots p_s are distinct, Eqs. (5.4) in unknowns $C_\alpha^{(s)}$ can always be solved so that the transformed equations always exist and the *transformation is nonsingular*; the latter circumstance permits determining η_α from Eq. (5.23). Suppose that this is done and we have

$$\eta_\alpha = \sum_{k=1}^{n} D_k^{(\alpha)} x_k + G_\alpha \xi \qquad \alpha = 1, \ldots, n \tag{5.31}$$

where $D_k^{(\alpha)}$ and $G_\alpha^{k=1}$ are certain known constants.

---

[1] For the details of the canonical transformation see Lur'e [2, Sec. 12, Chap. 4].

It remains now to express σ and $\dot{\sigma}$ in terms of the new variables; from (5.31) and (5.22) one obtains

$$\sigma = \sum_{k=1}^{n} \left[\sum_{\alpha=1}^{n} p_\alpha D_k^{(\alpha)} \right] x_k + \left[\sum_{\alpha=1}^{n} p_\alpha G_\alpha \right] \xi \tag{5.32}$$

Introducing the notations

$$\gamma_k = \sum_{\alpha=1}^{n} p_\alpha D_k^{(\alpha)} \qquad \gamma_{n+1} = \sum_{\alpha=1}^{n} G_\alpha p_\alpha \qquad k = 1, \ldots, n$$

$$-\gamma_k \rho_k = \beta_k \qquad \sum_{k=1}^{n+1} \gamma_k = -r' \qquad \xi = x_{n+1} \tag{5.33}$$

the canonical equations take the final form

$$\dot{x}_k = -\rho_k x_k + f(\sigma) \qquad k = 1, \ldots, n+1$$

$$\sigma = \sum_{k=1}^{n+1} \gamma_k x_k$$

$$\dot{\sigma} = \sum_{k=1}^{n+1} \beta_k x_k - r' f(\sigma) \tag{5.34}$$

$$\sum_{k=1}^{n+1} \gamma_k = -r'$$

According to different cases, system (5.34) may have different forms; we prefer to continue with the given form in order not to complicate the exposition; for other possibilities see Letov [1].

5.6   SOME APPLICATIONS TO CONTROL PROBLEMS

In his treatise, Letov [1] indicates a number of examples concerning the reduction of differential equations in control theory to various canonical forms; some of these differential equations were formed by Bulgakov, but here we are interested primarily in their reduction to the canonical form.   The following differential equations are called the *first problem* of Bulgakov (see Appendix).

$$T^2 \ddot{\psi} + U\dot{\psi} + \mu = 0 \tag{5.34a}$$

$$\dot{\mu} = f^*(\sigma) \qquad \sigma = a\psi + E\dot{\psi} + G^2 \ddot{\psi} - \frac{1}{l} \mu \tag{5.35}$$

Let us investigate first the significance of these equations.   Equation (5.34) relates to the system to be controlled; the coordinate ψ is the deviation of the system from its set value (for example, $\psi = 0$), and the terms $T^2 \ddot{\psi} + V\dot{\psi}$ have the obvious significance of inertia and velocity damping.   Clearly in this form one can conveniently consider the problem of automatic steering of a ship for small deviations ψ from the set course; the first two terms $T^2\ddot\psi + U\dot\psi$ characterize the moment due to the inertia of the ship in its angular motion and the velocity damping (in the first approximation the damping is considered to be a linear term $U\dot\psi$, since the angle ψ is assumed to be small).   The third term μ is a measure of the rudder moment, that is, the *control action* in some units.

The first equation in (5.35) characterizes the *regulating element*, which produces the control action; it is controlled in its rate of change $\dot\mu$ by a force (moment) $f^*(\sigma)$; the latter is the function of the control signal σ, which, in turn, is a linear function of ψ, $\dot\psi$, and $\ddot\psi$; the followup action reduces it continuously to zero.   Thus, ultimately, σ is the *error function*, which is the term used in control engineering.   We shall return to these questions later, but shall consider now the purely formal question of the reduction of (5.34) and (5.35) to the canonical form. Setting

$$\frac{U}{T^2\sqrt{r}} = -b_{22} \qquad \frac{lT^2}{T^2 + lG^2} = i \qquad \frac{i}{T^2} = r$$

$$-\frac{i}{rT^2} = -1 = n_2 \qquad a = p_1$$

$$\left(E - \frac{UG^2}{T^2}\right)\sqrt{r} = p_2 \qquad \frac{T}{\sqrt{2}} = t \qquad f(\sigma) = \frac{1}{i\sqrt{r}}\,f^*(\sigma)$$

$$\psi = \eta \qquad \dot\psi = \sqrt{r}\,\eta_2 \qquad \mu = i\xi$$

$$(5.36)$$

Eqs. (5.35) and (5.36) are reduced to the normal, and, at the same time, dimensionless, form:

$$\dot\eta_1 = \eta_2 \qquad \dot\eta_2 = b_{22}\eta_2 + \eta_2\xi \qquad \dot\xi = f(\sigma) \qquad \sigma = p_1\eta + p_2\eta_2 - \xi$$

$$(5.37)$$

In these equations differentiations are with respect to the dimensionless time.

The stationary solution (the equilibrium) is given by the set of algebraic equations

$$\eta_2 = 0 \qquad b_{22}\eta_2 + \eta_2\xi = 0 \qquad |p_1\eta_1 + p_2\eta_2 - \xi| < \sigma^* \qquad (5.38)$$

where σ^* is the upper limit of the "dead zone" (insensitivity) of the control equipment.

In carrying out the canonical transformation we determine first $D(\rho)$ and its derivatives; this gives

$$D(\rho) = \begin{vmatrix} \rho & 0 \\ 1 & \rho + b_{22} \end{vmatrix} = \rho(\rho + b_{22}) \qquad D'(\rho) = 2\rho + b_{22} \qquad (5.39)$$

The roots of Eq. (5.2) are $\rho_1 = 0$ and $\rho_2 = -b_{22}$.

Here intervenes the calculation of the coefficients of the transformation. (We refer to Letov [1].)

The normal system (5.37) is ultimately reduced to the canonical form

$$\dot{x}_1 = f(\sigma) \qquad \dot{x}_2 = -\rho_2 x_2 + f(\sigma) \qquad \dot{\sigma} = \beta_1 x_1 + \beta_2 x_2 - f(\sigma) \qquad (5.40)$$

where

$$\beta_1 = \frac{-p_1}{\rho_2} \qquad \beta_2 = \frac{p_1 - \rho_2 p_2}{\rho_2} \qquad x_1 = \xi \qquad x_2 = \rho_2 \eta_2 + \xi$$

As the next problem one can consider definition (5.4) for $f^*(\sigma)$ instead of its abridged definition (5.4a) and obtain another form of the canonical equations

$$\dot{x}_1 = f(\sigma) \qquad \dot{x}_2 = -\rho_2 x_2 + f(\sigma) \qquad \dot{x}_3 = -\rho_3 x_3 + f(\sigma)$$

$$\sigma = \beta_2 x_2 + \beta_3 x_3 \tag{5.41}$$

in which the values of the constants are different.

In Letov [1] one will find a great number of examples in which different forms of canonical transformations are indicated. It is to be noted that these examples concern only the *reduction to the canonical form*; this must be carried out *before* one can undertake the investigation of the problem of stability outlined in the following section.

Most of these problems follow the steps which are indicated in this section, but the discussion differs according to the form of the differential system. Without going through the voluminous material concerning the various particular cases, we shall merely mention some of them without reproducing the intermediate procedure that connects the initial differential systems (5.34) and (5.35) to their corresponding canonical form (5.41).

Letov designates by the term "second problem of Bulgarov" the case in which the initial differential equations [corresponding to (5.34) and (5.35) of the "first problem"] are

$$T^2 \ddot{\psi} + U\dot{\psi} + k\psi + \mu = 0 \tag{5.42}$$

$$\dot{\mu} = f^*(\sigma) \qquad \sigma = a\psi + E\dot{\psi} + G^2\ddot{\psi} - \frac{1}{l}\mu \tag{5.43}$$

Note that the only difference between the "second" and the "first" problems is the presence of the term $k\psi$ in (5.42); it is missing in (5.34). In other words, the "first problem" may correspond, for example, to the problem of the automatic steering of a craft in *azimuth*, since in such a case the term $k\psi$ is missing. In other words, a craft has no natural "preference" for any particular course, and one has to produce *artificially* a definite direction to be steered (by means of a connection with a compass). In the "second problem" the term $k\psi$ is supposed to exist;[1] such a case would correspond, for instance, to antirolling stabilization, in which case ψ is the coordinate defining the angle of deviation from the vertical. Clearly if the craft is stable (that is, if the center of gravity is below the center of suspension), the *natural term* $k\psi$ exists [as indicated in Eq. (5.42)].

Omitting the intermediate calculations, since they are analogous to those indicated in connection with Eqs. (5.34) and (5.35), one obtains the following canonical system of equations [cf. Eq. (5.41)]:

$$\dot{x}_1 = -\rho_1 x_1 + q_1 f(\sigma)$$

$$\dot{x}_2 = \epsilon_1 x_1 + \rho_1 x_2 + q_2 f(\sigma) \tag{5.44}$$

$$\dot{\sigma} = \beta_1 x_1 + \beta_2 x_2 - f(\sigma)$$

It can be seen that the presence of the static stability term $k\psi$ in (5.42), which is absent in (5.34), accounts for a somewhat different form of the canonical equations; that is, the term $-\rho_1 x_1$, which was missing in (5.41), now appears in the differential equation for $\dot{x}_1$. This is obvious, since this degree of freedom has its own static stability; for the second equation (with $\dot{x}_2$) in addition to the terms x_2 and $f(\sigma)$ [as in (5.41)], the static stability term with a coefficient ϵ_1 intervenes again. Likewise, the expression for $\dot{\sigma}$ is also different in Eqs. (5.41) and (5.42).

The results in themselves do not represent anything of interest, since the reduction of the initial differential systems [for example, systems such as (5.34) and (5.35), or (5.42) and (5.43)] could be done in a number of different ways.

The important point, however, is that these ultimate "canonical systems" [such as (5.41) or (5.44)] have the property of facilitating the

---

[1] The "second" problem covers the case of automatic steering (in azimuth), inasmuch as in this case the term $k\psi$ obviously exists if one agrees to designate by ψ the angle of departure from the set course; the term $k\psi$ in this case is obtained by establishing a connection between the rudder and the gyro compass (see Appendix).

application of Liapounov's second method. This will be shown in Sec. 5.9.

5.7 ASTATIC CONTROL

In his treatise Letov [1, Sec. 6, Chap. 2] gives an interesting analysis of astatic control which is based on an American publication.

The term *astatic* (or *isodromous*) control intervenes each time that control action is derived from the integral $\int \psi \, dt$ of the deviation. This control action appears when, instead of controlling this action *directly*, one controls (from instruments) its rate of change only. The differential systems [analogous to systems (5.34) and (5.35), or (5.42) and (5.43)] in this case are (see Appendix I)

$$T^2\ddot{\psi} + U\dot{\psi} + k\psi + \mu = \chi \qquad \dot{\mu} = f^*(\sigma) \tag{5.46}$$

$$\sigma = a\psi + E\dot{\psi} + G^2\ddot{\psi} + \frac{1}{N}\int \psi \, dt - \frac{1}{l}\mu \tag{5.47}$$

It can be observed that the only difference between (5.46) and (5.47), on the one hand, and (5.42) and (5.43) on the other, is in the presence of the term χ in (5.46) and $(1/N)\int \psi \, dt$ in (5.47). These terms characterize the astatic action by which a constant disturbance χ acting on the system does not affect its setting owing to the "integral," or astatic, control term.

If one carries out the process of reduction to the canonical form that was indicated in the preceding section, one obtains, after somewhat lengthy calculations,[1] the following canonical system:

$$\begin{aligned} \dot{x}_1 &= -\rho_1 x_1 + q_1 f(\sigma) \qquad \dot{x}_2 = \epsilon x_1 - \rho_1 x_2 + q_2 f(\sigma) \\ \dot{x}_3 &= f(\sigma) \qquad \dot{\sigma} = \beta_1 x_1 + \beta_2 x_2 + \beta_3 x_3 - f(\sigma) \end{aligned} \tag{5.48}$$

Comparing this system with (5.44) which is the same as that studied here but *without* the static control, one notes that the latter introduces an additional "degree of freedom" x_3 and contains a modification of the form of the expression for $\dot{\sigma}$.

It may be useful to mention at this point that these long reductions of differential systems (from their usual form to the "normal" form and from the latter to the "canonical" form) are guided by purely formal arguments intended to reduce parameters to a convenient form.

---

[1] See Letov [1, pp. 96–102] for these calculations.

No attention is paid to the physical significance of the quantities involved. Because of this it is very difficult to see what the canonical equations actually mean after the variables have gone through so many transformations.

For instance, in this problem [systems (5.46) and (5.47)] it is convenient to introduce an additional equation: $\dot{\varphi} = \psi$. Reduction to the normal form and to dimensionless variables results in the intermediate system:

$$\dot{\eta}_1 = \eta_2 \qquad \dot{\eta}_2 = b_{21}\eta_1 + b_{22}\eta_2 + \eta_2\xi \qquad \dot{\eta}_3 = b_3\eta_1$$

$$\dot{\xi} = f(\sigma) \qquad \sigma = p_1\eta_1 + p_2\eta_2 + p_3\eta_3 - \xi \tag{5.49}$$

The long passage from the "normal" form (5.49) to the canonical form (5.48) results in a great number of intermediate relations which we do not write here.

As a result of this the simplicity of equations such as Eq. (5.48) *is only apparent* because each of the variables, such as x_1, x_2, or x_3, is expressible in terms of rather complicated relations; for that reason it is impossible to see the whole picture of the process. It is possible to see only some "cross sections" of the manifold of variables, as well as parameters which are ultimately useful for the problem of stability. This is investigated in the following section.

5.8   STABILITY OF CONTROL SYSTEMS

After the somewhat long reduction of control equations to the *canonical form*, one can approach the principal question—that of *stability of control systems*.

Assume that equations of a control system have been reduced to the canonical form

$$\dot{x}_k = -\rho_k x_k + f(\sigma) \qquad \sigma = \sum_{k=1}^{n+1} \gamma_k x_k \qquad \dot{\sigma} = \sum_{k=1}^{n+1} \beta_k x_k - rf(\sigma)$$

$$\sum_{k=1}^{n+1} \gamma_k = -r \qquad k = 1, \ldots, n+1 \tag{5.50}$$

where ρ_k, γ_k, β_k, and r are known numbers. System (5.50) may have either one trivial solution (the state of equilibrium) or a continuum of trivial solutions (within the interval of the "dead zone"). For the trivial solution we shall use the notation $x_k = x_k^*$ (see Sec. 5.2).

Between the solutions of the canonical system (5.50) and those of the original system, there exists a single-valued correspondence.

Assume that among n roots of Eq. (5.28) there are s real roots $\rho_1, \ldots, \rho_s$ and $\frac{1}{2}(n - s)$ pairs of conjugate complex roots $\rho_{s+1}, \ldots, \rho_n$.

In view of this, all the constants $\gamma_1, \ldots, \gamma_s, \beta_1, \ldots, \beta_s$ will be real. The quantities $\gamma_{s+1}, \ldots, \gamma_n$ and $\beta_{s+1}, \ldots, \beta_n$, and also the variables $x_{s+1}, \ldots, x_n$, will be conjugate complex by pairs.

We still suppose that

$$\text{Re } \rho_k > 0 \qquad k = 1, \ldots, n \tag{5.51}$$

and that the roots are distinct. (One of the real roots may vanish, however.)

The problem is to determine those values of the parameters for which the stability of the trivial solution

$$x_k = x_k^* \qquad k = 1, \ldots, n + 1 \tag{5.52}$$

is guaranteed.

Before formulating this problem, it is useful to establish first two lemmas:

Lemma 1   A quadratic form:

$$F(a_1 x_1, \ldots, a_{n+1} x_{n+1}) = \sum_{i=1}^{n+1} \sum_{k=1}^{n+1} \frac{a_k a_i}{\rho_k + \rho_i} x_k x_i \tag{5.53}$$

in which $a_1, \ldots, a_s$ are real and $a_{s+1}, \ldots, a_{n+1}$ are couples of conjugate complex roots, is *positive definite in the variables* x_k.

In fact

$$\frac{1}{\rho_k + \rho_i} = \int_0^\infty e^{-(\rho_i + \rho_k)\tau} \, d\tau$$

so that (5.53) can be written as

$$F = \sum_{i=1}^{n+1} \sum_{k=1}^{n+1} \left[a_k a_i \int_0^\infty e^{-(\rho_i + \rho_k)\tau} \, d\tau \right] x_k x_i = \int_0^\infty \left(\sum_{k=1}^{n+1} a_k x_k e^{-\rho_k \tau} \right)^2 d\tau \tag{5.54}$$

Because there is a square of a real number under the integral (since the complex roots enter in conjugate pairs), and because the integral vanishes only when x_k vanish, clearly F is a positive definite function of $x_1, \ldots, x_{n+1}$.

Lemma 2   Consider another quadratic form

$$\Phi(x_1, \ldots, x_{n+1}) = \frac{1}{2}(A_1 x_1^2 + \cdots + A_s x_s^2) + C_1 x_{s+1} x_{s+2} + \cdots$$
$$+ C_{n-s} x_n x_{n+1} \tag{5.55}$$

in which $A_1, \ldots, A_s$ and $C_1, \ldots, C_{n-s}$ are real positive numbers. It is clear that Φ is real. Since Φ vanishes only at the origin, it is also positive definite.

We also note that for (5.7)

$$\int_0^\delta f(\sigma)\, d\sigma \tag{5.56}$$

is positive for any $|\sigma| > \sigma^*$ and is zero for $|\sigma| < \sigma^*$. The same property exists in the case of the integral.

$$\int_0^\delta \varphi(\sigma)\, d\sigma \tag{5.57}$$

in which $\varphi(\sigma)$ is a function defined by Eq. (5.8).

There is one difference, however, between (5.56) and (5.57). For normal characteristics the limit of (5.56) for $\sigma \to \infty$ is ∞, whereas for (5.57) the same limit may be finite; this circumstance is of some importance for the construction of the functions V.

Lure's theorem   We shall study now the stability of the trivial solution (5.52) and consider a positive definite function

$$V = \Phi + F + \int_0^\delta f(\sigma)\, d\sigma \tag{5.58}$$

Its Eulerian derivative (Chap. 4) is

$$\frac{dV}{dt} = \sum_{k=1}^s A_k x_k [-\rho_k x_k + f(\sigma)] + C_1 x_{s+2}[-\rho_{s+1} x_{s+1} + f(\sigma)] \tag{5.59}$$

$$+ C_1 x_{s+1}[-\rho_{s+2} x_{s+2} + f(\sigma)] + \cdots + \sum_{i=1}^{n+1} \sum_{k=1}^{n+1} \frac{a_i a_k}{\rho_k + \rho_i}$$

$$\times \{x_k[-\rho_i x_i + f(\sigma)] + x_i[-\rho_k x_k - f(\sigma)]\} + f(\sigma)\left[\sum_{k=1}^{n+1} \beta_k x_k - rf(\sigma)\right]$$

Taking into account that

$$\sum_{i=1}^{n+1} \sum_{k=1}^{n+1} a_k a_i x_k x_i = \sum_{k=1}^{n+1} a_k x_k \sum_{i=1}^{n+1} a_i x_i = \left(\sum_{k=1}^{n+1} a_k x_k\right)^2$$

$$\sum_{i=1}^{n+1} \sum_{k=1}^{n+1} \frac{a_k a_i}{\rho_k + \rho_i}(x_k + x_i) = 2 \sum_{i=1}^{n+1} \sum_{k=1}^{n+1} \frac{a_k a_i}{\rho_k + \rho_i} x_k$$

$$\tag{5.60}$$

and adding t_0 and subtracting from the right-hand side

$$2\sqrt{r} f(\sigma) \sum_{k=1}^{n+1} a_k x_k \tag{5.61}$$

the Eulerian derivative can be written as:

$$\frac{dV}{dt} = -\sum_{k=1}^{s} \rho_k A_k x_k{}^2 - C_1(\rho_{s+1}^{+} + \rho_{s+2}) x_{s+1} x_{s+2} - \cdots - C_{n-s}$$

$$\times (\rho_n + \rho_{n+1}) x_n x_{n+1} - \left(\sum_{k=1}^{n+1} a_k x_k\right)^2 - [\sqrt{r} f(\sigma)]^2 - 2\sqrt{r} f(\sigma) \sum_{k=1}^{n+1} a_k x_k$$

$$+ f(\sigma) \sum_{k=1}^{s} \left(A_k + \beta_k + 2\sqrt{r} a_k - 2a_k \sum_{i=1}^{n+1} \frac{a_i}{\rho_k + \rho_i}\right) x_k \qquad (5.62)$$

$$+ f(\sigma) \sum_{\alpha=1}^{n+1-s} \left(C_\alpha + \beta_{s+\alpha} + 2\sqrt{r} a_{s+\alpha} + 2a_{s+\alpha} \sum_{i=1}^{n+1} \frac{a_i}{\rho_{s+\alpha} + \rho_i}\right) x_{s+\alpha}$$

where for the convenience of writing in the last parentheses one has set

$$C_1 = C_2 \qquad C_3 = C_4, \ldots, C_{n-s} = C_{n-s+1}$$

The Eulerian derivative dV/dt of the sign opposite to V will be certainly obtained if the coefficients of $f(\sigma)$ in (5.62) vanish. If one designates $\sum_{k=1}^{s}$ and $\sum_{\alpha=1}^{n+1-s}$, multiplying $f(\sigma)$ by Γ_1 and Γ_2, respectively, and sets

$$\Gamma_1 = 0 \qquad \Gamma_2 = 0 \qquad\qquad\qquad (5.63)$$

it is seen that the Eulerian derivative dV/dt is certainly negative, since on the right-hand side of the remaining terms in (5.62) positive definite functions with negative signs appear.

In view of (5.63) Eqs. (5.62) can be written as

$$\frac{dV}{dt} = -\sum_{k=1}^{s} \rho_k A_k x_k{}^2 - C_1(\rho_{s+1} + \rho_{s+2}) x_{s+1} x_{s+2}$$

$$\cdots C_{n-s}(\rho_n + \rho_{n+1}) x_n x_{n+1} - \left[\sum_{k=1}^{n+1} a_k x_k + \sqrt{r} f(\sigma)\right]^2 \quad (5.64)$$

Hence if (5.63) is fulfilled, Liapounov's stability criterion holds, and the stability of the trivial solution of (5.56) is guaranteed.

The *sufficient* character of the criterion is seen from this discussion.

In fact, *it is not necessary* that (5.63) be fulfilled. Stability exists so long as Γ_1 and Γ_2 are different from zero and positive, provided that the absolute value of the last terms [with $f(\sigma)$ as factor] *is less* than the absolute value of the essentially negative terms.

A more detailed study of the functions Γ_1 and Γ_2 permits forming a conclusion about the range in which the Liapounov criterion holds, that is, about the *extent of stability in the large*.

In fact the functions Γ_1 and Γ_2 contain arbitrary constants of which $A_1, \ldots, A_s, C_1, C_2, \ldots, C_{n-s+1}$ are either real $(a_1, \ldots, a_s)$ or conjugate complex $(a_{s+1}, \ldots, a_{n+1})$. We shall be interested not in the values of these constants but in the possibility of determining them under conditions (5.63).

Assume, for example, that $A_1 = 0, \ldots, A_s = 0$, and $C_1 = 0, \ldots, C_{n-s} = 0$. In such a case (5.63) reduces to equations

$$\beta_k + 2\sqrt{r}a_k + 2a_k \sum_{i=1}^{n=1} \frac{a_i}{\rho_k + \rho_i} = 0 \qquad k = 1, \ldots, n+1 \tag{5.65}$$

If the constants of the regulating system satisfy inequalities of the form

$$F_k(\beta_1, \ldots, \beta_{n+1}, 0, \ldots, 0) > 0 \tag{5.66}$$

this shows that the trivial solution is stable.

5.9   MODIFICATIONS OF LUR'E'S THEOREM

Lur'e's general theorem, outlined in the preceding section, gave rise to numerous papers which tried to simplify it for some special cases.

Thus, for example, if one returns to the calculations of the Eulerian derivative, beginning with the form of V given by Eq. (5.58) and transforming it [in order not to use (5.61)], conditions (5.63) can be obtained in a somewhat different form; that is,

$$\beta_k + 2a_k \sum_{i=1}^{n+1} \frac{a_i}{\rho_k + \rho_i} = 0 \qquad k = 1, \ldots, n+1 \tag{5.67}$$

(This supposes that $A_k = C_a = 0$.) Lur'e's theorem will still hold, but with conditions (5.63) in the form of Eq. (5.67).

Likewise, if instead of (5.58) one takes

$$V = F = \sum_{k=1}^{n+1} \sum_{i=1}^{n+1} \frac{a_k a_i}{\rho_k + \rho_i} x_k x_i \tag{5.68}$$

and calculates its Eulerian derivative, one obtains

$$\frac{dV}{dt} = -\left(\sum_{k=1}^{n+1} a_k x_k \right)^2 + 2f(\sigma) \sum_{k=1}^{n+1} \sum_{i=1}^{n+1} \frac{a_k a_i x_k}{\rho_k + \rho_i} \tag{5.69}$$

This change can be obtained by transforming the right-hand side of $\dot{V}$. In fact, if one adds the term

$$-f(\sigma)\left[\sigma - \sum_{k=1}^{n=1} \gamma_k x_k \right] \equiv 0 \tag{5.70}$$

the Eulerian derivative becomes

$$\frac{dV}{dt} = -\left[\sum_{k=1}^{n+1} a_k x_k\right]^2 - \sigma f(\sigma) + f(\sigma)\sum_{k=1}^{n+1}\left[\gamma_k + 2a_k\sum_{k=1}^{n+1}\frac{a_i}{\rho_k + \rho_i}\right]x_k$$

and one sees at once that the condition

$$\gamma_k - 2a_k\sum_{k=1}^{n+1}\frac{a_i}{\rho_k + \rho_i} = 0 \qquad k = 1,\ldots,n+1 \tag{5.71}$$

guarantees the absolute stability of the control system.

It should be noted that there is no definite rule concerning the choice of the function V; this explains why, depending on the particular choice, there are a number of criteria of stability.

As a rule, one has to try and select a function V whose Eulerian derivative is in the form

$$\frac{dV}{dt} = -[+] - [+] + \Gamma \tag{5.72}$$

where $[+]$ designates some positive definite functions and Γ is a function of which nothing can be said a priori—that is, whether it is positive definite, negative definite, or neither. Sometimes such functions are said to be of a "variable sign."

If by means of some transformations, the Eulerian derivative can be brought to the form of (5.72), then the condition $\Gamma = 0$ immediately gives the criterion for absolute stability. But, as already mentioned, this criterion is *sufficient* but not necessary.

5.10 SIMPLIFIED CRITERIA OF STABILITY

It follows from the remark at the end of the preceding section that Liapounov's second method is a very broad principle; with it the condition of stability can be ascertained *without integrations*, which generally constitute a difficult or, often, impossible task. This broadness can, however, be a drawback. In fact, since there are no definite rules for establishing the V function appropriate to each particular case, the matter becomes, to some extent, *an art*, rather than a definite mathematical procedure. However, once the Liapounov criterion is obtained, there is nothing else to discuss except, possibly, the ascertaining of the limit of *stability in the large*. This requires an investigation of how far one can go in admitting $\Gamma > 0$ without impairing criterion (5.72) (with $\Gamma = 0$).

Because of this, Liapounov's second method stirred up an extraordinary amount of activity.   This activity is still in progress, and has resulted in hundreds of papers on the subject.[1]   For this reason it is necessary to limit this chapter to the most essential topics only.

Before terminating our review of applications of the second method, it may be useful to say a few words about some simplifications in the use of Liapounov's criteria due to Malkin [4].

Let us assume, as before, that we have real and distinct roots ρ_k of the characteristic equation and that none of them is equal to zero. Consider also a real negative definite quadratic form

$$W = -\frac{1}{2} \sum_{\alpha=1}^{n+1} \sum_{\beta=1}^{n+1} A_{\alpha\beta} x_\alpha x_\beta \tag{5.73}$$

According to the Silvester criterion the coefficients $A_{\alpha\beta}$ must satisfy the inequalities

$$\Delta_1 = A_{11} > 0; \qquad \Delta_2 = \begin{vmatrix} A_{11} & A_{12} \\ A_{21} & A_{22} \end{vmatrix} > 0; \ldots$$

$$\Delta_{n+1} = \begin{vmatrix} A_{11} & \cdots & A_{1,n+1} \\ \cdots\cdots\cdots\cdots\cdots \\ A_{n+1,1} & \cdots & A_{n+1,n+1} \end{vmatrix} > 0 \tag{5.74}$$

Consider also another real quadratic form

$$F = \frac{1}{2} \sum_{\alpha=1}^{n+1} \sum_{\beta=1}^{n+1} B_{\alpha\beta} x_\alpha x_\beta \tag{5.75}$$

It can be shown that this function is of constant sign and is positive everywhere if the coefficients B of (5.75) are defined by the formula

$$B_{\alpha\beta} = \frac{A_{\alpha\beta}}{\rho_\alpha + \rho_\beta} \qquad \alpha_1\beta = 1, \ldots, n+1 \tag{5.76}$$

The following discussion is similar to that explained in Sec. 5.9. We select a positive definite function

$$V = F + \int_0^\sigma f(\sigma) \, d\sigma \tag{5.77}$$

and calculate its Eulerian derivative.

---

[1] In particular, in a recent publication of N. N. Krasovsky [5], Chapter 4, 202 international references are cited for the last decade or so.

In view of (5.50) one obtains

$$\frac{dV}{dt} = \frac{1}{2} \sum_{\alpha=1}^{n+1} \sum_{\beta=1}^{n+1} [-(\rho_\alpha + \rho_\beta)x_\alpha x_\beta + f(\sigma)(x_\alpha + x_\beta)]B_{\alpha\beta} +$$

$$+ f(\sigma)\left[\sum_{\alpha=1}^{n+1} \beta_\alpha x_\alpha - f(\sigma)\right] \quad (5.78)$$

However, by (5.73) and (5.76) one can write

$$\frac{1}{2} \sum_{\alpha=1}^{n+1} \sum_{\beta=1}^{n+1} B_{\alpha\beta}(\rho_\alpha + \rho_\beta)x_\alpha x_\beta = -\dot{W}$$

so that (5.78) becomes

$$\frac{dV}{dt} = W - rf^2(\sigma) + f(\sigma)\sum_{\alpha=1}^{n+1}\left[\beta_\alpha + \frac{1}{2}\sum_{\beta=1}^{n+1}(B_{\alpha\beta} + B_{\beta\alpha})\right]x_\alpha \quad (5.79)$$

If all x_α were zero, dV/dt would be negative definite. Since this does not happen as a rule, it is necessary to establish the sign of the quadratic form $-dV/dt$ of the variables $x_1, \ldots, x_{n+1}, f(\sigma)$.

Its determinant is

$$\Delta = \begin{vmatrix} A_{11} & \cdots & A_{1,n+1}P_1 \\ A_{21} & \cdots & A_{2,n+1}P_2 \\ \cdots\cdots\cdots\cdots\cdots\cdots\cdots \\ A_{n+1,1} & \cdots & A_{n+1,n+1}P_{n+1} \\ P_1 & \cdots & P_{n+1}r \end{vmatrix} \quad (5.80)$$

where

$$2P_\alpha = \beta_\alpha + \frac{1}{2}\sum_{\beta=1}^{n+1}(B_{\alpha\beta} + B_{\beta\alpha}) \qquad \alpha = 1, \ldots, n+1 \quad (5.81)$$

The sequence of its diagonal minors is precisely (5.74). Since these minors are positive, the fact that (5.80) is positive shows that (5.79) is negative definite, so that the condition

$$\Delta > 0 \quad (5.81a)$$

is the only one which guarantees stability of the system. The method is general, since a number of different cases can be treated on this basis.

Thus, for example, we have the different canonical forms

1. $\dot{x}_k = -\rho_k x_k + f(\sigma)$ $k = 1, \ldots, n$ $\dot{\sigma} = \sum_{k=1}^{n} \beta_k x_k - r' f(\sigma)$

2. $\dot{x}_k = -\rho_k x_k + f(\sigma)$ $k = 1, \ldots, m+1$ $\sigma = \sum_{k=1}^{m+1} \gamma_k x_k$

$\dot{\sigma} = \sum_{k+1}^{m+1} \beta_k x_k - r' f(\sigma)$

3. $\dot{x}_k = -\rho_k x_k + f(\sigma)$ $k = 1, \ldots, m+1$

$\dot{\sigma} = \sum_{k=1}^{m+1} \beta_k x_k - r' f(\sigma)$

Systems 2 and 3 are the same.   The desired inequalities serving as the criterion of stability can be obtained from (5.80) and (5.81) by means of a change in the number of lines and columns in the determinants associated with corresponding changes in the summation indices.

A number of other criteria exist; they depend on particular special conditions to be imposed on the problem.   We shall consider one due to Letov, which represents the abovementioned criterion in a somewhat different form.

If one selects the coefficients in (5.79) such that they have the relations

$$\beta_\alpha + \frac{1}{2} \sum_{\beta=1}^{n+1} (B_{\alpha\beta} + B_{\beta\alpha}) = 0 \qquad \alpha = 1, \ldots, n+1 \qquad (5.82)$$

one can make $\dot{V}$ negative definite.   In view of (5.76) one will have

$$\beta_\alpha + \frac{1}{2} \sum_{\beta=1}^{n+1} \frac{A_{\alpha\beta} + A_{\beta\alpha}}{\rho_\alpha + \rho_\beta} = 0 \qquad \alpha = 1, \ldots, n+1 \qquad (5.83)$$

or

$$\beta_\alpha + \sum_{\beta=1}^{n+1} \frac{A_{\alpha\beta}}{\rho_\alpha + \rho_\beta} = 0 \qquad \alpha = 1, \ldots, n+1 \qquad (5.84)$$

If the choice of $A_{\alpha\beta}$ is dictated only by inequalities (5.74), one can obtain another criterion of stability.

In fact, suppose that one has solved system (5.84) and that one has

$$A_{\alpha\beta} = A_{\alpha\beta}^* |\beta_1, \ldots, \beta_{n+1}| \qquad \alpha, \beta = 1, \ldots, n+1 \qquad (5.85)$$

This is always possible if the roots ρ_k are distinct, although the solution may not be single valued.   The criteria of stability will be then

$$A_{11}^* > 0 \qquad \begin{vmatrix} A_{11}^* & A_{12}^* \\ A_{21}^* & A_{22}^* \end{vmatrix} > 0 \qquad \begin{vmatrix} A_{11}^* & \cdots & A_{1,n+1}^* \\ \cdots\cdots\cdots\cdots\cdots \\ A_{n+1,1}^* & \cdots & A_{n+1,n+1}^* \end{vmatrix} > 0 \qquad (5.86)$$

These inequalities contain parameters of the control system.

The essence of this modification is as follows.   For absolute stability of a system of form (1) above (for which the roots of the characteristic equation are distinct and Re $\rho_k > 0$) it is sufficient to choose the values (5.86) as parameters in which the numbers $A_{\alpha\beta}^*$ are solutions of Eqs. (5.84).

Refer to Letov [1] for a complete discussion of this and a number of other simplified methods.   It is to be noted that most of them are based on the discussion of the positive definiteness of certain quadratic forms which are used in these problems of stability in order to bring the problem to a form in which the sufficient condition of stability [such as that yielded by Eq. (5.63)] becomes manifest.

5.11   THE PRACTICALITY OF LIAPOUNOV'S CRITERIA

Since by its very nature Liapounov's second method leads to the *sufficient criteria* for stability (see the end of Sec. 5.9) there was a certain doubt initially that the use of these criteria for the design of control systems might lead to too stringent conditions, that is, conditions which are really *not necessary*.   This question has not been fully answered, but a certain limited amount of information can be obtained from Letov [1, pages 243–251].   We shall mention only that if one considers the second problem of Bulgakov and compares the *sufficient* conditions of the Liapounov criterion with the simplified criteria based on the equations of the first approximation (which are linear and thus can be discussed on that basis) which yield the necessary and sufficient criteria, one finds that the difference under normal conditions is not great.

The conclusion obtained by Letov was that the curve limiting the region of the absolute stability built according to Lur'e's theorem (Sec. 5.9) is the envelope of the family of curves depending on the parameter defined by

$$\left[\frac{df^*(\sigma)}{d\sigma} \right]_{\sigma=0} = h \qquad 0 < h < \infty \qquad (5.87)$$

for the whole interval $(0 < h < \infty)$ which limits partial regions of stability calculated on the basis of the first approximation.

There is one point to be clarified.   It was seen that if the conditions of Lur'e's theorem are fulfilled, then the control system is stable for any function $f(\sigma)$ of class A.   The question remains: if the system is stable for any *linear* function $f(\sigma) = h\sigma$, $0 < h < \infty$, will it be stable for *any* function $f(\sigma)$ so long as it is of class A, in accordance with Lur'e's theorem?   These questions are now being discussed.   There is one possibility for reaching a conclusion, that is, if Liapounov's criteria can be narrowed so that they are not only *sufficient* but also *necessary*. There have been some attempts to obtain this generalization.

REFERENCES

1. Letov, A. M.: "Stability of Non-linear Control Systems," 2d ed., Moscow, 1962.   This book contains an extensive bibliography.

2. Lur'e, A. I.: *Prikl. Mat. i Mekh.*, vol. 11, no. 4, 1947; *Automatika i Tel.*, vol. 8, no. 5, 1947, and vol. 9, no. 5, 1947; "Einige nichtlineare probleme," Akademie-Verlag, Berlin, 1957.

3. Lur'e, A. I., and V. N. Postnikov: *Prikl. Mat. i Mekh.*, vol. 8, no. 3, 1944.

4. Malkin, I. G.: "Theory of Stability of Motion," page 401, Goztehizdat, Moscow, 1952.

CHAPTER SIX
RELAY SYSTEMS
(GENERAL THEORY)

6.1 INTRODUCTORY REMARKS

Control systems that include relays are the most important examples of nonlinear control systems. Moreover, the theory of relay systems has recently inspired two important trends in control theory: (1) the method of harmonic linearization (Chap. 7); and (2) the theory of piecewise linear systems (Chap. 8). The name of J. Z. Tsypkin [6] is associated with the recent developments in the theory of relay control systems, and in this chapter we shall follow his work closely.

Although the relay was used for many years, for a long time it was considered merely as a detail in electric circuits. Only during the last 10 years or so has the role of the relay as a *functional transformer* (Chap. 9) been understood; when this became known, the studies of relay systems appeared as forerunners of much broader studies concerning nonlinearities in control systems (Chap. 2).

Before a level could be reached at which these important generalizations could be perceived, a number of difficult problems had to be solved—the problem of stability was probably the most difficult. The problem of stability is based on the concept of continuity by its very nature. In fact, all methods and definitions in the theory of stability (Chaps. 4 and 5) are based on conclusions which can be obtained if a system is deviated very little (theoretically by an infinitely small amount) from its equilibrium position. This analysis forms the essence of the method of variational equations (Chap. 1). Similarly, in Liapounov's second method the criterion is based on studying the sign of a certain Eulerian derivative; this again involves the concept of continuity.

In the case of a relay, either a finite change in the dependent variable y or no change at all corresponds to an infinitely small change in the independent variable x. This constitutes a major difficulty, which for a long time handicapped studies of relay control systems; recently, however, two different approaches have been found.

In one of them (Sec. 6.9) the procedure is to some extent similar to the definition of the Dirac δ function as the limit of a family of continuous functions; it is shown that the problem reduces to an asymptotic case when a certain parameter tends to infinity.

Quite recently, another approach (Popov [5]) was formulated, in which it is shown that the absolute stability of a relay control system can be determined in terms of the frequency characteristics (Secs. 6.15 and 6.16). This theory is not yet completely explored, but apparently it offers a simpler approach than does the asymptotic method outlined in Secs. 6.9 and 6.10.

Studies of relay control systems brought attention to other problems, such as the determination of the periodic solutions; sometimes such solutions (oscillations) are undesirable; in other problems, on the contrary, they are useful phenomena. We shall postpone the study of these questions and concentrate our attention in this chapter on some general problems in the theory of relay control systems and on the question of stability in particular.

6.2 DIFFERENT MODES OF RELAY ACTIONS

Being the simplest, and at the same time the most typical, nonlinearity in control theory, the relay must first be studied together with the part of the system that is supposed to be linear.

In fact, at present most applied problems in control theory reduce to a simple scheme: R (relay) and M (linear part) (Fig. 6.1). This simple combination of R and M yields a number of cases according to the particular features of these component parts.

In the first case (Fig. 6.1a) the linear part M may be stable (S), unstable (I), or neutral (N); the parameters of the linear part M may be lumped (l), distributed (d), or retarded (r). The relay itself may have different features: symmetrical (Sm) or asymmetrical (As); it may have a dead zone (z) or not have it (OZ); it may have hysteresis or not have it, etc.

Tsypkin condensed these cases in the form shown in Fig. 6.1.

Part (a) shows a simple case of a symmetrical theoretically perfect (no dead zone, no hysteresis) relay; the variety of cases is associated, rather, with the outside linear circuit. The diagram is self-explanatory; thus, for example, if one follows the sequence *MSl*, this means that an ordinary (ideal) relay is operating in a stable system with lumped parameters.

Perhaps this is the most important case. Clearly it ultimately results in a differential equation perturbed by the quasidiscontinuities

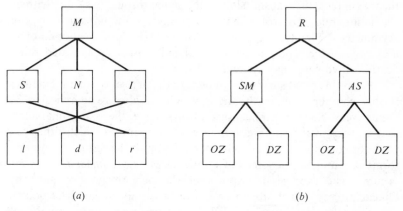

(a)   (b)

Fig. 6.1

(that is, idealized by discontinuities) produced by the relay. If one follows another path, *MSd*, this corresponds to a stable (linear) system with distributed parameters. (This is a case about which we know very little.) In any of these cases the phenomena are governed not by the differential equation but by *partial differential equations*, and again these partial differential equations are perturbed by discontinuities. It is possible that such phenomena may be discovered in long transmission lines, in which case one would attempt to introduce a discontinuous regulation (relays or sampled data).

Finally, if one tries to follow the third path, *MSr*, one definitely encounters what are called *retarded phenomena*.

Here we know still less, since these are amenable to the so-called difference differential equations (Minorsky [3, Chap. 21]), and these always lead to complicated transcendental problems. In problems involving relays all this becomes still more complicated, although some recent attempts have been made to approach the problem in a somewhat simplified manner.

One could let our path go through *N* and *I* on Fig. 6.1a, but there are no available studies of this at the present time.

In Fig. 6.1b the ramifications relate to the relay itself; without the symmetrical case Sm, the asymmetrical case As is generally more complicated. The asymmetrical cases are always characterized by the presence of the constant component in the Fourier series which results from the operation of the relay, as opposed to the Fourier series without constant terms, as in the Sm case.

It is interesting to note that this asymmetrical performance has turned out to be the most important one from the standpoint of control theory; in fact, the transmission of the signal through a system with an oscillating relay control (Chap. 7) is always accompanied by this asymmetry. Finally, the presence (or absence) of a dead zone or of hysteresis further complicates these already rather complicated ramifications involving relay systems.

From this rapid survey it can be seen that a relay system introduces further complications in situations which are already complicated by themselves. Such complications always have the same character; that is, they introduce discontinuities in phenomena which otherwise might be continuous. And, since the relay, plus the rest of the system, forms one unit, a phenomenon known as *piecewise linear idealization* occurs. The average description of the phenomenon is made by "linear pieces," which are to be joined at certain nonanalytic points.

Thus the trivial mechanism for opening or closing a circuit that was known for nearly a century turned out to be the center of the most complicated algorithms that have appeared in control theory during the last decade.

6.3 LINEAR PARTS OF CONTROL SYSTEMS

We shall first consider the linear part of a control system; this should be well known,[1] and we shall merely summarize the results. There are two ways of characterizing linear systems: (1) by the time characteristic; and (2) by the frequency characteristic. The *time characteristic* $h(t)$ is the response of the system at the output when the unit impulse is applied at its input; this also gives the definition of the transfer function.

The unit function is the function defined by conditions

$$y(t) = \begin{cases} 1 & \text{for } t > 0 \\ 0 & \text{for } t < 0 \end{cases}$$

---

[1] It is assumed that the reader is acquainted with the elements of Laplace's transform theory, which is used extensively in Secs. 6.3 to 6.9.

The characteristic $h(t)$ may also be regarded (physically) as the *reaction* of the linear system on $y(t)$ so defined.

Since the image of $y(t)$ is $Y(p) = 1/p$, the image of $h(t)$ will be

$$H(p) = W(p)\frac{1}{p} \tag{6.1}$$

where $W(p)$ is the transfer function (or rather its image). The time characteristic $h(t)$ is thus the original of

$$H(p) = \int_0^\infty h(t)e^{-pt}\,dt$$

The general expression for $W(p)$ usually appears in the form:

$$W(p) = \frac{P(p)}{Q(p)} \tag{6.2}$$

where P and Q are operational polynomials in $p = d/dt$, the degree of P being not greater than that of Q.

If $W(p)$ has n poles: $p_1, \ldots, p_n$ [i.e., zeros of $Q(p)$] which are distinct and different from zero, according to the decomposition formula (Berg [2]) one has

$$h(t) = \frac{P(0)}{Q(0)} + \sum_{\nu=1}^{n} \frac{P(p_\nu)}{Q'(p_\nu)p_\nu} e^{p_\nu t} \tag{6.3}$$

In the case in which $W(p)$ is given by the ratio of transcendental functions the number of poles may become infinity; this happens in the case of *retarded phenomena*, which were mentioned in the preceding section. The second characteristic is obtained when the input is a sinusoidal function of time $\tilde{y}(t)$.

$$y(t) = \tilde{y}(t) = y_m \cos(\omega t + \psi) = y_m e^{j(\omega t + \psi)} = \tilde{y}_m e^{j\omega t} \tag{6.4}$$

where

$$j = \sqrt{-1} \qquad \tilde{y}_m = e^{j\psi}$$

The image of $y(t)$ is $Y(p) = \tilde{y}_m/(p - j\omega)$; the image of the output is obtained by multiplying $Y(p)$ by the transfer function in which p is replaced by $j\omega$:

$$Z(p) = W(p)\frac{\tilde{y}_m}{p - j\omega} \tag{6.5}$$

In addition to the poles of $W(p)$, the image $Z(p)$ has also the pole $p = j\omega$.

Formula (6.3) is a particular case of a more general case $W(p)$ and has multiple poles; in this case one has

$$h(t) = \sum_{v=0}^{s} \sum_{\mu=0}^{r_v-1} c_{v\mu} \frac{t^\mu}{\mu!} e^{(p_v t)} = \sum_{v=0}^{s} \sum_{\mu=0}^{r_v-1} \frac{c_{v\mu}}{\mu!} \frac{d^\mu}{dp_v{}^\mu} e^{p_v t} \tag{6.6}$$

where

$$c_{v\mu} = \frac{1}{\gamma!} \frac{d^\gamma}{dp^\gamma} \left[\frac{P(p)}{Q(p)p} (p - p_v)^{r_v} \right]_{p=p_v} \tag{6.5a}$$

$$\gamma = r_\gamma - \mu - 1$$

where r_v is the multiplicity of the pole and the sum of multiplicities is equal to the degree of denominator $Q(p)$ of the transfer function $W(p)$. In the general case the output $z(t)$ is given by the formula

$$z(t) = W(j\omega)\bar{y}_m e^{j\omega t} + \sum_{r=1}^{s} \sum_{\mu=1}^{r_v-1} \bar{y}_\mu c_{\gamma\mu} \frac{t^\mu}{\mu!} e^{p_v t} \tag{6.6}$$

In this formula the first term is the periodic component and the second is the transient part.

If the poles of $W(p)$ have negative real parts, the transient part of $z(t)$ dies out, and only the forced oscillation remains in the long run; that is

$$z(t) = W(j\omega)\bar{y}_m e^{j\omega t} = W(j\omega)\bar{y}(t) \tag{6.7}$$

where $\bar{y}(t)$ is the stationary process.

The quantity $W(j\omega)$ is termed the *frequency characteristic*. One can also write

$$W(j\omega) = W_0(\omega)e^{j\theta(\omega)} \tag{6.8}$$

where $W_0(\omega)$ is the amplitude and $\theta(\omega)$ is the phase. Hence, in the steady state one has the expression

$$\bar{z}(t) = W_0(\omega)y_m e^{j(\omega t + \theta(\omega) + \psi)} \tag{6.9}$$

This shows that both amplitude and phase vary with ω.

In the real notations, (6.9) is written as

$$\bar{z}(t) = W_0(\omega)y_m \cos [\omega t + \theta(\omega) + \psi] \tag{6.10}$$

Equation (6.8) in the complex notations is written as

$$W(j\omega) = U(\omega) + jV(\omega) \tag{6.11}$$

From Euler's identity, $e^{(j\theta)} = \cos \theta + j \sin \theta$, one obtains

$$U(\omega) = W_0(\omega) \cos \theta(\omega) \qquad V(\omega) = W_0(\omega) \sin \theta(\omega) \tag{6.12}$$

which leads to the usual amplitude, that is, phase diagrams, which we shall not discuss at present.   (For the material in this chapter see also Tsypkin [6].)

6.4   CONTROL SYSTEMS WITH RELAYS

A control system with a relay R can be reduced to the scheme shown in Fig. 6.2, where M is the linear part with the transfer function $W(p)$.

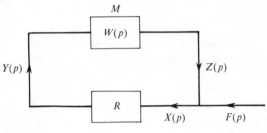

Fig. 6.2

Part M holds the relation

$$Z(p) = W(p)Y(p) \tag{6.13}$$

The input $Y(p)$ is here

$$Y(p) = L\{\Phi[x(t)]\} \tag{6.14}$$

the symbol L meaning "Laplace's transformation."   The condition for the closed system (in the originals) is

$$x(t) = f(t) - z(t) \tag{6.15}$$

and in the images is

$$X(p) = F(p) - Z(p) \tag{6.16}$$

$f(t)$ being the external action.
     If one eliminates $Z(p)$ between these equations, one gets

$$X(p) = F(p) - W(p)L\{\Phi[x(t)]\} \tag{6.17}$$

or, in a more homogeneous form,

$$L[x(t)] = L[f(t)] - W(p)L\{\Phi[x(t)]\} \tag{6.18}$$

This makes use of the relations

$$X(p) = L[x(t)], \ldots$$

Written in terms of the output $z(t)$, this relation is

$$L[z(t)] = W(p)L\{\Phi[f(t) - z(t)]\} \tag{6.19}$$

These equations, (6.18) and (6.19), cannot be solved, since they contain the images of the nonlinear functions $\Phi[x(t)]$.

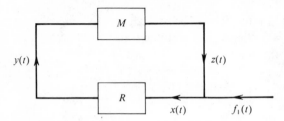

Fig. 6.3

As an example, consider the relay-controlled followup system shown in Fig. 6.3. The linear part M includes here a motor with reducing gearing and a measuring device. The equation for this part is obtained in the usual manner and is

$$T_a T_M \dddot{\theta}(t) + T_M \ddot{\theta}(t) + \dot{\theta}(t) = k_m y(t) \tag{6.20}$$

where $\theta(t)$ = angle of rotation of servomotor shaft
    $y(t)$ = voltage across armature
    T_a and T_M = time constants of armature and electromechanical element
    k_m = dimensional coefficient of amplification of motor, together with the reducing gearing

The transfer function of this part of the system is

$$K_1(p) = \frac{k_m}{T_a T_m p^3 + T_m p^2 + p} \tag{6.21}$$

For the measuring device: $K_2(p) = k_a$ so that the transfer function of the linear part will be

$$W(p) = K_1(p)K_2(p) = \frac{k_l}{T_a T_M p^3 + T_M p^2 + p} \tag{6.22}$$

where $k_l = k_m k_a$. In this case there are two external actions: $f_1(t)$—the control action—and $\tilde{f}(t)$—the harmonic action. This produces the linearization (see Chap. 7).

In terms of the images one has:

$$L[x(t)] = F_1(p) + F_k(p) + \frac{k_l}{T_a T_{MP}^3 + T_{MP}^2 + p} L\{\Phi[x(t)]\} \qquad (6.23)$$

where $F_1(p)$, $F_k(p)$ are images of $f_1(t)$ and $\tilde{f}_k(t)$, respectively.

This example merely shows how to form equations in terms of the images, but the essential element in the scheme is $L\{\Phi[x(t)]\}$, the image of the nonlinear function $\Phi[x(t)]$, which introduces a new feature.

6.5 EQUATIONS OF RELAY ELEMENTS

Assuming that the inertia of the relay is negligible, its equation can be written in the form

$$y = \Phi(x) \qquad (6.24)$$

where $\Phi(x)$ is a discontinuous function of x.

A few typical characteristics of relays are shown in Fig. 6.4.   In

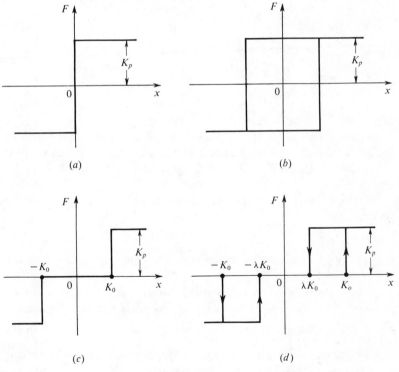

(a)

(b)

(c)

(d)

Fig. 6.4

this family of characteristics, part (a) represents an ideal relay; (b) represents a relay with symmetrical hysteresis with respect to the origin; (c) shows the characteristic with a dead zone; and (d) is the general characteristic which combines the characteristics (b) and (c).

These four characteristics are often encountered; the corresponding equations are:

a. $y = \Phi_1(x) = k_p \sin x$

b. $y = \Phi_2(x) = \begin{cases} k_p \, \text{sign} \, (x - k_0) & \text{for } \dot{x} > 0 \\ k_p \, \text{sign} \, (x + k_0) & \text{for } \dot{x} < 0 \end{cases}$ $\qquad$ (6.25)

c. $y = \Phi_3(x) = \dfrac{k_p}{2} \, [\text{sign} \, (x - k_0) + \text{sign} \, (x + k_0)]$

d. $y = \Phi_4(x) = \begin{cases} \dfrac{k_p}{2} \, [\text{sign} \, (x - k_0) + \text{sign} \, (x + \lambda k_0)] & \text{for } \dot{x} > 0 \\ \dfrac{k_p}{2} \, [\text{sign} \, (x + k_0) + \text{sign} \, (x - \lambda k_0)] & \text{for } \dot{x} < 0 \end{cases}$

We have the function

$$\text{sign} \, x = \begin{cases} 1 & \text{for } x > 0 \\ 0 & \text{for } x = 0 \\ -1 & \text{for } x < 0 \end{cases}$$

The coefficient λ of "return" is given by $0 \leqslant \lambda \leqslant 1$.

It should be noted that although only the coordinate x enters in the formulas, the velocity $\dot{x}$ appears implicitly as a parameter, since in (b) and in (d), the formulas for $\Phi(x)$ are different depending on the sign of $\dot{x}$.

In view of this, instead of (6.24) the relay formulas should be written as

$$y = \Phi(x, \dot{x}) \qquad (6.26)$$

but very often, when no confusion is anticipated, one can use formula (6.24).

For asymmetrical characteristics, as mentioned above, one must also introduce the constant term y_0, and the relay equation becomes

$$y = y_0 + \Phi(x - x_0) \qquad (6.27)$$

In this equation x_0 and y_0 indicate the displacement of the normal characteristic (6.24) along the x and y axes.

The essential feature of a relay is that its output changes discon-tinuously when its input goes through some threshold values.

If one applies an alternating quantity to the input (e.g., voltage) whose values exceed these thresholds, the output will be a constant quantity k_p (in some cases this may be zero) of different signs and of

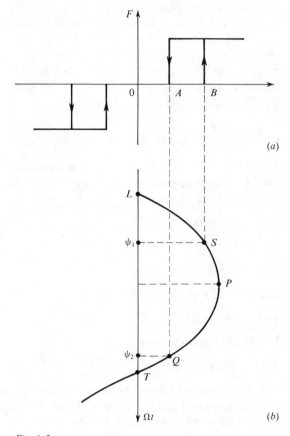

Fig. 6.5

different duration.   In some cases it is convenient to represent these relations graphically, as shown in Fig. 6.5 (Popov and Pal'tov [4]).

In Fig. 6.5a the characteristic (d) of the relay in Fig. 6.4 is shown. Part 6.5b shows the variable quantity applied to the input (e.g., voltage) plotted against t or, preferably, against the angle $\psi = \Omega t$, where Ω is the frequency.

This construction permits correlating the two parts by an obvious construction. Thus, for the increasing signal, the x relay will remain open until the point B is reached; the point S on the curve, and hence the "angular time" ψ_1, corresponds to this point on part (*b*). For a further increase of ψ, the relay will be closed until the sinusoidal signal, having passed through its maximum value P, reaches the value ψ_2 (corresponding to the point Q on the sinusoidal curve). At this instant ψ_2 the relay will open the circuit. This sequence of actions will be the same for $x < 0$, since everything is symmetrical with respect to 0.

It follows from this discussion that the relay will be closed when the arc SPQ is traversed and will be open on arcs LS and QT. This construction is due to Popov and Pal'tov [4, Chap. 7] and is very convenient for analyzing the time-space relationships of relay circuits.

6.6 EQUATIONS OF RELAY SYSTEMS

In investigations of relay systems it is customary to reduce the whole system to its simplest form, such as the one shown in Fig. 6.2. The equation of the linear part M is

$$Z(p) = W(p)Y(p) \tag{6.28}$$

and that of the relay element R is

$$Y(p) = L\{\Phi[x(t)]\} \tag{6.29}$$

The condition for a closed system is

$$x(t) = f(t) - z(t) \tag{6.30}$$

Written in terms of images, it is

$$X(p) = F(p) - Z(p) \tag{6.31}$$

In this formula the control signal is expressed in terms of the images of the external signal and the reaction $z(t)$ of the linear part. Eliminating $Y(p)$ and $Z(p)$ in these equations, one obtains the equation of a closed relay system

$$X(p) = F(p) - W(p)L\{\Phi[x(t)]\} \tag{6.32}$$

In more homogeneous notations this can be written as

$$L[x(t)] = L[f(t)] - W(p)L\{\Phi[f(t) - z(t)]\} \tag{6.33}$$

It should be noted that if one can determine either $x(t)$ or $z(t)$ in some manner, there is no difficulty in determining the other variables.

Assume also that besides $f(t)$ there is some other external action $f_1(t)$. Then, designating by $W_f(p)$ the transfer function connecting the image of the output from M and $F_1(p)$, one can find the image of the external action reduced to the output of the linear part in the form $W_f(p)F_1(p)$. Hence such a system with the additional external action can be considered as the type of system shown in Fig. 6.6b, in which the image of

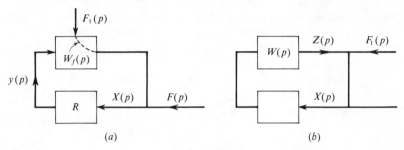

(a)   (b)

Fig. 6.6

the external action applied to the input of relay is $-W_f(p)F_1(p)$. Note that the quantity in which we are interested, $Z_f(p)$, is obtained by adding the quantity $-W_f(p)F_1(p)$ to $Z(p)$.

Equation (6.33) may be regarded as the general equation of a closed relay system. The equation cannot be solved for $L[x(t)] = X(p)$ or $L[x(t)] = Z(p)$, since Eq. (6.33) is nonlinear, and the linear theory (the Laplace transform) does not apply here.

6.7   TRANSIENT PROCESSES IN RELAY SYSTEMS

If one follows Tsypkin's theory, the physical aspect of the relay control presents itself in the following manner. We have a linear system, with well-known behavior, which we can analyze by means of existing linear theory. At certain instants, when the variable $x(t)$, the input to the relay, passes through certain "threshold values" (as, for instance, the "angular instants" ψ_1, ψ_2, . . . , in Fig. 6.5), the relay releases discontinuous actions in one direction or another.

It is clear that these actions, the impulses, disturb the conditions which existed *before* the instant at which the impulse was released. If, on the other hand, we consider this previous situation in terms of a certain Fourier series, it is clear that at each relay operation the Fourier series is perturbed; this perturbation concerns not only the fundamental but also the whole spectrum of its harmonics. On the other hand, if one admits that the modification of this spectrum inevitably modifies these threshold values $\psi_1, \psi_2, \ldots$, and, hence, reacts again on the whole Fourier series, one can readily conceive that, in its full generality, the problem of relay-controlled systems is beyond solving with our present means.

Attempts have been made to try and follow step by step (that is, with each impulse) the graphical constructions set up to show how a given impulse modifies the preceding history. One obtains in this manner a sequence of exponential transients joined at the nonanalytic points, i.e., at the instants at which the relay operates (either in closing or in opening the circuit).

The difficult part of this procedure is to *predetermine* the points at which these discontinuities occur; the problem becomes *transcendental*

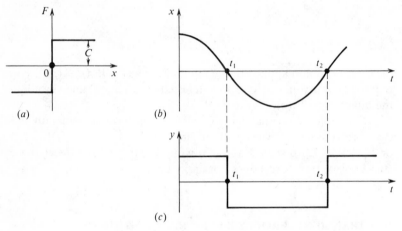

Fig. 6.7

precisely at this point.   We shall discuss in Chap. 8 recent attempts to approach these questions mathematically by introducing the concept of *piecewise linear functions* (sometimes the term "piecewise *analytic*" is used).

In this section we shall first indicate the graphical procedure for the steady state, which is relatively easy, and later indicate a similar procedure for the transient state.   To simplify the problem still further, we shall consider the case in which the nonlinear characteristic of the relay has the form shown in Fig. 6.7a; that is, the case in which it corresponds to the ideal relay (without either hysteresis or a dead zone).

Figure 6.7b shows the time variation of x supposed to be a sinusoidal function.   Figure 6.7c indicates the response [the output

$y(t)$] of the relay. Since the characteristic is assumed to be ideal, the reversals of relay occur at the instants $t_1, t_2, \ldots$, when the input $x(t)$ goes through zero.

From this, one observes that a relay, by its very nature, is a *functional transformer*. It transforms a sinuisoidal input $x(f)$ into the output $y(t)$, which is represented by a Fourier series whose coefficients can be easily determined by the well-known Fourier procedure. This remark will be important for what follows.

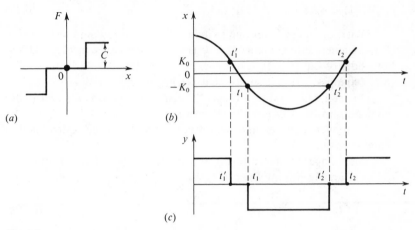

Fig. 6.8

If the characteristic of the relay contains a dead zone (Fig. 6.8) the same argument leads to the obvious graphical conclusion. The constant quantity C (introduced by the relay)[1] disappears at the instant t_1', but the relay *reverses* only at the instant t_1. Thus the dead zone in the characteristic is reproduced as the *time interval* $t_1't_1$ in Fig. 6.8c, which gives the response of the relay. One can easily apply this argument to more complicated cases, for example, cases having both a dead zone and hysteresis. All this is presumably known to the reader, and we mention it only to connect these simple concepts with the more complicated ones which appear when the transient state is studied.

Attempts have been made to follow *formally* this simple intuitive argument. Let us consider, for example, the case of an ideal characteristic (Fig. 6.4a). Clearly the instants t_k of "switchings" (when the relay operates) are the roots of the equation:

$$x(t_k) = 0 \qquad (6.34)$$

---

[1] In this chapter the constant quantity C (introduced by the relay) is indicated occasionally as k_p, the latter notation being used by Tsypkin [6].

In view of Eq. (6.30) this condition is also equivalent to

$$f(t_k) = z(t_k) \tag{6.35}$$

Moreover, as is seen directly from Fig. 6.8, the instants of switchings t_k must also satisfy the condition

$$\dot{x}(t_k)(-1)^k > 0 \tag{6.36}$$

and [again in view of (6.3)] the condition

$$f(t_k)(-1)^k > \dot{z}(t_k)(-1)^k \tag{6.37}$$

When one goes from one switching to the following one, the sign of these inequalities changes; if k is even, one can cancel $(-1)^k$ on both sides of Eq. (6.37); if, however, k is odd, the sign of the inequality (6.37) changes.   It is assumed that $\dot{x}(t_1) < 0$.

One can call condition (6.34) the *condition of switching* and (6.36) the condition for a *proper direction* of switchings.

Moreover, between any two instants t_k and t_{k+1} the control action remains constant k_p.

The image of an impulse of the height $(-1)^k k_r$, of duration $t_{k+1} - t_k$ and beginning for $t = t_k$, is

$$(-1)^k \frac{k_p}{p} \left(e^{-pt_k} - e^{-pt_{k+1}} \right) \tag{6.37a}$$

The image of the control action is the sum of the images of these impulses, so that

$$L[y(t)] = L\{\Phi[x(t)]\} = L\{\Phi[f(t) - z(t)]\}$$
$$= k \sum_{k=0}^{\infty} \frac{(-1)^k}{p} \left(e^{-pt_k} - e^{-pt_{k+1}} \right) \tag{6.38}$$

In view of this, the equation

$$L[z(t)] = W(p)L\{\Phi[f(t) - z(t)]\} \tag{6.39}$$

can be written as

$$L[z(t)] = W(p)k_p \sum_{k=0}^{\infty} \frac{(-1)^k}{p} \left(e^{-pt_k} - e^{-pt_{k+1}} \right) \tag{6.40}$$

Taking into account that the original of the image is the time characteristic $h(t)$, that is, $L[h(t)] = W(p)(1/p)$, in view of the theorem of the lag, one obtains

$$L[h(t - t_k)] = \frac{W(p)}{p} e^{-pt_k} \qquad h(t - t_k) = 0 \qquad \text{for } t < t_k \tag{6.41}$$

Omitting some further intermediate steps (Tsypkin [6, page 95]), one ultimately obtains the formula

$$z(t) = k_p\left[h(t) + 2\sum_{k=1}^{\infty}(-1)^k h(t - t_k)\right] \qquad t_n < t < t_{n+1} \qquad (6.42)$$

This formula gives the value of $z(t)$—the reaction of the linear part—after n operations of relay, that is, in the interval $t_n < t < t_{n+1}$. It is clear that this gives a procedure for calculating the process once the function $h(t)$ is determined.

One thus has the following sequence

$$z(t) = \begin{cases} k_p h(t) & \text{for } 0 < t < t_1 \\ k_p h(t) - 2k_p h(t - t_1) & \text{for } t_1 < t < t_2 \\ k_p h(t) - 2k_p h(t - t_1) + 2k_p(t - t_2) & \text{for } t_2 < t < t_3 \\ \cdots\cdots\cdots\cdots\cdots\cdots\cdots\cdots\cdots\cdots\cdots\cdots \end{cases} \qquad (6.43)$$

These formulas thus determine the *transient process*; they show that this process is represented by the sum of component impulses which have taken place previously; it is also clear that the more distant the part impulses are from the present moment the less the action of them is felt.

This formula represents the essence of the *direct* method, which gives rise to corresponding graphical interpretations; in Tsypkin [6] the reader can find examples of the use of this method for different relay characteristics. For a given characteristic it permits obtaining as many steps of the process as one may wish.

The procedure is straightforward but requires many calculations unless they are made all at once in the form of tables arranged in terms of different parameters, such as $k_p n$, and different forms of the functions $h(t)$. Examples of such tables can be found in Tsypkin [6, pages 102, 106, etc.].

6.8 STABILITY OF RELAY SYSTEMS

As discussed in Sec. 1, the question of stability in relay systems is particularly difficult. In some cases (e.g., when a dead zone exists) there is natural stability, but it is more correct to say that the dead zone is a region of *insensitivity* to which the concept of stability does not, properly speaking, apply; in such systems one frequently has the condition

$$y = \Phi(0) = 0 \qquad (6.44)$$

It is of greater importance to consider the problem of stability when the relay has an ideal characteristic (Fig. 6.4a); in this case conditions become more definite.

One should also be guided by certain similar concepts which exist in the theory of continuous sytems, but they are less definite in the case of relay systems.

In fact, although it is possible to see how a relay system behaves close to the equilibrium point in general, one cannot form any idea about the limit of the zone of stability.   The major difficulty, as we mentioned in Sec. 6.1, is the impossibility of obtaining *directly* the variational equations (Sec. 1.2), which is possible only when the system is continuous and when Taylor's expansion around the equilibrium point is possible.

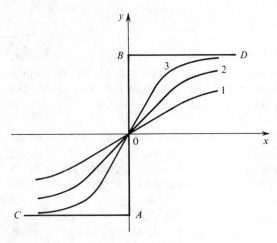

Fig. 6.9

Although there is seemingly no normal way of forming the necessary variational equations, an interesting attempt to do this was made by setting up an *indirect argument*, which consisted in considering a purely discontinuous function $CAOBD$ (Fig. 6.9) as the limit of a continuous sequence of functions 1, 2, 3, ...   This is similar to the approach usually made in connection with the Dirac δ function.   The fundamental idea in this approach (Tsypkin [6, Sec. 14]) is as follows. Suppose that a small change of coordinate occurs at $t - t_0$; one may consider this as a change of initial conditions which permits us to associate a certain impulse with this change.   This impulsive action will produce some deviations of $z_1(t)$, $z_2(t)$, and $x(t)$ (see Fig. 6.10) from their equilibrium values by the quantities $\xi_1(t)$, $\xi_2(t)$, and $\xi(t)$, respectively.   Clearly $\xi(t) = x(t)$, since for the equilibrium $x(t_0) =$ $x(0) = 0$. $\xi_1(t)$ and $\xi_2(t)$ coincide with $z_1(t)$ and $z_2(t)$, so long as no external actions are involved.

One can therefore try to interpret the scheme shown in Fig. 6.10 in that sense.   The only difference is that we consider an impulse $F(p)$

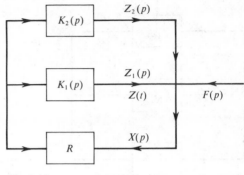

Fig. 6.10

applied to the system, and, instead of $Z_1(p)$ and $Z_2(p)$ we consider their deviations from zero.   One approximates the nonlinear function $\Phi(x)$ linearly by setting $\Phi(x) \simeq kx \simeq k\xi$, the angular coefficient k being equal to the derivative of $\Phi(x)$ for $x = \xi = 0$; that is,

$$k = \Phi'(0) \tag{6.45}$$

It remains to ascertain the significance of $\Phi'(0)$ in this case.   For continuous characteristics one clearly has

$$k = \Phi'(0) = \tan \alpha \tag{6.46}$$

where α is the slope of the curve at the origin ($x = \xi = 0$).   If $\alpha \to \pi/2$, $k \to \infty$, so that for the ideal relay characteristic one should have

$$k = \Phi(0) = \infty. \tag{6.47}$$

The proper interpretation of this condition must be made in connection with the scheme of Fig. 6.11.

On this basis it is clear that the stability of equilibrium of a relay system reduces to the stability of equilibrium of a *linear system which is obtained if the relay is replaced by a linear amplifier whose coefficient of amplification increases indefinitely.*

A scheme of this nature is shown in Fig. 6.11 in which $F_*(p)$ indicates the image of the equivalent impulsive action $f_*(t)$ corresponding to the initial conditions, and $k_f(p)$ is the transfer function of the part of the system from the point of application of the impulsive action up to the point corresponding to the output $\xi_1(t)$.

This linear system for $k \to \infty$, according to Tsypkin, will be the variational system in the case of a relay.

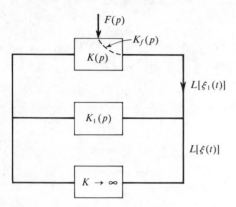

Fig. 6.11

One can obtain the same result directly from Fig. 6.11 using the images $\xi(t)$ and $\xi_1(t)$ in the form

$$L[\xi(t)] = -\left\{\frac{K_f(p)}{1 + k[K(p) + K_1(p)]}\right\}F_*(p) \tag{6.48}$$

$$L[\xi_1(t)] = \frac{K_f(p)}{1 + kK(p)/[1 + kK_1(p)]}\, F_*(p) \tag{6.49}$$

If one takes into account the transfer function of the linear part of the system

$$W(p) = K(p) + K_1(p) \tag{6.50}$$

Eqs. (6.48) and (6.49) can be written in the form

$$L[\xi(t)] = -\left[\frac{K_f(p)}{1 + kW(p)}\right]F_*(p) \tag{6.51}$$

$$L[\xi_1(t)] = \frac{K_f(p)[1 + kK_1(p)]}{1 + kW(p)}\, F_*(p) \tag{6.52}$$

Equations (6.51) and (6.52) will correspond to the variational equations of the relay system if the coefficient of amplification $k \to \infty$; in the meantime this gives the criterion for stability of equilibrium.

As is seen from these equations, the poles of the transfer function of the linear system are zeros of $[1 + kW(p)]$. If one replaces

$W(p) = P(p)/Q(p)$ and equates to zero the numerator of the expression $[Q(p) + kP(p)]/Q(p)$, one obtains the characteristic equation of the linear part

$$\frac{1}{k} Q(p) + P(p) = 0 \tag{6.53}$$

For $k \to \infty$ a part m of the roots of (6.53) tends to the roots of

$$P(p) = 0 \tag{6.54}$$

The remaining $(n - m)$ roots increase indefinitely in their absolute values. It should be recalled that the degrees of P and Q are m and n respectively, with $m \leqslant n$.

Equation (6.54) may be regarded as that of a *limit system* which is obtained from the given system if $k \to \infty$. In fact, if one makes $k \to \infty$ in (6.52), one obtains

$$L[\xi_1(t)] = \frac{K_f(p)K_1(p)F_*(p)}{W(p)} \tag{6.55}$$

The poles of this function are the zeros of $W(p)$, and this explains the limit equation (6.54).

If one replaces in (6.55) the quantity $W(p)$ by its value (6.50), the limit equation (6.55) can be written as

$$L[\xi_1(t)] = \frac{K_f(p)}{1 + \dfrac{K(p)}{K_1(p)}} F_*(p) = \frac{K_f(p)}{1 + W^*(p)} F_*(p) \tag{6.56}$$

According to this equation such a limit system may be represented by Fig. 6.12. This limit system is obtained from that shown in Fig. 9.11 by replacing the amplifier and the element with the transfer function $K_1(p)$ by means of an element whose transfer function is $1/K_1(p)$.

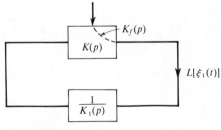

Fig. 6.12

This somewhat delicate argument shows that the problem of stability of equilibrium in relay systems reduces to the investigation of stability of the linear system shown in Fig. 6.11, in which the coefficient of amplification k increases indefinitely. This, in turn, requires a study regarding the location of roots in the complex plane when $k \to \infty$.

6.9 CRITERIA FOR STABILITY OF EQUILIBRIUM

We shall review briefly another procedure for ascertaining the stability of equilibrium of a relay directly, by means of the transfer function $W(p)$, or by the frequency characteristic $W(j\omega)$.

It should be recalled that the transfer function $W(p)$ is given by the formula

$$W(p) = \frac{P(p)}{Q(p)} = \frac{b_0 p^m + b_1 p^{m-1} + \cdots + b_{m-1} p + b_m}{a_0 p^n + a_1 p^{n-1} + \cdots + a_{n-1} p + a_n} \tag{6.57}$$

where b_i and a_i are constant coefficients depending on parameters of the system; moreover $m \leqslant n$.

One begins by developing $W(p)$ according to the negative powers of p (Voronov [7]):

$$W(p) = \frac{1}{(n-m)!} \frac{d^{n-m}}{dp^{n-m}} \left[W(p) \right]_{p \to \infty} p^{-(n-m)}$$

$$+ \frac{1}{(n-m+1)!} \frac{d^{n-m+1}}{dp^{n-m+1}} \left[W(p) \right]_{p \to \infty} p^{-(n-m+1)} + \cdots \tag{6.58}$$

Writing this differently, we have

$$W(p) = \sum_{k=0}^{\infty} \frac{d_k}{p^{n-m+k}} \tag{6.59}$$

where

$$d_k = \frac{1}{(n-m+k)!} \frac{d^{n-m+k}}{dp^{n-m+k}} \left[W(p) \right]_{p=\infty} \tag{6.60}$$

After some transformations which we omit (see Tsypkin [6, pages 129 to 131]), one obtains the expressions for

$$d_k = \frac{1}{a_0^{k+1}} \begin{vmatrix} a_0 & 0 & \cdots & b_0 \\ a_1 & a_0 & \cdots & b_1 \\ \cdots & \cdots & \cdots & \cdots \\ a_k & a_{k-1} & \cdots & b_k \end{vmatrix} \tag{6.61}$$

in which a_i and b_i, for $i > n$ and $i > m$, must be replaced by zeros.

If one replaces p by $j\omega$ [in (6.53)] and solves it with respect to $-1/k$, one has [in view of (6.57) and (6.58)]

$$-\frac{1}{k} = W(j\omega) = \frac{d_0}{(j\omega)^{n-m}} + \frac{d_1}{(j\omega)^{n-m+1}} + \cdots \tag{6.62}$$

For large ω the behavior of the frequency characteristic is determined by the first terms of its decomposition in series in terms of $1/j\omega$. Thus, for the first term of (6.62) and for $n - m > 0$, the characteristic $W(j\omega)$ approaches zero for large values of ω along the line whose slope is $-(n - m)(\pi/2)$. The form of the curve $W(j\omega)$ is determined by the first two terms of the series $W(j\omega)$. Figure 6.13 shows the approach

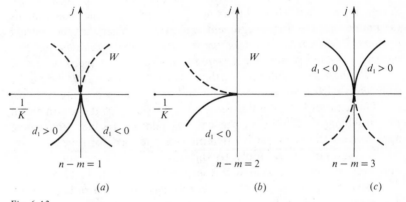

Fig. 6.13

of the curve to the origin for $n - m = 1$, part (a); for $n - m = 2$, part (b); and for $n - m = 3$, part (c).

These curves correspond to large values of ω and represent the corresponding behavior of the curve $W(p)$ near the origin; it is assumed that $d_0 > 0$, but d_1 may be of both signs.

The subsequent discussion is rather long and is not reproduced here (see Tsypkin [6, pages 133 to 135]); we give only the results of this asymptotic analysis (for $k \to \infty$); that is, the position of equilibrium is stable if one of the following three criteria is fulfilled.

1. The transfer function $W(p)$ of the linear part has all zeros [i.e., roots of $P(p)$] with negative real parts and for $p = \infty$ has a zero of an order not higher than two (that is, $n - m \leqslant 2$). The coefficients d_0 and d_1 [of decomposition of $W(p)$ according to the powers of $1/p$] satisfy the relations $d_0 > 0$ for $n - m = 1$ and $d_0 > 0$, $d_1 < 0$ for $n - m = 2$.

2. The limit system ($k \to \infty$) is stable, and the frequency characteristic for $\omega \to \infty$ is situated in the lower half-plane; its form is analogous to a characteristic given by an equation of degree not higher than two.

3. The limit system is stable, and the time characteristic $h(t)$ has the following property:

If $h(0) = 0$ then $\dot{h}(0) > 0$

If $h(0) = \dot{h}(0) = 0$ then $\ddot{h}(0) > 0, \dddot{h}(0) < 0$ (6.63)

The stability of the limit system can be studied by the usual linear criteria (Routh, Hurwitz, Nyquist, Michailov, etc.).

Summing up this long discussion, we can say that the stability of a relay system depends on the form of the transfer function $W(p)$. Since $W(p) = P(p)/Q(p)$, $P(p)$ and $Q(p)$ are algebraic polynomials (assuming that the linear argument is used), it is clear that the *concept of stability ultimately depends on the somewhat implicit relations existing between $P(p)$ and $Q(p)$ in the asymptotic case ($k \to \infty$) under study.*

We shall not elaborate further, since the procedure should be sufficiently clear from what has been said in this and preceding sections.

One cannot fail to notice the great complexity of the treatment of the problem of stability in the case of relays. In fact, the whole approach to this problem is attempted on the basis of linear theory, which does not really apply to this essentially discontinuous case. However, in order to deal with the purely nonlinear feature of this discontinuous problem, it is necessary to make use of a rather delicate argument (outlined in Sec. 6.8), which concerns the asymptotic approximation ($k \to \infty$). All this contributes to the considerable difficulties encountered in reaching the ultimate criteria.

6.10 SELF-EXCITED OSCILLATIONS IN SYSTEMS WITH RELAYS

The existence of self-excited oscillations in relay control systems has been known for many years; they were known long before modern control theory was formed. Even today, however, this field is relatively little explored in comparison with similar phenomena in continuous sytems.

The reason for this is the fact that the discontinuities caused by relay actions preclude the use of classical analytical theory (of Poincaré), which would greatly facilitate such studies.

In this section we shall outline briefly the essence of the approach we have been analyzing so far. (The same questions are treated somewhat differently in Chap. 8, which analyzes an approach due to Aiserman and his associates. We shall, however, follow here the argument of Tsypkin, which gives a clear picture of this difficult subject.)

It was shown in Sec. 6.7 that the passage of the input variable $x(t)$ through certain *threshold values* results in discontinuities in the output variable $y(t)$ and that this accounts for the role of a *functional transformer* generally played by the relay (see Chap. 10).

In general, the problem is of great complexity, and the problem of the *existence* of a periodic solution for systems with relays has not yet

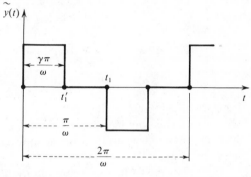

Fig. 6.14

been solved. (We shall postpone consideration of this question to Chap. 8.) However, if one *assumes* that such a solution exists, it is possible to proceed formally and to draw certain useful conclusions.

Hence, if one assumes that the output $y(t)$ is periodic [we shall indicate this by the symbol $\tilde{y}(t)$], one can write

$$\tilde{y}(t) = \frac{1}{2} \sum_{r=-\infty}^{\infty} C_r e^{jr\omega t} \tag{6.63a}$$

where $C_r = |C_r| e^{-jq_r}$ is a complex coefficient and $j = e^{i\pi/2}$.

For the periodic functions limited by horizontal parts (such as relay characteristics), the quantities C_r are represented by the formula

$$C_r = \frac{1}{j\pi r} \sum_{i=1}^{s+1} D\tilde{y}(t_i)e^{-jr\omega t_i} \tag{6.64}$$

where $D\tilde{y}(t_i)$, $i = 1, \ldots, s + 1$ means the discontinuity (or "jump") of $\tilde{y}(t)$ for certain instants t_i. Owing to the discontinuities, it is necessary to consider separately the values "to the right" (i.e., for $t_i + 0$) of the discontinuity and those "to the left" (i.e., for $t_i - 0$) and to define the jump $D\tilde{y}(t_i)$ by the expression

$$D\tilde{y}(t_i) = \tilde{y}(t_i + 0) - \tilde{y}(t_i - 0) \tag{6.65}$$

We shall deal with these new concepts in more detail in Chap. 8, and shall be interested here only in the formal representation of these quasidiscontinuous actions.

If $\tilde{y}(t)$ is symmetrical, $C_r = 0$ if r is even, and one has merely to replace r [in (6.64)] by $(2m - 1)$, where m is an integer. Instead of the complex notation one can use the real notation. Thus, for instance, for a symmetrical function $\tilde{y}(t)$ one has

$$\tilde{y}(t) = \frac{1}{2} \sum_{m=-\infty}^{\infty} |C_r| e^{j(r\omega t - \varphi_r)} \qquad r = 2m - 1 \tag{6.66}$$

in the complex form; in the corresponding real form one will have

$$\tilde{y}(t) = \frac{C_0}{2} + \sum_{r=1}^{\infty} |C_r| \cos (r\omega t - \varphi_r) \qquad r = 2m - 1 \tag{6.67}$$

In this way the representation of $\tilde{y}(t)$ as a sum of harmonic components reduces to the determination of the complex coefficients $C_r = |C_r| e^{-j\varphi_r}$, which requires the determination of absolute values $|C_r|$ and also of phase angles φ_r.

If $\tilde{y}(t)$ has the form corresponding to the dead zone (Fig. 6.4c) the discontinuities in this case occur for $t_1' = \gamma\pi/\omega$, $t_1 = \pi/\omega$, and the jumps of the function in these points are $D\tilde{y}(\gamma\pi/\omega) = 0 - k_p = -k_p$, k_p being the "height" of the rectangular curve. From (6.64) (always for $r = 2m - 1$) one obtains

$$C_r = -\frac{2k_p}{j\pi r} (e^{-jr\gamma\pi} - e^{-jr\pi}) = \frac{2k_p}{j\pi r} (1 - e^{-jr\gamma\pi})$$

since $e^{-jr\pi} = -1$. After a few further transformations one obtains the following real notation (we continue to write r instead of $2m - 1$):

$$\tilde{y}(t) = \frac{4k_p}{m} \sum_{m=1}^{\infty} \frac{1}{r} \sin \frac{r\gamma\pi}{2} \cos \left[r\omega t - \frac{\gamma r\pi}{2} \right] \tag{6.68}$$

These formulas give the output quantity of a relay with a dead zone. If the latter is absent, it is sufficient to set $\gamma = 1$. In such a case the matter becomes simpler (we omit some intermediate trigonometric transformations), and in this case one gets

$$\tilde{y}(t) = \frac{4k_p}{\pi} \sum_{m=1}^{\infty} \frac{1}{r} \sin r\omega t \qquad r = 2m - 1 \tag{6.69}$$

Formulas (6.68) and (6.69) remain in cases in which the relay element has hysteresis; this follows from the fact that the presence of hysteresis merely introduces a lag between $\tilde{x}(t)$ and $\tilde{y}(t)$ without any changes in other relations.

For the calculation of $\tilde{z}(t)$ one must determine the reaction of the linear part on the sequence of impulses $\tilde{y}(t)$. In this case the sequence consists of harmonic components [(6.68) or (6.69)]. Since this concerns the linear part, the principle of superposition holds, so that $z(t)$ is merely the sum of stationary reactions to each harmonic component. One obtains for this reaction $z(t)$ the expression for a relay with a dead zone:

$$\tilde{z}(t) = \frac{4k_p}{\pi} \sum_{m=1}^{\infty} \frac{W_0(r\omega)}{r} \sin \frac{\gamma r \pi}{2} \cos \left(r\omega t - \frac{\gamma r \pi}{2} + \theta r\omega \right) \tag{6.70}$$

where again we have written r instead of $2m - 1$. If one sets $\gamma = 1$ in this formula, one obtains the reaction of a relay without the dead zone. For the steady-state periodic processes there are simplifications in that the instants of switchings t_k are determined by the frequency and are multiples of each other, so that it is sufficient to carry out calculations for a finite number of impulses and not for $m \to \infty$. In this case calculations are conducted as follows. The reaction of a linear part on a unit impulse starting at $t = t_0$ is $h(t - t_0)$ for $t > t_0$, the unit impulse being

$$1(t - t_0) = \begin{cases} 1 & \text{for } t > t_0 \\ 0 & \text{for } t < t_0 \end{cases}$$

This reaction on a rectangular impulse of height k_p and duration $\gamma\pi/\omega$ beginning at $t = t_0$ can be found in the form

$$k_p \Delta h\left(t - t_0 - \frac{\gamma\pi}{\omega} \right) = k_p\left[h(t - t_0) - h\left(t - t_0 - \frac{\gamma\pi}{\omega} \right) \right] \tag{6.71}$$

for $t_0 + \gamma\pi/\omega < t$. In this formula Δh means the first difference of the time characteristic $h(t)$ with the duration $\gamma\pi/\omega$.

If one adds reactions of the linear part on the sequence of the preceding impulses (for $t \le t_0$), one obtains the expression

$$\tilde{z}(t) = k_p\left[h(t) + \sum_{k=1}^{\infty} (-1)^k \Delta h\, \tau \right] \qquad \tau = t + \frac{(k - \gamma)\pi}{\omega}$$

$$0 \le t \le \frac{\gamma\pi}{\omega} \tag{6.72}$$

$$\tilde{z}(t) = k_p \sum_{k=0}^{\infty} [(-1)^k \Delta h\, \tau] \qquad \frac{\gamma\pi}{\omega} \le t < \frac{\pi}{\omega}$$

where $\Delta h(\tau) = h(t + k\pi/\omega) - h[t + (k - \gamma)\pi/\omega]$.

The first expression in Eqs. (6.72) determines $\bar{z}(t)$ in the interval $0 \leqslant t < \gamma\pi/\omega$, when the impulse exists, and the second determines $\bar{z}(t)$ when it does not exist, $\gamma\pi/\omega \leqslant t < \pi/\omega$.

From that point one can proceed graphically by tracing the reaction for these two intervals which are fitted at nonanalytic points (points with two distinct tangents), at which these two kinds of intervals replace each other. Refer to Tsypkin [6, pages 151 to 154] for these graphical constructions.

6.11   CONDITIONS FOR EXISTENCE OF SELF-EXCITED OSCILLATIONS

We shall here indicate briefly certain considerations concerning the existence of self-excited oscillations in a simple form, *under the assumption that the periodic state exists.* This, of course, has nothing to do with the *proof of existence* of a periodic solution, which is still more or less an open question, as we explain in Chap. 8.

It is clear that if the periodic state exists, all variables $x(t)$, $y(t)$, $z(t)$, and possibly others, are periodic; this will be indicated by sign $\bar{x}(t)$, etc. It is also clear that in the self-excited state

$$\bar{x}(t) = -\bar{z}(t) \tag{6.73}$$

Moreover, using the notation of the preceding section, the instants of switching are determined by the *form* of the oscillation (which we also assume); thus $t_k = k\pi/\omega_0$; $t'_{k+1} = (k + \gamma)\pi/\omega_0$; etc.

One can formulate a number of relations which are merely the consequences of the formulas given in Sec. 6.8. It can be shown that:

1. In the absence of a dead zone and hysteresis:

$$\bar{x}\left(\frac{k\pi}{\omega_0}\right) = 0 \qquad \dot{\bar{x}}\left(\frac{k\pi}{\omega_0}\right)(-1)^k > 0 \tag{6.74}$$

2. With hysteresis:

$$\bar{x}\left(\frac{k\pi}{\omega_0}\right) = (-1)^k k_0 \qquad \dot{\bar{x}}\left(\frac{k\pi}{\omega_0}\right)(-1)^k > 0 \tag{6.75}$$

3. With a dead zone ($\lambda = 1$):

$$\bar{x}\left(\frac{k\pi}{\omega_0}\right) = (-1)^k k_0 \qquad \dot{\bar{x}}\left(\frac{k\pi}{\omega_0}\right)(-1)^k > 0 \tag{6.76}$$

$$\bar{x}\left[\frac{(k + \gamma)\pi}{\omega_0}\right] = (-1)^k k_0 \qquad \dot{\bar{x}}\left[\frac{(k + \gamma)\pi}{\omega_0}\right](-1)^k < 0 \tag{6.76a}$$

4. With a dead zone and hysteresis ($\lambda \neq 1$):

$$\tilde{x}\left(\frac{k\pi}{\omega_0}\right) = (-1)^k k_0 \qquad \dot{\tilde{x}}\left(\frac{k\pi}{\omega_0}\right)(-1)^k > 0 \tag{6.77}$$

$$\tilde{x}\left(\frac{(k+\gamma)\pi}{\omega_0}\right) = (-1)^k \lambda k_0 \qquad \dot{\tilde{x}}\left(\frac{(k+\gamma)\pi}{\omega_0}\right)(-1)^k < 0 \tag{6.77a}$$

In these notations k is the index of the instant t_k, and k_0 is the width of the zone of hysteresis (in which case on the return one has λk_0; $0 \leqslant \lambda \leqslant 1$) or of the dead zone.

If one substitutes $k = 1$ in (6.75) and (6.77) and $-k = 0$ in (6.77a), one obtains, in the presence of hysteresis,

$$\tilde{x}\left(\frac{\pi}{\omega_0}\right) = -k_0 \qquad \dot{\tilde{x}}\left(\frac{\pi}{\omega_0}\right) < 0 \tag{6.78}$$

and, in the presence of the dead zone,

$$\tilde{x}\left(\frac{\pi}{\omega_0}\right) = -k_0 \qquad \dot{\tilde{x}}\left(\frac{\pi}{\omega_0}\right) < 0 \tag{6.79}$$

$$\tilde{x}\left(\frac{\gamma\pi}{\omega_0}\right) = \lambda k_0 \qquad \dot{\tilde{x}}\left(\frac{\gamma\pi}{\omega_0}\right) < 0 \tag{6.80}$$

These conditions determine ω_0 and γ, that is, the frequency of oscillations and the relative duration of impulses.

Following this argument and assuming a sinusoidal $\tilde{x}(t)$, one constructs $y(t)$ depending on the location of thresholds (which was explained in Sec. 6.7). The calculation of $z(t)$ is more complicated, since it involves calculations of coefficients and phase angles of the Fourier series.

In general, the phase angle between $\tilde{x}(t)$ and $\tilde{z}(t)$ is different from 180 degrees and depends on the frequency of the input action $\tilde{x}(t)$. If the frequency is made to vary, it may happen that this phase angle is equal to 180 degrees so that $z(t) = -x(t)$. It is clear that at this point the external action can be removed, and the system will continue to work in a state of self-excited oscillation. If one takes into account the condition $\tilde{x}(t) = -\tilde{z}(t)$, one obtains the conditions under which the self-excited system operates,

$$\tilde{x}\left(\frac{\pi}{\omega_0}\right) = 0 \qquad \dot{\tilde{x}}\left(\frac{\pi}{\omega_0}\right) < 0$$

which were mentioned earlier.

It is useful to emphasize once more that the contents of this and of the preceding sections must not be considered as theorems of the existence of periodic solutions in systems with relays; these conclusions must be considered only as the results of an assumption that the periodic state exists.

Attempts to establish the actual conditions necessary for the existence of periodic solutions in the relay (or similar) systems are yet in progress and are closely related to the theory of so-called *piecewise linear systems*, which are studied in Chap. 8. This theory actually establishes the conditions for the existence of periodic solutions in systems of relays; they are similar to those obtained on a topological basis (Chap. 9). We emphasize this point in order to call attention to the subject, which is outlined in some detail, in Chaps. 8 and 9.

6.12   CHARACTERISTICS OF RELAY SYSTEMS

We shall indicate briefly some results of this simplified theory, which *presupposes* that the periodic state exists and merely derives some conclusions from this assumption. In such a nonanalytic domain and in the absence of any algorithm, this course was probably the only one available. In view of the lack of an adequate mathematical algorithm, effort was directed toward establishing some provisional criteria justified by their agreement with observed results.

In this manner the definition of the characteristic of a relay system was formed:

$$I(\omega) = -\frac{1}{\omega} \dot{\bar{z}}\left(\frac{\pi}{\omega}\right) - j\bar{z}\left(\frac{\pi}{\omega}\right) \tag{6.81}$$

Thus,

$$\operatorname{Re} I(\omega) = -\frac{1}{\omega} \dot{\bar{z}}\left(\frac{\pi}{\omega}\right) \qquad \operatorname{Im} I(\omega) = -\bar{z}\left(\frac{\pi}{\omega}\right) \tag{6.82}$$

In these expressions $\bar{z}(t)$ is determined by its values in Eq. (6.66) or Eq. (6.68).

For relay systems with dead zones the characteristics are determined by the formulas

$$I_1(\omega) = -\frac{1}{\omega} \dot{\bar{z}}\left(\frac{\pi}{\omega}\right) - j\bar{z}\left(\frac{\pi}{\omega}\right)$$

$$I_\gamma(\omega) = -\frac{1}{\omega} \dot{\bar{z}}\left(\frac{\gamma\pi}{\omega}\right) - j\bar{z}\left(\frac{\gamma\pi}{\omega}\right) \tag{6.83}$$

In these formulas $\bar{z}(\pi/\omega)$ and $\bar{z}(\gamma\pi/\omega)$ are determined by (6.66), in which the parameter γ appears. For $\gamma = 1$ the two characteristics $I_1(\omega)$ and $I_\gamma(\omega)$ become identical and equal to $I(\omega)$.

The significance of this representation can be seen from the vector diagram in Fig. 6.15; from this it is seen that if the frequency ω changes

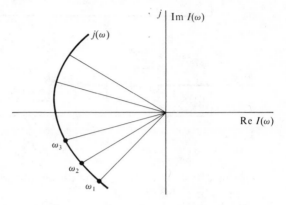

Fig. 6.15

the end of the vector, $I(\omega)$ describes the curve C, which is the characteristic in polar coordinates.

We shall not elaborate further on the question of characteristics, in view of that obvious theoretical significance. The applied character of the procedure is also clear. In fact, it is sufficient to develop the formulas of Sec. 6.11, replacing the quantities $\bar{z}(t)$ and $\dot{\bar{z}}(t)$ by their explicit values in terms of the corresponding Fourier series. The computational work for different forms of relay characteristics can be found in Tsypkin [6, pages 161 to 237] in great detail. This material, although of great interest to persons engaged in the design of relay systems, can hardly add anything further from a theoretical point of view to what has been outlined in the preceding section.

6.13 LATER DEVELOPMENTS

An alternative method for investigating stability of continuous systems and also of some systems with discontinuities of the first class was developed by V. M. Popov [5]. The application of this method to the relay systems was indicated by J. Z. Tsypkin [6]. In this section we shall discuss his approach briefly, referring to the above-cited references for details.

Consider a simple scheme (Fig. 6.16) containing a linear part M and a relay R; Fig. 6.16b shows the structural scheme corresponding to Fig. 6.16a.

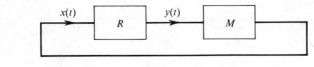

(a)

(b)

Fig. 6.16

Designating by $w(t)$ the impulse characteristic of M, which is assumed to be stable, one has

$$\lim_{t \to \infty} w(t) = 0 \tag{6.84}$$

and also

$$\int_0^\infty |w(t)| \, dt < \infty \tag{6.85}$$

The initial conditions can be represented by a certain equivalent action $f(t)$ applied to the input of the system.

Since the linear part M is stable, clearly

$$\lim_{t \to \infty} f(t) = 0 \tag{6.86}$$

and also

$$\int_0^\infty |f(t)| \, dt < \infty \qquad \int_0^\infty |f'(t)| \, dt < \infty$$

The convergence of integrals is due to the presence of the exponential functions in the integrands; such actions are said to be "vanishing."

The reaction $z(t)$ of M, as usual, is:

$$z(t) = \int_0^t w(t - \lambda) y(\lambda) \, d\lambda \tag{6.87}$$

If one assumes the ideal relay characteristic (Fig. 6.4a), one has:

$y(t) = \Phi[x(t)] = \operatorname{sign} x(t)$

$$\operatorname{Sign} x(t) = \begin{cases} 1 & \text{for } x(t) > 0 \\ 0 & \text{for } x(t) = 0 \\ -1 & \text{for } x(t) < 0 \end{cases} \tag{6.88}$$

For the closed system one also has to add the condition of closing

$$x(t) = f(t) - z(t) \tag{6.89}$$

If one eliminates $y(t)$ and $z(t)$ between (6.87), (6.88), and (6.89), one has the relation

$$x(t) = f(t) - \int_0^t w(t - \lambda)\Phi[x(\lambda)]\, d\lambda \tag{6.90}$$

between the originals, and it can be seen that it reduces to the Volterra integral equation of the second kind.

Applying Laplace's transformation to the linear part M and making use of the theorem of convolution, one has

$$Z(p) = W(p)Y(p) \tag{6.91}$$

where

$$Z(p) = \int_0^\infty e^{-pt}z(t)\, dt$$

$$W(p) = \int_0^\infty e^{-pt}w(t)\, dt$$

and

$$Y(p) = \int_0^\infty e^{-pt}y(t)\, dt \tag{6.92}$$

If these integrals converge, the replacement $p = j\omega$ yields

$$Z(j\omega) = W(j\omega)Y(j\omega) \tag{6.93}$$

in terms of the frequency characteristics.   If the linear part M is stable, all poles of the transfer function $W(p)$ have negative real parts.

For $f(t) = 0$, Eq. (6.87) has a trivial solution $x(t) = 0$ corresponding to the equilibrium point.   The problem of stability reduces in what follows to that of the equilibrium.

It is to be noted that for a relay system any small $x(t)$ produces a constant action $y(t)$; this is the typical feature of such a system.   This introduces a major difficulty, as we have mentioned already.   It is thus necessary to introduce certain new definitions.

We shall call a relay control system stable if for any $\epsilon > 0$ one can find $\eta(\epsilon) > 0$ such that for all vanishing $f(t)$ satisfying the condition

$$\sup |f(t)| < \eta \tag{6.94}$$

the error function $x(t)$ satisfies the inequality

$$|x(t)| < \epsilon \tag{6.95}$$

for any $t \geqslant 0$.

If, in addition to (6.95), one also has the condition

$$\lim_{t \to \infty} x(t) = 0 \tag{6.96}$$

the relay control system is *asymptotically stable*. In the case in which the asymptotic stability takes place only for a sufficiently small η, the stability is said to be "in the small"; if it occurs for any η, satisfying (6.86), it is said to be "in the large" (that form of stability is called also the *absolute stability*).

6.14 TSYPKIN'S THEORY REGARDING STABILITY IN THE LARGE

We shall give a brief review of a recent development of Tsypkin [6] (based on an earlier theory of Popov [5]). This theory is interesting in that it approaches the question of stability on the basis of the frequency characteristics; this resembles the principle of Nyquist's diagram, although the procedure is quite different, since we are concerned here with not only a nonlinear but even with a nonanalytic case.

Using the previous notations [$x(t)$, the action applied to the relay, and $z(t)$, the reaction of the linear part M], one first introduces two auxiliary functions:

$$y_T(t) = \begin{cases} y(t) = \Phi[x(t)] & \text{for } 0 \leqslant t \leqslant T \\ 0 & \text{for } t < 0, t > T \end{cases} \tag{6.97}$$

and

$$\psi_T(t) = -rz_T(t) - z'_T(t) \qquad r = \text{const} > 0 \tag{6.98}$$

and

$$z_T(t) = \int_0^\infty w(t - \lambda) y_T(\lambda) \, d\lambda \tag{6.99}$$

Identifying (6.99) with

$$z_T(t) \equiv z(t) \qquad 0 < t < T \tag{6.100}$$

one has

$$\rho_T = \int_0^\infty y_T(t)\psi_T(t)\, dt \tag{6.101}$$

which, according to the Parseval theorem, can be expressed in terms of the spectral functions

$$\rho_T = \frac{1}{2\pi} \int_{-\infty}^\infty y_T(-j\omega)\Psi_T(j\omega)\, d\omega \tag{6.102}$$

The subsequent calculation is long (see Popov [5]); it is sufficient here to mention that the expression for it is of the form

$$\rho_T = -\frac{1}{2\pi} \int_{-\infty}^\infty \Pi(j\omega)\, |\,Y(j\omega)|^2\, d\omega \tag{6.103}$$

where

$$j\omega = (r + j\omega)W(j\omega) \tag{6.104}$$

Since the integral of the imaginary part of (6.103) is zero, one has

$$\rho_T = -\frac{1}{2\pi} \int_{-\infty}^\infty \operatorname{Re} \Pi(j\omega)\, |\,Y_T(j\omega)|^2\, d\omega \tag{6.105}$$

The function $\Pi(j\omega)$ is called the *Popov function*, and it plays a fundamental role in the following material.   If

$$\operatorname{Re} \Pi(j\omega) > 0 \qquad 0 \leqslant \omega < \infty \tag{6.106}$$

clearly, from (6.84),

$$\lim_{\omega \to \infty} [\operatorname{Re} \Pi(j\omega)] \geqslant 0 \tag{6.107}$$

In such a case it follows from (6.103) that

$$\rho_T < 0 \tag{6.108}$$

There are also other forms for representing p_T (see Tsypkin [6]); we mention here only that (6.105) can also be written

$$r\int_0^T |x(t)|\, dt + |x(T)| < C_f(r) \tag{6.109}$$

where

$$C_f(r)^0 = \int_0^\infty [rf(t) + f'(t)]\, dt + x(0)$$

For vanishing actions, the integral on the right-hand side exists so that $C_f(r)$ is a finite positive quantity.   One has thus

$$\int_0^T |x(t)|\, dt < \frac{C_f(r)}{r} \qquad |x(t)| < C_f(r) \tag{6.110}$$

This intermediate calculation shows that a relay control system is stable but the stability is not asymptotic.   For asymptotic stability, it is necessary to differentiate (6.90), which leads to another calculation (see Tsypkin [6]) from which one finds that where the integral of the absolute value of the function $x(t)$ converges, its derivatives are bounded, and the function tends to zero when $t \to \infty$; that is,

$$\lim_{t \to \infty} x(t) = 0 \tag{6.111}$$

which corresponds to the asymptotic stability.   These somewhat long calculations based on the theory of the harmonic analysis strongly abridged here lead to the following theorem of Popov.

In order to make a relay control system stable "in the large," it is sufficient that for any real $\omega < \infty$ the inequality

$$\text{Re } j\omega W(j\omega) > 0 \tag{6.112}$$

be fulfilled [5].

This theorem also holds when the linear part M is neutral, that is, when the transfer function $W(p)$ has a simple pole at the origin.

6.15 CRITERIA FOR STABILITY "IN THE LARGE" FOR RELAY CONTROL SYSTEMS

As was shown previously [Eq. (6.106)], the criterion of stability is derived from the inequality

$$\text{Re } \Pi(j\omega) = \text{Re } j\omega W(j\omega) > 0 \tag{6.113}$$

Consider the function

$$\Pi(p) = pW(p) \tag{6.114}$$

which is obtained from (6.113) if one replaces $j\omega$ by p.   This function is called real and positive if (1) $\Pi(p)$ is real if p is real, and (2) $\text{Re } \Pi(p) > 0$, when $\text{Re } p \geqslant 0$.

With these conventions, the Popov criterion for asymptotic stability in a relay control system can be formulated as follows.   *The necessary conditions for asymptotic stability in a relay control system in the large are*

1. $\Pi(p) = pW(p)$ *must be real and positive.* To the inequality (6.113) corresponds another inequality

Im $W(j\omega) < 0$ (6.115)

From this follows the frequency criterion for asymptotic stability in the large (Fig. 6.17).

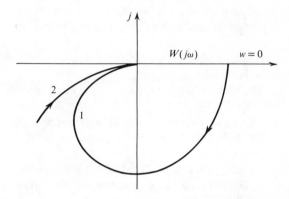

Fig. 6.17

2. *The frequency characteristic of the linear part of the system must be situated below the abscissa axis.*

Characteristic 1 is a static characteristic and characteristic 2 is an astatic one of the first order (Fig. 6.17).
Writing $W(j\omega)$ as

$W(j\omega) = |W(j\omega)|\, e^{j\theta(\omega)}$ (6.116)

the imaginary part will be

Im $W(j\omega) = |W(j\omega)|\sin\theta(\omega)$ (6.117)

Criterion 2 requires that $\sin\theta(\omega) \leqslant 0$; that is,

$-\pi \leqslant \theta(\omega) \leqslant 0$ (6.118)

This yields another condition:

3. *A relay control system will be stable "in the large" if the phase characteristic of its linear part for any ω in $(0,\infty)$ is negative and does not exceed π in the absolute value.*

It can be shown that the real positive function $\Pi(p) = pW(p)$ must have the following properties:

1. It must not have either poles or zeros in the right half-plane.
2. All poles or zeros situated on the imaginary axis must be simple, and the residues at the poles must be positive.
3. The difference of the degrees of the denominator and of the numerator must not be greater than one.

If one imposes these conditions on $W(p) = P(p)/Q(p)$, one can obtain additional conditions on the functions $P(p)$ and $Q(p)$; they are:

1. Polynomials $P(p)$ and $Q(p)$ must not have any zero in the right half-plane.
2. The zeros of $Q(p)$ on the imaginary axis must be simple and different from zero.
3. The difference of degree of polynomials $Q(p)$ and $P(p)$ must not exceed two.

These properties follow from a more detailed study of the asymptotic behavior of these polynomials for large p. (See Tsypkin [6, page 130].)

Ultimately we are led to the more detailed criterion:

For stability of a relay control system in the small it is necessary and sufficient that $P(p)$ should not have roots with positive real parts; that $n - m$ should be less than two; and that the coefficients of the expansion of $W(p)$ in negative powers of p should satisfy the conditions $d_0 > 0$ for $m = n - 1$ and $d_0 > 0$, $d_1 < 0$ for $m = n - 2$, where the constants d_0, d_1 are given by (6.60).

We shall limit ourselves to this short outline of Popov's theory and mention only one conclusion, which, perhaps, one can feel intuitively in approaching the study of relay systems. That is, the ultimate criterion of stability of this typically nonlinear system is hidden in the properties of its linear counterpart. In fact, the latter determines this reaction $z(t)$, which releases the action $x(t)$ at the input of the relay, and one feels that the stability *can* be obtained *for a very special interplay of these actions and reactions.* It was, however, a long time, and long detours were made, before this somewhat vague feeling found a mathematical justification in Popov's theory, which gives the real algorithm for an investigation of the stability of relay control systems.

It must be noted that this does not yet give any information regarding the conditions for the existence of oscillations in relay systems but deals only with the problem of asymptotic stability. The great merit of the theory is in reducing the problem to that of the frequency characteristics of the *linear part* of relay control systems.

6.16 CONCLUDING REMARKS

In this chapter, we reviewed the principal points of the theory of relay control systems. Since most of this material relates to a subject that is by no means organized at present, the exposition is, inevitably, a *provisional theory*. The first 13 sections follow the classical treatise of Tsypkin [6] which contains practically everything which was published up to that time; this chapter reproduces only a few of the most important points of his work.

The material in Secs. 6.14 and 6.15 relates to work done up to 1962, and outlines an entirely new approach.

The theory of relay systems has become so important recently probably because it is a particular (and, indeed, is the most important) case of *nonlinear control problems*, which have seemed to dominate the entire study of control theory in recent years.

The most difficult problem in this theory concerns the question of stability; we mentioned this point in Sec. 6.1 and gave a more detailed presentation in Secs. 6.8 to 6.13. In fact, in view of the lack of continuity, it was necessary to introduce the asymptotic approach (Sec. 6.8), which is generalized further in Sec. 6.9. This approach is not simple and brings to mind to some extent the difficulty which appeared in connection with the phenomenon of a quasidiscontinuous type idealized on the basis of the Dirac δ function. The theory is based on the asymptotic passage from continuously acting systems to quasidiscontinuous ones (idealized by the mathematical discontinuities of the first kind) when one of the parameters tends to infinity.

Sections 6.14 and 6.15 relate to a recent work of Popov's [5]; he has shown that the difficulties involved in asymptotic treatment can be avoided by a closer analysis of the linear part of the problem. It is shown that the latter, under certain conditions, may yield criteria under which a sufficient condition for the asymptotic stability can be obtained directly without any necessity for using the asymptotic procedure. This approach opens the door for a host of new possibilities in this field in which the continuous methods of analysis will be closely associated with discontinuities. For that reason the contents of this chapter have been partially directed toward a general exposition aiming primarily at the intuitive (physical) aspects of relay systems and partially toward the conditions of equilibrium.   The question of periodic solutions will be discussed in Chap. 8.

REFERENCES

1. Aiserman, M. A., and F. R. Gautmacher: "Absolute Stability of Control Systems," Moscow, 1963.
2. Berg, E. I.: "Heaviside's Operational Calculus," McGraw-Hill Book Company, New York, 1936.
3. Minorsky, N.: "Non-linear Oscillations," D. Van Nostrand, Inc., New York, 1962.
4. Popov and Pal'tov: Gostehizdat, Moscow.
5. Popov, V. M.: *Acad. RPR*, vol. 10, nos. 1 and 3, 1960; *Avtomatika i Tel.*, vol. 22, no. 8., 1961; vol. 24, no. 1, 1963.
6. Tsypkin, J. Z.: Stability of Relay Control Systems, *Isvestia Ac. Nauk Tech. Cibernetics*, 3, 1963.
7. Voronov, A. A.: "Theory of Automatic Control," Moscow, 1954.

CHAPTER SEVEN
METHOD OF
HARMONIC
LINEARIZATION

7.1 INTRODUCTORY REMARKS

In Secs. 3.5 to 3.8 we discussed briefly the method of harmonic linearization of Popov and Pal'tov [4]. We indicated the principal points of the method, leaving its applications and some applied aspects somewhat in the background.

As we mentioned already, the method of harmonic linearization is a kind of hybrid method having its roots in several disconnected theories; from that point of view, it is particularly interesting, since a theory so formed acquires definite aspects of a codified science. Thus, perhaps for the first time, one can begin to see the theory of nonlinear control systems in its entirety, instead of with regard to some isolated sectors.

Popov-Pal'tov's treatise, in which the method of harmonic linearization is used as a working tool, has many practical applications, and this is probably why it is of primary importance to engineers. Mathematicians, however, can also find a number of points of interest, since many theoretical points were left open, most of the authors' effort being directed primarily toward applied results. The method presents, therefore, a typical picture of a vigorous advance in an applied domain guided largely by a few fundamentals and by agreement with experimental results. Undoubtedly this "scientific offensive" will be followed by theoretical readjustments, but this is inevitable in the period of formation of *any* applied science.

The procedure used in the theory of harmonic linearization was briefly mentioned in Sec. 3.3.   We shall here give a brief outline of its mathematical fundamentals although the larger part of the chapter will be devoted to analysis of applied problems.

The starting point of this theory is the operational expression

$$Q(p)x + R(p)F(x,px) = 0 \qquad p = \frac{d}{dt} \tag{7.1}$$

in which $Q(p)$ and $R(p)$ are linear operators and $F(x,px)$ is a nonlinear operator.   The principal object of the theory is to replace $F(x,px)$ by a corresponding linear operator.   It is assumed that (7.1) has a solution of the form

$$x = A \sin \psi \qquad \psi = \Omega t \tag{7.2}$$

where A is the amplitude and Ω the frequency.   As mentioned above, the principal aim of the method is to determine the linearizing factors $q(A,\Omega)$ and $q'(A,\Omega)$, which are determined by the equations

$$q = \frac{1}{\pi A} \int_0^{2\pi} F(A \sin \psi, A\Omega \cos \psi) \sin \psi \, d\psi$$

$$q' = \frac{1}{\pi A} \int_0^{2\pi} F(A \sin \psi, A\Omega \cos \psi) \cos \psi \, d\psi \tag{7.3}$$

$$0 = \frac{1}{2\pi A} \int_0^{2\pi} F(A \sin \psi, A\Omega \cos \psi) \, d\psi$$

It is to be noted that the third equation in (7.3) is valid only for the symmetrical oscillations; for asymmetrical oscillations (Sec. 7.9), instead of a zero on the left side of the third equation in (7.3) there will be a certain function F^0.   If the solution (7.2) exists and the linearizing functions $q(A,\Omega)$ and $q'(A,\Omega)$ are determined and then substituted into (7.1), one obtains the *linearized* differential equation

$$L(p)x = \left[Q(p) + R(p)\left(q + \frac{q'}{\Omega} p \right) \right] x = 0 \tag{7.4}$$

From then on the problem is treated as linear.

The assumption of the periodic solution (7.2) implies that the polynomial $L(p)$ must have $p^2 + \Omega^2$ as a divisor, which results in $p = \pm j\Omega; j = \sqrt{-1}$.   This in turn means that in the expression

$$L(j\Omega) = X(A,\Omega) + j Y(A,\Omega) \tag{7.5}$$

one must have identically

$$X(A,\Omega) = 0 \qquad Y = (A,\Omega) = 0 \tag{7.6}$$

From these equations one obtains the values of A and Ω, in the case in which one has a nonhomogeneous expression instead of (7.1),

$$Q(p)x + R(p)F(x,px) = S(p)f(t) \tag{7.7}$$

where $Q(p)$, $R(p)$, and $S(p)$ are linear operators and $F(x,px)$ are, as previously, nonlinear, the procedure is different; instead of looking for the solution (7.2), one looks for a solution of the form

$$x = x_0 + x^* = x_0 + A \sin \psi \qquad \psi = \Omega t \tag{7.8}$$

This leads to the calculation of the linearizing functions of the form

$$q(x^0,A,\Omega) \qquad q'(x^0,A,\Omega) \qquad F^0(x^0,A,\Omega) \tag{7.9}$$

Upon the substitution of these functions in (7.7), one obtains

$$Q(p)(x^0 + x^*) + R(p)\left(F^0 + qx^* + \frac{q'}{\Omega}px^*\right) = S(p)f(t) \tag{7.10}$$

It is assumed that it is possible to split this system into two equations:

$$Q(p)x^0 + R(p)F^0 = S(p)f(t) \tag{7.11}$$

$$Q(p)x^* + R(p)\left(q + \frac{q'}{\Omega}p\right)x^* = 0 \tag{7.12}$$

For the symmetrical oscillations, (7.11) does not exist, since $x^0 \equiv 0$ and $F^0 \equiv 0$. For asymmetrical oscillations (Sec. 7.9), on the contrary, Eqs. (7.11) and (7.12) both must be taken into account. Equation (7.12) gives a periodic solution x^* [of the type (7.2)] if it exists. Equation (7.11) permits calculating the stationary error x^0 due to the nonautonomous form of (7.7). From the standpoint of applications the asymmetrical character of oscillations [when both (7.11) and (7.12) are valid] is of greater importance, since Eq. (7.12) specifies the stationary oscillation (i.e., the carrier wave) which carries the signal specified by Eq. (7.11).

In control systems based on the principle of harmonic linearization, one deals with asymmetrical oscillations, since the transmission of signals always involves asymmetrical behavior. However, from the standpoint of the theory associated with the method of harmonic linearization, all essential features are better seen from the study of symmetrical oscillations; in view of this, we shall begin our study with the last-mentioned oscillations and will not deal with the theory of asymmetrical oscillations until Sec. 7.9.

As in other methods of linearization, the principal advantage of the method of harmonic linearization is in the replacement of the original nonlinear system by the *equivalent linear* system, the term *equivalent* being understood in the Krylov-Bogoliubov sense (see Sec. 3.3). The advantage of the method is offset to some extent by certain complications resulting from the conditions of stability. In fact, since the linearized system is to be treated as linear, the condition of stability is determined by the Hurwitz criteria (and not by Liapounov's second method). If the physical system is devoid of self-excitation, the use of the Hurwitz criteria does not present any difficulty; if, however, the system is a self-excited type, the use of the criteria presents a certain difficulty, which is outlined in Secs 7.2 and 7.3.

In Sec. 7.4 we discuss another delicate point—one concerning the connection between the classical theories (of Poincaré and Krylov-Bogoliubov), which use the so-called "small-parameter method," and the present approach, which uses the concept of the "filter hypothesis" suggested by Aiserman (Sec. 7.2).

Beginning with Sec. 7.5 the applied part of the method of harmonic linearization is outlined in some detail; this is probably the most interesting part of the theory; unfortunately it was possible to give here only a few examples of a large number of problems which were treated in the original text of Popov and Pal'tov.

7.2 ADDITIONAL CONSIDERATIONS REGARDING STABILITY

It will be useful to supplement the outline of stability given in Sec. 3.8 by information which concerns the question of *variable damping*, which is often encountered in these problems. It should be remembered that in linear problems, the concept of *constant damping* appears in the exposition of the general solution. In linearized problems, particularly in those in which self-excited oscillations are present, it is more convenient to introduce the concept of a *variable damping* than to operate with the topology of the problem, as we did in Sec. 3.7.

There are several methods used in connection with the problem of stability of linearized equations.

The method of variational equations In this method, one tries to introduce in the basic equation [see Eq. (3.62)]

$$\left[Q(p) + R(p)\left(q + \frac{q'}{\Omega}p\right) \right]x = 0 \tag{7.13}$$

the concept of variational equations; Eq. (7.13) acquires then, for (7.1), the form

$$Q(p)\Delta x + R(p)\left[\left(\frac{\partial F}{\partial x}\right)^* \Delta x + \left(\frac{\partial F}{\partial px}\right)^* p\,\Delta x\right] = 0 \qquad (7.14)[1]$$

where the asterisk indicates that the partial derivatives are taken at the point corresponding to the nonperturbed solution (Chap. 1). The simplification in question consists of replacing (7.14) by the differential equation with constant coefficients:

$$[Q(p) + R(p)(k + k'p)]\,\Delta x = 0 \qquad (7.15)$$

where

$$k = \frac{1}{2\pi}\int_0^{2\pi}\left(\frac{\partial F}{\partial x}\right)^* d\psi \qquad k' = \frac{1}{2\pi}\int_0^{2\pi}\left(\frac{\partial F}{\partial px}\right)^* d\psi \qquad \psi = \Omega t$$

The treatment of stability then becomes linear.

This procedure cannot, however, be considered rigorous, since the replacement of (7.14) by (7.15) is justified only under certain conditions; if it is possible to do this, then the investigation of stability is facilitated. For example, consider the scheme of Fig. 7.9; the variational system in this case is

$$(T_1 p + 1)\,\Delta x_2 = -k_1\,\Delta x_4$$

$$\Delta x_3 = \left(\frac{\partial E}{\partial x}\right)^* \Delta x \qquad \Delta x = \Delta x_2 - k_{fb}\,\Delta x_4 \qquad (7.16)$$

$$(T_2 p + 1)p\,\Delta x_4 = k_2\,\Delta x_3$$

These variational equations are obtained from the equations of the structural scheme shown in Fig. 7.9 by replacing x_1, x_2, x_3, ... by Δx_1, Δx_2, Δx_3, ... The last equation (7.16) may be regarded as a dynamic system (servomotor), since it contains $p^2 = d^2/dt^2$; in this manner (3) (in Fig. 7.9) is to be considered as a servomotor.

It is clear that, owing to the relay, two self-excited oscillations (if any) will not be sinusoidal. Thus, for instance, the oscillation $x_3(t)$ will have a rectangular form even if the oscillation $x(t)$ is sinusoidal; this presupposes the ideal characteristic of the relay (Fig. 7.1). For characteristics of more complicated types, the form of $x_3(t)$ will be accordingly changed. We shall consider only the case of the

---

[1] We retain the notations of Popov and Pal'tov [4]; for instance, $\partial F/\partial px = \partial F/\partial \dot{x}$, as is usually written.

ideal characteristic and assume that there exists a periodic solution

$$x_3(t) = \sum_{r=1}^{\infty} B_r \sin (r\Omega t + \beta_r) \qquad (7.16a)$$

where B_r and β_r are the amplitude and the phase of the rth harmonic. Since the symmetry is odd, only odd harmonics are present.   Since the

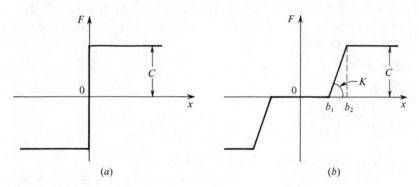

(a)   (b)

Fig. 7.1

signal $x_3(t)$ appears at the input of the linear link (3) the output x_4 will be

$$x_4(t) = \sum_{r=1}^{\infty} C_r B_r \sin (r\Omega t + \beta_r + \varphi_r) \qquad (7.16b)$$

In view of the inertial type of link (3), one has

$$C_r = \left| \frac{k_2}{p(T_2 p + 1)} \right|_{p=jr\Omega} = \frac{k_2}{\sqrt{T_2^2 r^2 \Omega^2 + 1}} \frac{1}{r\Omega}$$

$$\varphi_r = \arg \left(\frac{k_2}{p(T_2 p + 1)} \right)_{p=j\Omega r} = -\frac{\pi}{2} - \arctan (T_2 r\Omega) \qquad (7.16c)$$

These expressions show that higher harmonics go through link (3) with smaller amplification, so that this link acts as a low-pass filter.   In view of this one can assume, with a reasonable approximation, that

$$x_4(t) \simeq C_1 B_1 \sin (\Omega t + \beta_1 + \varphi_1) \qquad (7.16d)$$

which is the expression of the "filter hypothesis" of Aiserman (Chap. 8).   The subscript 1 means here the first harmonic.   One can thus write, approximately,

$$x = A \sin \Omega t \qquad (7.16e)$$

in which A and Ω are unknown.   Since all quantities are determined through the first harmonic $(x_3)_1$, clearly in the nonlinear function of link (2) one can conserve also only $(x_3)_1$; that is,

$$(x_3)_1 = |F(x)|_1 \simeq B_1 \sin \Omega t \tag{7.16f}$$

where

$$B_1 = \frac{1}{\pi} \int_0^{2\pi} F(A \sin \psi) \sin \psi \, d\psi \qquad \psi = \Omega t \tag{7.16g}$$

In view of $x = A \sin \Omega t$, one can write (7.16f) in the form

$$|x_3|_1 = |F(x)|_1 = qx \tag{7.17}$$

where q is determined from the expression

$$q = \frac{B_1}{A} = \frac{1}{\pi A} \int_0^{2\pi} F(A \sin \psi) \sin \psi \, d\psi$$

$$= \frac{1}{\pi A} \int_0^{\pi} c \sin \psi \, d\psi + \frac{1}{\pi A} \int_\pi^{2\pi} (-c) \sin \psi \, d\psi$$

so that ultimately

$$q = \frac{4c}{\pi A} \tag{7.18}$$

Note that in this form of linearization the nonlinear link is replaced by the linear link involving the linearizing factor q, but the latter becomes a function of the amplitude A.   If one replaces this value of q in the characteristic equation, one has

$$T_1 T_2 p^3 + (T_1 + T_2)p^2 + (1 + T_1 k_2 k_{fb} q)p + (k_1 + k_{fb})k_2 q = 0 \tag{7.19}$$

Setting $p = \pm j\Omega$; $j = \sqrt{-1}$, one obtains an expression of the form

$$X(q,\Omega) + jY(q,\Omega) = 0 \tag{7.20}$$

where

$$X = (k_1 + k_{fb})k_2 q - (T_1 + T_2)\Omega^2 = 0 \tag{7.21}$$
$$Y = (1 + T_1 k_2 k_{fb} q)\Omega - T_1 T_2 \Omega^3 = 0$$

From the first equation in (7.21) one obtains

$$\Omega^2 = \frac{4c(k_1 + k_{fb})k_2}{\pi A(T_1 + T_2)} \tag{7.22}$$

and, from the second [taking into account (7.22) and (7.18)],

$$A = \frac{4ck_2 T_1(T_2 k_1 - T_1 k_{fb})}{\pi(T_1 + T_2)} \tag{7.23}$$

From (7.22) one also obtains

$$\Omega^2 = \frac{k_1 + k_{fb}}{T_1(T_2 k_1 - T_1 k_{fb})} \tag{7.24}$$

Since A and Ω are positive, it follows from (7.23) and (7.24) that the condition for the existence of a periodic solution is

$$T_2 k_1 - T_1 k_{fb} > 0 \tag{7.25}$$

Since the quantities A and Ω are expressed in terms of the parameters of the system, the investigation of their influence on A and Ω does not present any difficulty.

There is another possibility of obtaining similar results directly from the characteristic equation, that is, without studying the process in the neighborhood of the unperturbed periodic solution. We shall start with the characteristic equation

$$L(p) = b_0 p^n + b_1 p^{n-1} + \cdots + b_{n-1} p + b_n = 0 \tag{7.26}$$

in which the coefficients b_i generally contain q and q', which appear in the linearized operational expression

$$Q(p) + R(p)\left(q + \frac{q'}{\Omega} p\right) = 0 \tag{7.27}$$

In the transient condition the amplitude A varies slowly around its unperturbed value, so that

$$q = q(a,\Omega) \qquad q' = q'(a,\Omega) \tag{7.28}$$

Sometimes q and q' depend on one variable only. From this point the argument is conducted directly on the change of the Hurwitzian criteria when the stationary state is either approached or, on the contrary, lost. It is essential that in using this argument one remain within the limits for which the linearization has been established.

If the steady-state condition is reached, it means that at this point (7.26) has at least two purely imaginary roots; if one divides $L(p)$ by $p^2 + \Omega^2$, one obtains

$$\frac{L(p)}{p^2 + \Omega^2} = L_1(p) \tag{7.29}$$

The remaining part $L_1(p)$ must have roots such that the corresponding solution tends to the periodic solution in both cases (i.e., whether one is outside or inside the limit cycle, if one thinks in terms of the topological representation).

The variational equations can be obtained in this case as they are usually obtained, that is, by replacing x^* by $x^* + \Delta x^*$; in this case the procedure is to replace the stationary amplitude A by $A + \Delta a$, a being the variation of the amplitude. This procedure is not quite legitimate, since a (or A) is not the unknown function but a parameter (generally also unknown). However, if one admits this for a moment, the variation Δa will displace all roots with respect to the imaginary axis; the former imaginary roots will then acquire small real parts according to whether the motion is stable or unstable in the Hurwitzian sense (see the discussion in Sec. 3.7).

The argument is thus somewhat delicate and consists of three steps: (1) all that is nonlinear is lumped into one linearized term, which is then treated as linear; (2) the conditions under which there exist at least two imaginary roots is determined; and, finally, (3) a kind of "pseudovariational equation" with respect to the amplitude a is introduced.

In spite of these not-quite-orthodox points in the arguments, the procedure seems to give fairly satisfactory results.

There are several ways to carry out this procedure; we shall indicate two.

The preceding argument shows that for $\Delta a > 0$ the characteristic equation must satisfy the Hurwitzian criteria (i.e., all real parts of the roots must be negative), whereas for $\Delta a < 0$, the next-to-last criterion H_{n-1} must not be fulfilled. This question has been already discussed in Sec. 3.8.

These considerations regarding the change of sign of H_{n-1} when the steady-state solution is crossed can be expressed in the form:

$$\left(\frac{\partial H_{n-1}}{\partial q} \frac{\partial q}{\partial a} + \frac{\partial H_{n-1}}{\partial q'} \frac{\partial q'}{\partial a} \right)^* > 0 \tag{7.30}$$

where the asterisk means that the derivatives are taken at the point $a = A$, which corresponds to the unperturbed motion. The sign of this expression must not change for small deviations of ω around its stationary value.

Another possibility is to use the procedure suggested by Mikhailov[1] instead of that of Hurwitz. It consists of replacing p by $j\omega$ in (7.26) (with b_i expressed as functions of q and q') and separating the real and the imaginary parts. If one considers the real part $X(\omega)$ as the X coordinate and $Y(\omega)$ as the Y coordinate of a curve C, this curve goes

---

[1] This criterion can be found in M. A. Aiserman [1, page 218].

through the origin.   At the point at which L goes through the origin
the parameter ω has the value Ω corresponding to the periodic solution.
If one gives a small deviation Δa to the amplitude from its stationary
value $a = A$, the curve will not pass through the origin.   For stability
it is necessary that for $\Delta > 0$ the criterion be fulfilled.   For $\Delta < 0$, on
the contrary, the criterion should not be fulfilled.

7.3 DAMPING FUNCTION

The difficulties with stability of self-excited oscillations on the basis of
the linear criteria led to another attempt to approach the subject—an
attempt based on the concept of *damping* used in linear theory.   In
this theory the damping coefficient is always constant.   An enlargement
of this concept leads to the definition of the variable damping.

If one replaces p in (7.26) by $\xi + j\omega$, ξ being the coefficient of
damping in the characteristic equation (7.26) in which some coefficients
contain q and q', the amplitude A ceases to be constant (as in the
stationary state) and becomes a certain function $a(t)$ slowly varying
around the value $a = A$.

This approach is justified in this particular case, in which it is
assumed that the linear part is stable and neutral and the Hurwitzian
minors are positive, except for H_{n-1}, which varies a little around its
$H_{n-1} = 0$ value.

If one separates the real and the imaginary parts, one has the
relations

$$X(a,\omega) + \xi X_1(a,\omega) = 0 \qquad Y(a,\omega) + \xi Y_1(a,\omega) = 0 \qquad (7.31)$$

From these equations one obtains the values of ω and ξ as functions of a (the amplitude) in the neighborhood of the periodic solution;
more specifically,

$$\xi = f(q,q') = \varphi'(a) \qquad (7.32)$$

Again, the stability condition is derived in a manner similar to that
by which (7.26) was obtained; that is,

$$\left(\frac{\partial \xi}{\partial a}\right)^* = \frac{\partial f}{\partial q}\left(\frac{\partial q}{\partial a}\right)^* + \frac{\partial f}{\partial q'}\left(\frac{\partial q'}{\partial a}\right)^* < 0 \qquad (7.33)$$

the notations being the same as before.

Thus, for example, using (7.19) and reducing it to the form (7.31) in which ω (or its powers) enters, it is possible to represent ξ in the form

$$\xi = -\frac{T_1 + T_2}{2T_1T_2}\frac{\Delta a}{Ha + D} \qquad H > 0, D > 0 \tag{7.34}$$

that is,

$$\left(\frac{d\xi}{da}\right)_{a=A} < 0 \tag{7.35}$$

since all other quantities on the right side of (7.34) are positive.

There are a number of other possible combinations (Popov and Pal'tov [4, Sec. 2.4]) from which similar criteria can be obtained. All of them are connected in one way or another with what was explained in Secs. 3.7 and 3.8.

From these discussions it is clear that the problem of stability of linearized equations becomes complicated in the case having self-excited oscillations. The reason for that is sufficiently clear; these oscillations indicate the nonlinearity of the system and any attempt to treat the question of stability on the linear basis is thus inevitably complicated, and requires changes in the Hurwitzian criteria according to whether one considers them *outside* or *inside* the limit cycle.

All this relates to the simple topological configuration *IS* (an unstable singular point *I* surrounded by a stable cycle *S*). More complicated configurations, such as, for example, *SIS* in these notations have been definitely ascertained in control systems. This is what is termed "hard self-excitation" in the theory of oscillations. In other words, a control system normally works without oscillations; if, however, it is perturbed by a violent impulse capable of bringing the representative point outside the inner (unstable) cycle *I*, the system becomes excited on the outer (stable) cycle *S* (Fig. 1.6b).

If one tried to linearize a system of this nature (apparently this has not been done yet) the difficulty would be presumably still greater in view of the necessity of imposing (Hurwitz, Mikhailov) still more conditions on the linear criteria; one would then have to ascertain whether all these conditions were consistent.

7.4 COMPARISON BETWEEN THE METHOD OF LINEARIZATION AND THE SMALL-PARAMETER METHOD

We have touched this subject on several occasions (for instance, in Chap. 3). The difficulty was that the theory of oscillations developed *prior* to the study of oscillations in control systems. ˙Hence when oscillations in control systems came to light, it was natural that attention was turned to the theory of nonlinear oscillations.

Unfortunately, this did not turn out to be easy for two principal reasons: (1) the nature of nonlinearities; and (2) the question of the "small parameter."

Because point 1 was investigated in Chap. 1, we shall stress here the second difficulty, since it considerably handicapped the development of the theory of nonlinear control systems.

It should be recalled that in the analytical theories (the early Poincaré theory and the later theories of van der Pol and Krylov-Bogoliubov) the solution is sought in the form of a series arranged according to the ascending powers of a small parameter μ; this holds for the "nearly linear" differential equation of the form

$$\ddot{x} + x + \mu f(x,\dot{x}) = 0$$

or more specifically: $\ddot{x} + \omega_0^2 x = \mu f(x,\dot{x})$.

This matter is well known and we shall not enter into further detail.

As mentioned above, one of the difficulties that appeared in nonlinear problems in control theory was that there are no "small parameters" of any kind in any equations in control theory.

We shall see (Chap. 8) that by a somewhat indirect argument (the "filter hypothesis") Aiserman succeeded in formulating the missing criterion of "near linearity" without involving any "small-parameter" concept.   For that reason a few remarks are noteworthy.

Consider first a relay with a hysteresis loop (Fig. 2.4c) in connection with the differential equation

$$T_1\ddot{x} + \dot{x} + k_1 F_1(x) = 0 \tag{7.36}$$

where $F_1(x)$ is a discontinuous two-valued function.   This equation has the form

$$\ddot{x} + F(x,\dot{x}) = 0 \tag{7.37}$$

If one sets

$$F(x,\dot{x}) = \frac{1}{T_1}\dot{x} + \frac{k_1}{T_1} F_1(x) \tag{7.38}$$

and assumes that (7.37) is reducible to the classical form

$$\ddot{x} + \omega_0^2 x = \mu f(x,\dot{x}) \tag{7.39}$$

one obtains, by the identification,

$$\mu f(x,\dot{x}) = \left(\omega_0^2 x - \frac{1}{T_1}\dot{x}\right) - \left[\frac{k_1}{T_1}F_1(x)\right] \tag{7.40}$$

where $\omega_0^2 x$ is yet unknown. The significance of this expression is that the hysteresis loop $F_1(x)$ contains both the amplification (corresponding to the term $\omega_0^2 x$) and the retardation features (the latter corresponding to $-1/T_1\dot{x}$).† In fact, if there were no hysteresis (but only discontinuity) the term $-(1/T_1)\dot{x}$ would be missing.

Furthermore, in control theory the differential equations appear generally in the form of (7.37) and not in the form (7.38). In other words, it is rather difficult to decide how the generating solution is to be introduced; in order to do that one uses a "short cut" introduced by Krylov and Bogoliubov. In fact, if one uses the equations of the first approximation of the asymptotic theory (Sec. 3.3) for (7.39), one has

$$x = a \sin \psi \qquad \dot{a} = \mu A_1(a) \qquad \omega = \dot{\psi} = \omega_0 + \mu B_1(a) \tag{7.41}$$

where expressions of A_1 and B_1 can be calculated.

From the last expression of (7.41) one forms ω^2. Dropping the term with μ^2 and replacing $B_1(a)$ by the expression

$$\mu B_1(a) = -\frac{1}{2\pi\omega_0 a}\int_0^{2\pi}\mu f(a \sin \psi, a\omega \cos \psi) \sin \psi \, d\psi \tag{7.42}$$

the expression for ω^2 reduces to

$$\omega^2 = \omega_0^2 - \frac{1}{\pi a}\int_0^{2\pi}\mu f(a \sin \psi, a\omega \cos \psi) \sin \psi \, d\psi \tag{7.43}$$

On the other hand, from a comparison of (7.37) and (7.39) one has

$$\mu f(x,\dot{x}) = \omega_0^2 x - F(x,\dot{x}) \tag{7.44}$$

Taking into account (7.44) formula (7.43) can be written

$$\omega^2 = \frac{1}{\pi a}\int_0^{2\pi}F(a \sin \psi, a\omega_0 \cos \psi) \sin \psi \, d\psi \tag{7.45}$$

Similarly, from (7.44) one can derive the expression

$$\dot{a} = -\frac{1}{2\pi\omega_0}\int_0^{2\pi}F(a \sin \psi, a\omega_0 \cos \psi) \cos \psi \, d\psi \tag{7.46}$$

---

† We reproduce here the argument given by Popov and Pal'tov [4, page 134].

Hence, for the periodic solution ($a = A = $ const; $\omega = \Omega = $ const) one has

$$\int_0^{2\pi} F(A \sin \psi, A\omega_0 \cos \psi) \cos \psi \, d\psi = 0 \tag{7.47}$$

$$\Omega^2 = \frac{1}{\pi A} \int_0^{2\pi} F(A \sin \psi, A\omega_0 \cos \psi) \sin \psi \, d\psi \tag{7.48}$$

It is seen that these expressions use directly the form which does not require any small parameter; the latter is, however, introduced in definition (7.44).

If (7.57) had to be treated by the method of harmonic linearization directly it would be written as

$$\ddot{x} + \frac{q'(A,\Omega)}{\Omega} \dot{x} + q(A,\Omega)x = 0 \tag{7.49}$$

so that its characteristic equation would be

$$p^2 + \frac{q'(A,\Omega)}{\Omega} p + q(A,\Omega) = 0 \tag{7.50}$$

and the requirement for a pair of purely imaginary roots would be

$$q'(A,\Omega) = 0 \qquad \Omega^2 = q(A,\Omega) \tag{7.51}$$

This shows that the method of harmonic linearization coincides with the asymptotic method.

7.5 LINEARIZATION OF SOME TYPICAL NONLINEARITIES

We shall study some results which can be obtained by the method of harmonic linearization. The study develops from the application of the fundamental operator

$$F(x,px) = \left[q(A,\Omega) + \frac{q'(A,\Omega)}{\Omega} p \right] x \tag{7.52}$$

to different functions F, assuming that

$$x = A \sin \psi \qquad \psi = \Omega t \tag{7.53}$$

and taking into account only the fundamental harmonic of the Fourier series

$$F(x,px) = F(A \sin \psi, A\Omega \cos \psi) \tag{7.54}$$

The coefficients of the harmonic linearization are given by [see (7.3)]

$$q(A,\Omega) = \frac{1}{\pi A} \int_0^{2\pi} F(A \sin \psi, A\Omega \cos \psi) \sin \psi \, d\psi \qquad (7.55)$$

$$q'(A,\Omega) = \frac{1}{\pi A} \int_0^{2\pi} F(A \sin \psi, A\Omega \cos \psi) \cos \psi \, d\psi \qquad (7.56)$$

We shall consider the following cases:

1. In Sec. 3.5 we investigated the case of a relay with hysteresis and a dead zone (Fig. 3.3). We found that

$$q(A) = \frac{2}{\pi A} \int_{\psi_1}^{\psi_2} F(A \sin \psi) \sin \psi \, d\psi = \frac{2}{\pi A} \int_{\psi_1}^{\psi_2} c \sin \psi \, d\psi \qquad (7.57)$$

$$= -\frac{2c}{\pi A} \cos \psi \Big|_{\psi_1}^{\psi_2} = \frac{2c}{\pi A} (\cos \psi_1 - \cos \psi_2)$$

If one expresses ψ_1 and ψ_2 in terms of the relay constants, one has

$$q(A) = \frac{2c}{\pi A} \left(\sqrt{1 - \frac{b^2}{A^2}} + \sqrt{1 - \frac{mb^2}{A^2}} \right) \quad \text{for} \quad A \geqslant b, -1 \leqslant m \leqslant 1 \qquad (7.58)$$

(The significance of constants b, mb, and c has been explained in Sec. 3.5.) With regard to amplitude A, clearly this formula holds if $A \geqslant b$. A similar calculation for q' gives

$$q'(A) = -\frac{2c}{\pi A} (\sin \psi_1 - \sin \psi_2) \qquad (7.59)$$

And again, with the explicit values of ψ_1 and ψ_2 one obtains

$$q'(A) = -\frac{2cb}{\pi A^2} (1 + |m|) \quad A \geqslant b \qquad (7.60)$$

One can also obtain some particular values of these formulas. Thus, for instance, for an ideal characteristic of a relay (Fig. 7.1a), one has $m = 0$, $b = 0$. In this case one obtains

$$q(A) = \frac{4c}{\pi A} \qquad q'(A) = 0 \qquad (7.61)$$

2. In the case of a characteristic with a dead zone and saturation (Fig. 7.1a), it is obvious that amplitude A must be greater than b_2 (Fig. 7.1b).

We omit the lower part of the diagram (cf. Fig. 3.3, Sec. 3.5), since it serves only for the graphical determination of the "angular time" $\psi_1, \psi_2, \ldots$.

Since $F(A \sin \psi) = 0$ in $0 \leqslant \psi \leqslant \psi_1$, it is sufficient to determine the value of the integral between ψ_2 and $\pi/2$ instead of between 0 and $\pi/2$ (since in view of the symmetry, it is sufficient to calculate the integral for one quarter-period); that is,

$$q(A) = \frac{4}{\pi A} \int_{\psi_1}^{\pi/2} F(A \sin \psi) \sin \psi \, d\psi \tag{7.62}$$

In these limits of integration, one can have two intervals, (ψ_1, ψ_2) and $(\psi_2, \pi/2)$, in which the integrands have the same values. One obtains thus

$$q(A) = \frac{4k}{\pi A} \int_{\psi_1}^{\psi_2} (A \sin \psi - b_1) \sin \psi \, d\psi + \frac{4c}{\pi A} \int_{\psi_2}^{\pi/2} \sin \psi \, d\psi$$

Carrying out these integrations and taking into account expressions for ψ_1 and ψ_2 in terms of the parameters $b_1, b_2, k,$ and c (see Fig. 7.1a), one ultimately obtains

$$q(A) = \frac{2k}{\pi} \left(\arcsin \frac{b_2}{A} - \arcsin \frac{b_1}{A} + \frac{b_2}{A} \sqrt{1 - \frac{b_2{}^2}{A^2}} - \frac{b_1}{A} \sqrt{1 - \frac{b_1{}^2}{A^2}} \right)$$

$$\tag{7.63}$$

Since $\psi_1 = \arcsin (b_1/A)$ and $\psi_2 = \arcsin (b_2/A)$,

$$q'(A) = 0 \qquad \text{for } A \geqslant b_2$$

If $A < b_2$, one must use formula (7.64) below.

3. For the characteristic with a dead zone but without saturation (Fig. 7.2), the preceding case is applicable if $A < b_2$ and $b = b_1$. In

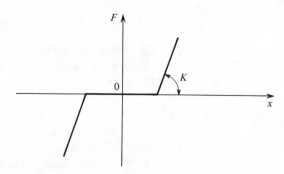

Fig. 7.2

this case $\psi_2 = \pi/2$, and Eq. (7.63) gives

$$q(A) = k - \frac{2k}{\pi}\left(\arcsin\frac{b}{A} + \frac{b}{A}\sqrt{1 - \frac{b^2}{A^2}}\right) \qquad (7.64)$$

$$q'(A) = 0 \qquad A \geqslant b$$

In this case everything happens as if the presence of the dead zone were giving a reduced coefficient of the linear amplification.

4. The characteristic with a dead zone, saturation, and a hysteresis loop (Fig. 7.3) is treated similarly. We omit again the lower part of the

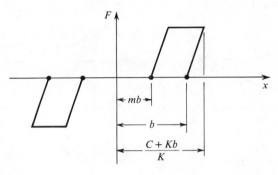

Fig. 7.3

graphical construction (from which one determines $\psi_1, \psi_2, \ldots$). Since in each interval (ψ_1,ψ_2), (ψ_2,ψ_3), $\ldots$, the function is known, the calculation of $q(A)$ reduces to the sum of integrals determined in these intervals.

We shall not reproduce these simple (but long) calculations and indicate only that with the explicit values of

$$\psi_1 = \arcsin\frac{b}{A} \qquad \psi_2 = \arcsin\frac{c + kb}{kA}$$

$$\psi_3 = \pi - \arcsin\frac{c + mkb}{kA} \qquad \psi_4 = \pi - \arcsin\frac{mb}{A}$$

one has

$$q(A) = \frac{k}{\pi}\left[\arcsin\frac{c + kb}{kA} + \arcsin\frac{c + mkb}{kA} - \arcsin\frac{b}{A}\right.$$

$$- \arcsin\left(\frac{mb}{A}\right) + \frac{c + kb}{kA}\sqrt{1 - \left(\frac{c + kb}{kA}\right)^2} + \frac{c + mkb}{kA}\sqrt{1 - \left(\frac{c + mkb}{kA}\right)^2}$$

$$\left.- \frac{b}{A}\sqrt{1 - \frac{b^2}{A^2}} - \frac{mb}{A}\sqrt{1 - \left(\frac{mb}{A}\right)^2}\right] \qquad \text{for } A \geqslant \frac{c + kb}{k} \qquad (7.64a)$$

A similar calculation for $q'(A)$ yields

$$q'(A) = -\frac{2bc(1-m)}{\pi A^2} \quad \text{for } A \geqslant \frac{c+kb}{k} \tag{7.65}$$

If $A \leqslant (c+kb)/k$, one has to use formula (7.66) below instead of (7.64) and (7.65).

5. The characteristic as it is in case 4, but without saturation, is shown in Fig. 7.4. In this case one can use the formulas (7.64) and (7.65)

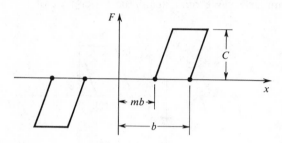

Fig. 7.4

by setting

$$\frac{c+kb}{k} = A \tag{7.66}$$

where c is a variable depending on A. Formulas (7.64) and (7.65) give

$$q(A) = \frac{k}{\pi}\Bigg\{\bigg[\frac{\pi}{2} + \arcsin\bigg[1 - \frac{b(1-m)}{A}\bigg] - \arcsin\frac{b}{A} - \arcsin\frac{mb}{A}$$

$$+\bigg[1 - \frac{b(1-m)}{A}\bigg]\sqrt{1 - \bigg[1 - \frac{b(1-m)}{A}\bigg]^2} - \frac{b}{A}\sqrt{1 - \Big(\frac{b}{A}\Big)^2} - \frac{mb}{A}$$

$$\times \sqrt{1 - \Big(\frac{mb}{A}\Big)^2}\Bigg\} \tag{7.67}$$

for $A \geqslant b$ and

$$q'(A) = -\frac{2kb}{\pi A}\bigg(1 - \frac{b}{A}\bigg)(1-m) \quad \text{always for } A \geqslant b \tag{7.68}$$

In Popov and Pal'tov [4, Chap.3], one can find many other formulas representing either particular cases of the preceding ones or new cases; among the latter we shall mention the so-called "power characteristics" (i.e., when nonlinear functions contain x^2, x^3, . . .).

6. A special form of nonlinearity occurs for (7.37) in the case

$$F(x_1,x_2) = kx_2{}^2 \text{ sign } x_1 \tag{7.69}$$

In this formula we assume that x_1 is the input quantity and x_2 the output. We assume that the solution of the output quantity is sought in the form

$$x_2 = A_2 \sin \Omega t \tag{7.70}$$

We shall suppose the input quantity to be of the same form but with different amplitude and phase, so that

$$x_1 = A_1 \sin (\Omega t - \varphi) \tag{7.71}$$

Relations between A_1 and A_2 and also φ are determined by the frequency characteristics of the linear part. Under these conditions one can write

$$F(x_1,x_2) = k(A_2 \sin \psi)^2 \text{ sign sin } (\psi - \varphi) \tag{7.72}$$

In this case the coefficients of linearization will depend not only on A but also on Ω.

We can determine coefficients $q(A_2,\Omega)$ and $q'(A_2,\Omega)$ for function (7.72).   Note that integrals (7.55) and (7.56) will be the same for each half-period.

If one carries out this calculation, one finds

$$q(A_2,\Omega) = \frac{4kA_2}{\pi} (\cos \varphi - \tfrac{1}{3} \cos^3 \varphi) \qquad \varphi = \varphi(\Omega) \tag{7.73}$$

$$q'(A_2,\Omega) = - \frac{4kA_2}{3\pi} \sin^3 \varphi \qquad \varphi = \varphi(\Omega) \tag{7.74}$$

If one sets $\varphi = 0$ in these formulas one has

$$\dot{q}(A_2) = \frac{8kA_2}{3\pi} \qquad q'(A_2) = 0 \tag{7.75}$$

which corresponds to

$$F(x_2) = kx_2{}^2 \text{ sign } x_2 \tag{7.76}$$

7.6   CONTROL OF MOTOR BY A RELAY

We shall investigate the relay control shown in Fig. 7.5.   Figure 7.5a consists of a motor with armature A and independent excitation F.

The relay R controls the change of polarity of the armature with respect to the impressed voltage.

The nonlinear characteristic of the relay is shown in part (b), and consists of a dead zone and a fixed voltage $\pm U$.

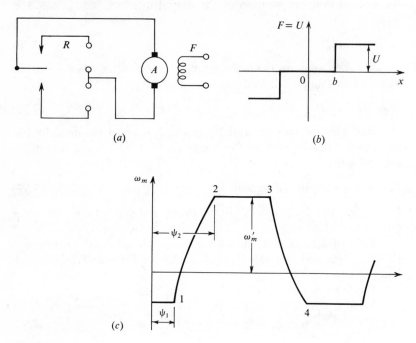

(a)   (b)

(c)

Fig. 7.5

If one neglects the effect of the load and assumes that the characteristic of the motor is linear, then normally (for closed contacts) the motor equation will be

$$(Tp + 1)\omega = kM \tag{7.77}$$

where ω = angular velocity of A
    M = starting moment
    T = time constant
    k = ratio of transmission between A and shaft

If contacts are open, the motor runs by inertia, and in this case

$$Ip\omega = 0 \tag{7.78}$$

I being the moment of inertia of the rotating element.

One must consider the relay and the motor together. If x varies sinusoidally ($x = A \sin \Omega t$), it is necessary to find a periodic solution which consists of pieces given by solutions (7.77) and (7.78), as well as by the relay characteristic.

Figure 7.5c indicates how the resultant characteristic (which we wish to be periodic) is formed; before arriving at point 1 the motor had a constant speed whose sign is determined by the preceding setting on relay contacts; the angle ψ_1 in this case is determined by the relation

$$\psi_1 = \text{arc sin} \frac{b}{A} \tag{7.79}$$

For the next interval 1–2 the solution of (7.77) appears, which gives

$$\omega = \omega^0 - (\omega^0 + \omega')e^{-\psi/2\pi} \tag{7.80}$$

where $\omega^0 = kM$ is the stationary speed, and ω' is the terminal speed when the contacts have been opened.

For the angle ψ_2 the second phase of motion enters, and one has

$$\psi_2 = T_1 - \arcsin \frac{b}{A} \tag{7.81}$$

The absolute value of the terminal speed on the interval 1–2 is obtained from (7.80) if one replaces ψ by its value for this interval.

$$\psi_{1\text{-}2} = \pi - 2\psi_1 \tag{7.82}$$

If one solves (7.80) with respect to ω', taking into account (7.81), one gets

$$\omega' = \frac{1-y}{1+y} \omega^0 \tag{7.83}$$

where

$$y = e^{-(\pi - 2\psi_1)/2\pi} \tag{7.83a}$$

The determination of coefficients of the harmonic linearization will depend on the form of the function $\omega(A \sin \psi)$ represented by Fig. 7.5c, and this will result in splitting the integration into intervals in which different solutions exist [see Eqs. (7.77) and (7.78)]. One thus has the following expression

$$q(A) = \frac{1}{2\pi} \int_0^{2\pi} \omega(A \sin \psi) \sin \psi \, d\psi = \frac{2}{\pi A} \left\{ \int_0^{\psi_1} (-\omega' \sin \psi) \, d\psi \right.$$

$$+ \int_{\psi_1}^{\psi_2} [\omega^0 - (\omega^0 + \omega')e^{-\psi/2\pi}] \sin \psi \, d\psi + \int_{\psi_2}^{\pi} \omega' \sin \psi \, d\psi$$

$$= \frac{2}{\pi A} \left\{ [\omega'(\cos \psi_2 + \cos \psi_1) + \omega^0(\cos \psi_1 - \cos \psi_2)] \right.$$

$$+ \frac{4\pi^2}{1 + 4\pi^2} (\omega^0 + \omega') \left[e^{-\psi_2/2\pi} \left(\frac{1}{2\pi} \sin \psi_2 + \cos \psi_2 \right) \right.$$

$$\left. \left. - e^{-\psi_1/2\pi} \left(\frac{1}{2\pi} \sin \psi_1 + \cos \psi_1 \right) \right] \right\} \tag{7.84}$$

Comparing (7.79) and (7.81), one gets

$$\cos \psi_2 = -\cos \psi_1 \qquad \sin \psi_2 = \sin \psi_1 \tag{7.85}$$

and taking into account the values of ω^0 and ω', one obtains finally

$$q(A) = \frac{4kM}{\pi A} \left\{ \sqrt{1 - \frac{b^2}{A^2}} + \frac{4\pi^2}{(1 + 4\pi^2)(1 + y)} \left[e^{-\psi_2/2\pi} \left(\frac{b}{2\pi A} - \sqrt{1 - \frac{b^2}{A^2}} \right) \right. \right.$$

$$\left. \left. - e^{-\psi_1/2\pi} \left(\frac{b}{2\pi A} + \sqrt{1 - \frac{b^2}{A^2}} \right) \right] \right\} \tag{7.86}$$

where y is given by (7.83a) and ψ_1 and ψ_2 by (7.79) and (7.81).

One obtains a similar formula for $q'(A)$, which we give in the final form, omitting some intermediate calculations, as

$$q'(A) = -\frac{4kM}{\pi A(1 + y)} \left\{ \frac{b(1 - y)}{A} + \frac{4\pi^2}{1 + 4\pi^2} \left[e^{-\psi_2/2\pi} \right. \right.$$

$$\left. \left. \times \left(\frac{1}{2\pi} \sqrt{1 - \frac{b^2}{A^2}} + \frac{b}{A} \right) + e^{-\psi_1/2\pi} \left(\frac{1}{2\pi} \sqrt{1 - \frac{b^2}{A^2}} - \frac{b}{A} \right) \right] \right\} \tag{7.87}$$

We shall not pursue this subject further, since the procedure should already be clear and can be summarized as follows.

1. One starts from the expression (7.52) in which one knows the representation of the function $F(x,px)$ in which one is interested.
2. The next step is to determine the "angular times" $\psi_1, \psi_2, \ldots$, at which discontinuities in F occur. This permits ascertaining the significant intervals $0, \psi_1; \psi_1, \psi_2; \ldots$, in which F is constant, or zero, or linear, etc.

3. Knowing the intervals and the corresponding values of F in each of them, one carries out integrations and the resultant values for q and q' are obtained by adding their values for different intervals.

4. Once everything is expressed in terms of $\psi_1, \psi_2, \ldots$, etc., it is convenient to replace these quantities in terms of the parameters, such as b, mb, c, $\ldots$, etc., which is more convenient for engineering calculations.

In Popov and Pal'tov [4] the reader can find a considerable number of such formulas for symmetrical and for asymmetrical oscillations (the latter are investigated in the following section).

It is possible that with a further advance in nonlinear methods of synthesis many seemingly long calculations of $q(A)$ and $q'(A)$ can be avoided by preparing tables of at least some of these functions. If one looks through these formulas, one cannot fail noticing that in many of them one encounters expressions such as

$$\sqrt{1 - \frac{b^2}{A^2}} \quad \sqrt{1 - \frac{m^2b^2}{A^2}}, \ldots$$

All this can be easily tabulated, and calculations will be accordingly reduced. Finally the *number* of schemes is not too great anyhow, and it is always possible to draw a number of tables (one for each particular characteristic) with b, mb, c, $\ldots$, etc., as parameters.

It must be noted however that all this can be done (and probably will be done) only if the method leads to a practical solution. This, as we have tried to emphasize on several occasions, is always the case if the "filter hypothesis" (of Aiserman) is fulfilled. In the case in which *it is not* fulfilled, the procedure becomes so complicated that it becomes impractical.

7.7 FOLLOWUP SYSTEM OF THE THIRD ORDER

We shall investigate a followup system whose structural scheme is shown in Fig. 7.6, in which A is an electronic amplifier, EF is the field winding of a generator, AR is the armature of a servomotor, m is the

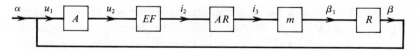

Fig. 7.6

motor, and R is a reducing gearing. It will be assumed that in the motor part one has to include dry friction, quadratic friction, and the lost motion in R.

Equations for different links of the system are as follows.

1. Error function (input to A):

$$u_1 = k_1(\alpha - \beta) \quad \text{for } \alpha = 0, \, u_1 = -k_1\beta \qquad (7.88)$$

2. Amplifier:

$$u_2 = k_y u_1 \qquad (7.89)$$

3. Field winding of the generator:

$$(T_1 p + 1)i_2 = k_2 u_2 \qquad (7.90)$$

4. Circuit of armatures (of generator and motor), assuming that its inductance is neglected:

$$i_3 = k_3 i_2 - k_4 p\beta_1 \qquad (7.91)$$

5. Equation of the motion of motor's armature (together with the load), taking the angle β of the shaft as variable (not taking into account the nonlinear friction):

$$M_T = F_1(p\beta_1)$$

If one takes into account the nonlinear friction, the equation of motion of armature will be

$$(T_2'p)p\beta_1 = k_5 i_3 - \frac{F_1(p\beta_1)}{k_\beta} \qquad (7.92)$$

Combining (7.91) and (7.92), one obtains

$$(T_2 p + 1)p\beta_1 = \frac{k_3 k_5}{1 + k_4 k_5} \, i_2 - \frac{F_1(p\beta_1)}{k_\beta(1 + k_4 k_5)} \qquad (7.93)$$

where $T_2 = T_2'/(1 + k_4 k_5)$.

6. Equation of the reducing gearing, taking into account the lost motion:

$$\beta = F_2(\beta_1) \qquad (7.94)$$

One looks for a harmonic solution for the variable β_1; that is, $\beta_1 = A \sin \psi$; $\psi = \Omega t$. If one applies the formulas of harmonic linearization for dry and for quadratic friction one obtains, respectively,

$$F_1(\beta_1) = \frac{q_1'(A) \, p\beta_1}{\Omega} \qquad F_1(\beta_1) = q_{1*}'(A)\Omega p\beta_1 \qquad (7.95)$$

The first formula holds for the dry (coulomb) friction with $q_1' = 4c/\pi A$, and the second one holds for the quadratic friction with $q_{1*}' = 8k_* A/3\pi$. In the first formula c is the constant value of the moment of the dry friction.

The first relation in (7.95) corresponds to the dry friction characteristic in which the static moment (for speed equal to zero) is not considered; this is an approximation, which can be accepted in the first study.

For nonlinear characteristics caused by the lost motion in the reducing gearing, the harmonic linearization

$$\beta = F_2(\beta_1) = \left[q_2(A) + \frac{q_2'(A)}{\Omega} p \right] \beta_1 \tag{7.96}$$

where

$$q_2(A) = \frac{K_6}{\pi} \left[\frac{\pi}{2} + \arcsin\left(1 - \frac{2b}{A}\right) \right.$$
$$\left. + 2\left(1 - \frac{2b}{A}\right)\sqrt{\frac{b}{A}\left(1 - \frac{b}{A}\right)} \right] \tag{7.97}$$

for $A \geqslant b$ and

$$q_2'(A) = -\frac{4k_6 b}{\pi A}\left(1 - \frac{b}{A}\right) \qquad A \geqslant b$$

In these formulas b is the half-width of the zone of lost motion (dead zone) and k_6 is the transmission ratio of the reducing gearing.

If one substitutes the values of (7.95) into (7.96), one obtains for the dry friction and for the quadratic friction, respectively, the expressions

$$\left[T_2 p + 1 + \frac{q_1'(A)}{k_\beta (1 + k_4 k_5)\Omega} \right] p\beta_1 = \frac{k_3 k_5}{1 + k_4 k_5} i_2 \tag{7.98}$$

$$\left[T_2 p + 1 + \frac{q_{1*}'(A)\Omega}{k_\beta (1 + k_4 k_5)} \right] p\beta_1 = \frac{k_3 k_5}{1 + k_4 k_5} i_2 \tag{7.99}$$

Combining Eqs. (7.88) to (7.90) with Eqs. (7.98) and (7.99), and replacing (7.97), one ultimately obtains the system

$$\left\{ T_1 T_2 p^3 + (T_1 + T_2)p^2 + \left[1 + \frac{k' q_1'(A)}{\Omega} + \frac{k_i q_2'(A)}{\Omega} \right] p \right.$$
$$\left. + k_i q_2(A) \right\} \beta_1 = 0 \quad (7.100)$$

$$\left\{ T_1 T_2 p^3 + (T_1 + T_2)p^2 + \left[1 + k' q_{1*}'(A)\Omega + \frac{k_i q_2'(A)}{\Omega} \right] p \right.$$
$$\left. + k_i q_2(A) \right\} = 0 \quad (7.101)$$

The characteristic equations for some particular cases are as follows.

1. Linear system (without dry friction and lost motion):

$$T_1 T_2 p^3 + (T_1 + T_2)p^2 + p + k = 0 \tag{7.102}$$

where $k = k_l k_6$ is the general coefficient of amplification.

2. When only the dry friction is present:

$$T_1 T_2 p^3 + (T_1 + T_2)p^2 + \left[1 + \frac{k' q_1'(A)}{\Omega}\right] p + k = 0 \tag{7.103}$$

3. When only the quadratic friction is present:

$$T_1 T_2 p^3 + (T_1 + T_2)p^2 + [1 + k' q_{1*}(A)\Omega]p + k = 0 \tag{7.104}$$

4. When only the lost motion is present:

$$T_1 T_2 p^3 + (T_1 + T_2)p^2 + \left[1 + \frac{k_l q_2'(A)}{\Omega}\right] p + k_l q_2(A) = 0 \tag{7.105}$$

Equation (7.102) permits ascertaining stability when nonlinearities are not essential; in this case one has the condition

$$T_1 + T_2 > k T_1 T_2 \tag{7.106}$$

and the limit value of amplification factor (for which the system is at the limit of stability) is

$$k^* = \frac{T_1 + T_2}{T_1 T_2} \tag{7.107}$$

For $k < k^*$ the system is stable; for $k > k^*$ it will be unstable.

In Eq. (7.103) the substitution $p = j\Omega$ yields the equations for the determination of A and Ω; they are

$$k - (T_1 + T_2)\Omega^2 = 0 \qquad \Omega + k' q_1'(A) - T_1 T_2 \Omega^3 = 0 \tag{7.108}$$

The stability of the periodic solution determined by (7.108) according to the criterion

$$\left(\frac{\partial X}{\partial a}\right)^* \left(\frac{\partial Y}{\partial \omega}\right)^* - \left(\frac{\partial X}{\partial \omega}\right)^* \left(\frac{\partial Y}{\partial a}\right)^* > 0 \tag{7.109}$$

and applied to functions

$$X(a,\omega) = k - (T_1 + T_2)^2 \qquad Y(a,\omega) = \omega + \frac{k' q_1'(a)}{\omega}\omega - T_1 T_2 \omega^3 \tag{7.109a}$$

after some intermediate calculations (which we omit), and with $q_1'(A)$ derived from (7.108), gives the criterion

$$\left(\frac{\partial Y}{\partial \omega}\right)^* = -2T_1 T_2 \Omega^2 < 0 \tag{7.110}$$

From the remaining expressions

$$\left(\frac{\partial X}{\partial a}\right)^* = 0 \qquad \left(\frac{\partial Y}{\partial a}\right)^* < 0 \qquad \text{and} \qquad \left(\frac{\partial X}{\partial \omega}\right)^* < 0$$

it is seen [in conjunction with (7.110)] that the criterion (7.109) is not fulfilled. The periodic solution corresponding to (7.108) merely corresponds to the limit of stability *in the small*.

The frequency of the periodic solution is determined from the first equation in (7.108) and is

$$\Omega = \sqrt{\frac{k}{T_1 + T_2}} \tag{7.111}$$

If one substitutes this value, as well as that of $q_1'(A)$, into the second equation of (7.108), one obtains the amplitude

$$A = \frac{4k'c}{\pi \sqrt{\dfrac{k}{T_1 + T_2}\left(\dfrac{T_1 T_2 k}{T_1 + T_2} - 1\right)}} \tag{7.112}$$

and it is seen that the periodic solution is possible if

$$T_1 T_2 k > T_1 + T_2 \tag{7.113}$$

This shows that the critical coefficient k of amplification (which separates the region in which a periodic solution is possible from that in which it is impossible) is

$$k = k_{\mathrm{cr}} = \frac{T_1 + T_2}{T_1 T_2} \tag{7.114}$$

It is observed that for $k = k_{\mathrm{cr}}$, $A \to \infty$ and for $k \to \infty$, $A \to 0$. This relation can be represented graphically in the form of the curve shown in Fig. 7.7, which is self-explanatory.   In fact in the region of

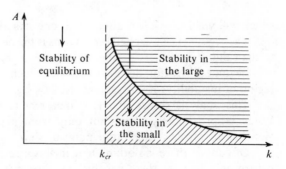

Fig. 7.7

stability of equilibrium, the only solution is $A \to 0$, which is shown by the arrow in that region. Beginning with the value $k = k_{cr}$ the hyperbolically shaped curve separates the zones of instability "in the large" (above the curve) from stability "in the small" (below it).

If one adds the quadratic friction to the linear one [Eq. (7.104)], one has for the determination of X and Y the following relations

$$X(a,\omega) = k - (T_1 + T_2)\omega^2$$

$$Y(a,\omega) = \omega + [1 + k'q'_{1*}(A)\Omega]\omega - T_1 T_2 \omega^3 \qquad (7.115)$$

One can verify easily that in this case criterion (7.109) is fulfilled, so that the solution is stable.

We omit some intermediate calculations (which are of the same character as previous ones; that is, they tend to determine k_{cr}) and mention only the following conclusion.

Quadratic friction releases self-oscillations in the region of parameters, in which the linear system (without quadratic friction) was unstable.

The preceding analysis permits forming certain conclusions of a more general character, namely, with a gradual increase of the coefficient of amplification k three subsequent regions are traversed. For small values of this coefficient $0 < k < k_{cr}$ there is a region of stability of equilibrium. The value of k_{cr} can be calculated if one eliminates Ω between two equations

$$k = \frac{\pi(T_1 + T_2)\Omega^2}{\dfrac{\pi}{2} + \arcsin\left(1 - \dfrac{2b}{A}\right) + 2\left(1 - \dfrac{2b}{A}\right)\sqrt{\dfrac{b}{A}\left(1 - \dfrac{b}{A}\right)}} \qquad (7.116)$$

$$k = \frac{\pi(\Omega - T_1 T_2 \Omega^3)}{4\dfrac{b}{A}\left(1 - \dfrac{b}{A}\right)} \qquad (7.117)$$

which will yield $k = k(A)$, after which one sets $dk/dA = 0$.

The region of self-excited oscillations is the next one; it corresponds to the value $k_{cr} \leqslant k \leqslant k'_{cr}$, where $k'_{cr} = (T_1 + T_2)/T_1 T_2$.

Beyond this region lies the third one, which is characterized by the region of instability; it corresponds to $k > k'_{cr}$.

This analysis shows that it is incorrect to consider a nonlinear system approximately linear not only from a quantitative point of view but also from a qualitative point of view.

Of course, there is nothing new in this assertion, and we mention it here only because these conclusions appear *in spite of the fact that the original system has been linearized.*

In fact, in these three regions one can recognize three typical areas included in the classical theory of oscillations: (1) stability of the singular point; (2) instability of the singular point that is supplemented by the presence of a stable limit cycle; and (3) instability of the saddle point.

In the above discussion these conclusions were reached by rather indirect linearization arguments, which were supplemented by a discussion of the nature of equilibrium in different regions of the kA plane.

7.8 ASYMMETRICAL OSCILLATIONS

The fundamental concepts of asymmetrical oscillations were outlined in Sec. 3.10. It was shown that, quantitatively, asymmetry may be regarded as a parallel transfer of the abscissa axis x by a constant quantity x^0; an oscillation takes, then, the form

$$x = x^0 + x^* = x^0 + A \sin \Omega t \tag{7.118}$$

Figure 7.8 shows this situation; the sinusoidal curve $x^* = A \sin \Omega t$ is now referred to the continuous line $M'M'$ for the abscissa (Fig. 7.8b) instead of the broken line MM, which was the case with symmetrical oscillation. If this curve $x(t)$ is input to the relay whose nonlinear characteristic is shown in Fig. 7.8a, the response of the relay will be a

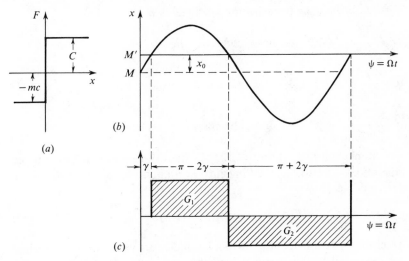

Fig. 7.8

rectangular Fourier series in which the areas G_1 are not necessarily equal to the areas G_2, so that in the Fourier representation there will be a constant term (as mentioned in Chap. 3).

Thus, in addition to the definition of the coefficients of linearization by the following formulas for the symmetrical oscillations

$$q = \frac{1}{\pi A} \int_0^{2\pi} F(A \sin \psi, A\Omega \cos \psi) \sin \psi \, d\psi$$

$$q' = \frac{1}{\pi A} \int_0^{2\pi} F(A \sin \psi, A\Omega \cos \psi) \cos \psi \, d\psi$$

$$(7.119)$$

a third coefficient will be added for asymmetrical ones:

$$F^0 = \frac{1}{2\pi} \int_0^{2\pi} F(x^0 + A \sin \psi, A\Omega \cos \psi) \, d\psi \qquad (7.120)$$

Thus, in the theory of asymmetrical oscillations, instead of the two equations for $q(A)$ and $q'(A)$, with which we have been concerned so far in the theory of symmetrical oscillations, there will be three relations:

$$F^0 = F^0(x^0,A,\Omega) \qquad q = q(x^0,A,\Omega) \qquad q' = q'(x^0,A,\Omega) \qquad (7.121)$$

This means that the fundamental function $F(x,px)$ becomes now

$$F(x,px) = F^0 + qx^* + \frac{q'}{\Omega} px^* \qquad (7.122)$$

Written in full, the linearization coefficients become

$$F^0 = \frac{1}{2\pi} \int_0^{2\pi} F(x^0 + A \sin \psi, A\Omega \cos \psi) \, d\psi$$

$$q = \frac{1}{\pi A} \int_0^{2\pi} F(x^0 + A \sin \psi, A\Omega \cos \psi) \sin \psi \, d\psi \qquad (7.123)$$

$$q' = \frac{1}{\pi A} \int_0^{2\pi} F(x^0 + A \sin \psi, A\Omega \cos \psi) \cos \psi \, d\psi$$

Replacing (7.118) and (7.122) in the differential equation (in the operational form), and taking into account the external disturbance $f(t)$, one has

$$Q(p)(x^0 + x^*) + R(p)\left(F^0 + qx^* + \frac{q'}{\Omega} px^*\right) = S(p)f(t) \qquad (7.124)$$

where $S(p)$ is an operational polynomial. In what follows we shall be interested in the case in which the terms x^0 and $x^* = A \sin \Omega t$ in

(7.18) have a different order of frequencies; more particularly, we shall consider the frequency of x^* to be relatively high as compared with that of x^0 (which may be even a constant in some cases). One can define the significance of the terms "high" and "low" (as applied to frequencies) better, for instance, by the obvious relations

$$|f(t + T) - f(t)| \ll |f(t)| \qquad \text{or} \qquad \left|\frac{df}{dt}\right| T \ll |f(t)| \tag{7.125}$$

where $T = 2\pi/\Omega$, Ω being the frequency of the oscillations.

Instead of (7.125) one can define this concept in terms of velocities

$$|pf(t + T) - pf(t)| \ll |pf(t)| \qquad \text{or} \qquad \left|\frac{dpf}{dt}\right| T \ll |pf(t)| \tag{7.126}$$

The same conditions permit us to consider the low-frequency quantity as *approximately constant* during one period of the high-frequency quantity. It is recalled that this is the principal point in the derivation of equations in the first approximation of the Krylov-Bogoliubov theory (Sec. 3.2).

It can be seen that the three coefficients q, q', and F^0, given by Eqs. (7.119) and (7.120), are functions of three variables: x_0, A, and Ω. One thus has

$$F^0 = F^0(x^0, A, \Omega) \qquad q = q(x^0, A, \Omega) \qquad q' = q'(x^0, A, \Omega) \tag{7.127}$$

(In some cases these relations may be simpler.)

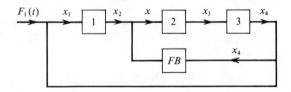

Fig. 7.9

Say that x, as given by (7.118), is substituted into the basic differential equation

$$Q(p)x + R(p)F(x, px) = S(p)f(t) \tag{7.128}$$

where in the right-hand side one has external perturbations [affected by their operator $S(p)$]. It is assumed in this theory that in such a case the differential equation (7.128) can be separated into two differential equations:

$$Q(p)x^0 + R(p)F^0 = S(p)f(t) \tag{7.129}$$

$$Q(p)x^* + R(p)\left(q + \frac{q'}{\Omega}p\right)x^* = 0 \tag{7.130}$$

The authors do not state any reason why this is legitimate, but the hypothesis seems to be plausible enough on the basis of the first approximation.

These two component equations play an important role in what follows. Equation (7.130) relates clearly to the theory of symmetrical oscillations that was discussed in Sec. 7.5, but the differential equation (7.124) gives something new.

The delicate point in the argument is this. Although it is assumed that the fundamental equation (7.128) can be split into two component equations [Eqs. (7.129) and (7.130)] of widely different frequencies, the two equations are not altogether independent, since there is a certain nonlinear relation between them. This relation is connected with the coefficients q and q', which, according to Eq. (7.128), depend not only on A and Ω but also on x^0. This point is left somewhat open, and the argument is, very likely, guided by considerations of plausibility rather than by formal ones.

In view of this additional variable x^0 the usual procedure of separating the real and the imaginary quantities (once $j\omega$ has been substituted for p) yields here

$$X(x^0,A,\Omega) = 0 \qquad Y(x^0,A,\Omega) = 0 \tag{7.131}$$

One thus has two equations for the determination of the three unknowns x^0, A, Ω. As a result, two of them depend on the third, so that

$$A = A(x^0) \qquad \Omega = \Omega(x^0) \tag{7.132}$$

For that reason the further steps are mostly graphical; one builds families of curves of equations giving q and q' for different values of the parameter x^0; once relations (7.132) are obtained from (7.131), one determines numerically or graphically the so-called "function of the shift"

$$F^0 = \Phi(x^0) \tag{7.133}$$

which characterizes the behavior of the nonlinear link in question with respect to the slowly varying parameter x^0. This function is generally a smooth curve, even for systems with relays (Fig. 7.10).   Once $\Phi(x^0)$ is determined it is possible to find also the explicit value

$$x^0 = x^0(t) \tag{7.134}$$

from (7.129) and (7.133). We do not, however, insist on these intermediate steps, which are semigraphical and semianalytical.

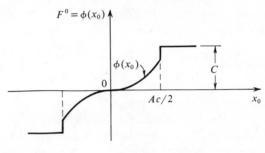

Fig. 7.10

In the case in which $x^0 = $ const and the right-hand side of (7.129) is also a constant, say M_0, Eq. (7.129) becomes

$$Q(0)x^0 + R(0)F^0 = M^0 \tag{7.135}$$

In this case the original differential equation is reduced to an algebraic equation with one variable x^0, which is also contained in F^0. In most cases, this equation is transcendental, and requires a graphical procedure.   According to one procedure, one can try to obtain a representation of A and Ω as functions of x^0 [see Eq. (7.132)].   One then determines the relation (7.133) by substituting (7.132) into the first relation of (7.127).

The authors indicate other methods by which x^0 can be determined; we shall not reproduce these various attempts to determine x^0 as a function of t from the form of the differential equation.   Apparently the problem has not yet been definitely settled.

7.9   STATIC AND STATIONARY ERRORS

If one admits that, by one method or another, it is possible to obtain relations (7.135) for a self-excited system (and this requires a further elaboration of the computing procedure, which we omit), one can analyze the problem further.

Assume first that we wish to explore the behavior of the system when $x^0 = $ const (and, hence, when A and Ω are constants).   In this case the behavior of the system is determined by the algebraic equation (7.128), that is,

$$Q(0)x^0 + R(0)F^0 = M^0 \qquad (7.136)$$

In this formula we replace F^0 by its value (7.120). If the transfer function of the linear part $R(p)/Q(p)$ has one zero root in the denominator, that is, when $Q(p) = pQ_1(p)$, one obtains from (7.136) the equation

$$\Phi(x^0) = \frac{M^0}{R(0)} \qquad (7.137)$$

and this permits determining the static deviation $x^0(M^0)$.

The authors discuss at length the question of errors due to nonlinearities. More specifically, it is stated that the presence of nonlinearities modifies the static error of the linear part of the system. Since the discussion at this point is rather lengthy and not very clear, we shall not include it here; we quote only the conclusion.

IN CALCULATION OF STATIC AND STATIONARY ERRORS OF NONLINEAR SYSTEMS WORKING IN THE SELF-EXCITED STATE, ONE MUST REPLACE THE NONLINEAR FUNCTION $F(x,px)$ BY THE FUNCTION $\Phi(x^0)$ OF THE SHIFT. THIS SITUATION ILLUSTRATES THE LACK OF THE SUPERPOSITION PRINCIPLE IN NONLINEAR SYSTEMS.[1]

This point needs further clarification. In fact, the only information regarding the manifestation of nonlinearities in this analysis is contained in the fact that Eq. (7.124) depends on three variables; the resulting equation, Eq. (7.128), is not necessarily linear. This is, of course, a rather indirect criterion for nonlinearity, and is based not on the differential equation itself but on its solution, whose explicit form is not given.

On the other hand, if the nonlinearity is felt in the errors, then the separation of the fundamental equation (7.125) into two equations, (7.129) and (7.130), does not seem to be quite obvious, since the original equation is nonlinear. Apparently, as we said above, there is still something missing in the argument. From the point of view of physics the matter is sufficiently clear, as we mentioned in connection with followup systems. It is useful, however, to emphasize once more that in the theory of relay systems, as treated by the method of harmonic linearization, there is always a self-excited state; when the system does

---

[1] Popov and Pal'tov [4, page 357].

not transmit any signal, this state leads to symmetrical oscillations; if, however, signals are transmitted, the self-excited oscillation becomes asymmetrical. This leads to the abovementioned complications in the argument. If one can admit that the basic differential equation can be split into two differential equations, (7.129) and (7.130), then there is no further difficulty, since one differential equation deals with x^* and the other with x^0. The former concerns the "carrier" signal, so to speak, and the latter deals with the signal that this carrier transmits.

Up to this point the argument is clear. However, when one begins to investigate the errors, then the existence of a nonlinear error is postulated indirectly [on the algebraic basis of Eqs. (1.131) and (1.132)] and not directly on the basis of the differential equation itself. This equation has been linearized and for that reason is treated as linear [this is evidenced by the "separation" of Eqs. (7.129) and (7.130)].

Very likely all this is again a manifestation of linearization. Such linearization is useful in facilitating the determination of amplitude and frequency, but it does bring about a complication in the theory of stability of the linearized equations (see Sec. 3.7). Here one also discovers certain difficulties in the justification of the separation of Eqs. (7.129) and (7.130) on the one hand and in the presence of nonlinear relations between x^* and x^0 on the other hand.

To reiterate, the theory seems to be sufficiently clear on physical grounds, but a further justification of the above two points is desirable.

7.10 FORCED OSCILLATIONS

An important case of forced oscillations occurs when a relay system is acted on by an external periodic excitation of frequency close to that of the self-excited oscillations of the system. In such a case it usually happens that the relay system falls into synchronization with the frequency of the external excitation. This is the well-known phenomenon of *synchronization* (or of *entrainment*) of frequency, which has been analyzed in the theory of nonlinear oscillations (Minorsky [3]).

We note in passing that if the abovementioned condition of synchronization cannot be obtained, there is no periodic solution (or oscillation), but there is always an "almost periodic" (or quasiperiodic) oscillation consisting of the "beats" (or interference) of two oscillations—the heteroperiodic (or external) and the autoperiodic (or self-excited). This case does not present any applied interest.

Hence, whenever one speaks about forced oscillations in control systems, one always means the *synchronized condition* in which there exists only one frequency, namely, the one corresponding to the external periodic excitation. Having recalled these preliminaries, we propose to continue the outline of the method of harmonic linearization in connection with this particular question.

We assume that the differential equation of the system is

$$Q(p)x + R(p)F(x,px) = S(p)f(t) \qquad (7.138)$$

where $f(t)$ is now a periodic function with period sufficiently close to that of the right-hand term of (7.138). Moreover, we assume that the synchronized condition exists, so that

$$x = A_e \sin (\Omega_e t + \varphi) \qquad (7.139)$$

where by the subscript e attached to A and Ω we mean *external* excitation; thus A_e and Ω_e are the amplitude and the frequency, respectively, when the synchronized condition exists.

In such a case the solution x must necessarily include the phase angle φ [as in (7.139)], since from the theory of this phenomenon we know that the process of synchronization always imposes a certain phase angle between the autoperiodic and the heteroperiodic oscillations by which the "entrainment" of the former by the latter is produced.

It is noted from the above that the unknowns in this problem will be A_e and φ, whereas Ω_e is a known quantity, since it represents the frequency of the external periodic oscillation; we shall, however, attach the subscript e to Ω; that is, we shall write Ω_e merely in order to indicate that Ω_e is the *given frequency* of the external excitation.

It is convenient to transform the expression for $f(t)$ by writing

$$f(t) = B \sin \left[(\Omega_e t + \varphi) - \varphi \right] = B \cos \varphi \sin (\Omega_e t + \varphi)$$

$$- B \sin \varphi \cos (\Omega_e t + \varphi) \qquad (7.140)$$

where B is the amplitude of the external periodic action.

Taking into account (7.139) and the corresponding expression for px, we have

$$px = A_e \Omega_e \cos (\Omega_e t + \varphi) \qquad (7.141)$$

One can write (7.140) as

$$f(t) = \frac{B}{A_e} \left(\cos \varphi - \frac{\sin \varphi}{\Omega_e} p \right) x \qquad (7.142)$$

Substituting this expression in the differential system (7.138) one can write it as

$$\left[Q(p) - S(p) \frac{B}{A_e} \left(\cos \varphi - \frac{\sin \varphi}{\Omega_e} p \right) \right] x + R(p)F(x,px) = 0 \qquad (7.143)$$

In this manner the nonhomogeneous differential equation (7.138) is reduced to the homogeneous differential equation (7.143), which is obvious, since there is a definite solution (7.139) with the heteroperiodic frequency; thus the problem, at least formally, appears as if it were autoperiodic (subject to some additional conditions, which will be outlined later).[1]

Since we are certain that in this case there is a periodic sinusoidal solution, this can be expressed by requiring that the polynomial

$$Q(p) - S(p)\frac{B}{A_e}\left(\cos\varphi - \frac{\sin\varphi}{\Omega_e}p\right) \tag{7.144}$$

must have neither purely imaginary roots nor roots with positive real parts.   One has to verify this condition for $Q(p)$, and, after the solution has been determined, for (7.144) also.

Moreover, one has to show that the "filter hypothesis" is reasonably fulfilled; that is, one has

$$\left|\frac{R(jk\Omega_e)A_e}{Q(jk\Omega_e)A_e - S(jk\Omega_e)B}\right| \ll \left|\frac{R(j\Omega_e)A_e}{Q(j\Omega_e)A_e - S(j\Omega_e)B}\right| \tag{7.145}$$

It is also required that the nonlinear term $F(x,px)$ admit symmetrical oscillations, so that

$$\int_0^{2\pi} F(A_e \sin\psi, A_e\Omega_e \cos\psi)\, d\psi = 0 \tag{7.146}$$

In this case [since (7.143) is homogeneous], one can carry out the harmonic linearization

$$F(x,px) = qx + \frac{q'}{\Omega_e}px \tag{7.147}$$

where

$$q = \frac{1}{\pi A_e}\int_0^{2\pi} F(A_e \sin\psi, A_e\Omega_e \cos\psi)\sin\psi\, d\psi$$
$$q' = \frac{1}{\pi A_e}\int_0^{2\pi} F(\quad)\cos\psi\, d\psi \tag{7.148}$$

In these formulas $\psi = \Omega_e t + \varphi$, which does not introduce any changes in the calculation of q and q'. One can therefore use previously established formulas, replacing A and Ω by A_e and Ω_e.

One thus obtains the characteristic operator of the first approximation:

$$Q(p) - S(p)\frac{B}{A_e}\left(\cos\varphi - \frac{\sin\varphi}{\Omega_e}p\right) + R(p)\left(q + \frac{q'}{\Omega_e}p\right) = 0 \tag{7.149}$$

---

[1] This statement is correct so long as the synchronized condition exists; this is assumed in this chapter.

If one replaces p by $j\Omega_e$, one obtains

$$Q(j\Omega_e) - S(j\Omega_e)\frac{B}{A_e}(\cos\varphi - j\sin\varphi) + R(j\Omega_e)(q + jq') = 0 \quad (7.150)$$

Since

$$\cos\varphi - j\sin\varphi = e^{-j\varphi}$$

one obtains

$$A_e\frac{Q(j\Omega_e) + R(j\Omega_e)(q + jq')}{S(j\Omega_e)} = Be^{-j\varphi} \quad (7.151)$$

From that point one can proceed in two ways: (1) graphically; or (2) analytically.

In method 1 one builds in the complex plane (X, j, Y) the curve

$$Z(A_e) = A_e\frac{Q(j\Omega_e) + R(j\Omega_e)(q + jq')}{S(j\Omega_e)} \quad (7.152)$$

which corresponds to the left-hand side of (7.151). The right-hand side is a circle of radius B. The intersection of this circle with the

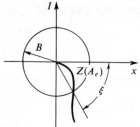

Fig. 7.11

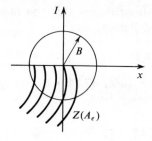

Fig. 7.12

curve $Z(A_e)$ gives a solution determining both the amplitude and the phase of the forced oscillation (Fig. 7.11). The dependence of A_e on Ω_e can be obtained if one traces a number of curves $Z(A_e)$ (Fig. 7.12) for different Ω_e. This method also applies for other parameters, such as k.

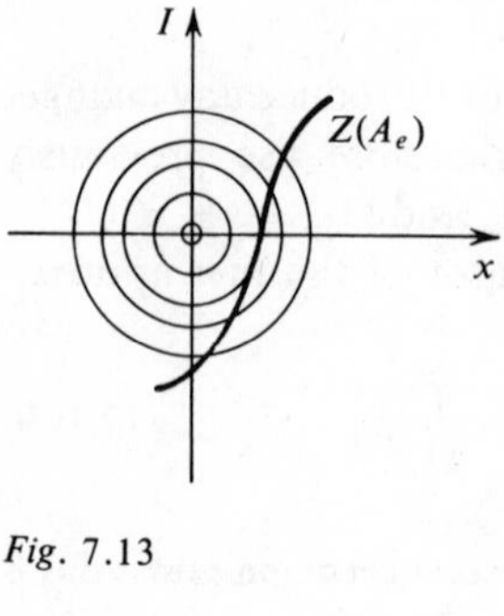

For the determination of the dependence of A_e on the amplitude of the external excitation B, one traces a number of concentric circles (Fig. 7.13). Here two cases are possible:

1. The point of intersection of a circle with the curve $Z(A_e)$ can exist for any B, in which case the curve $A_B(B)$ is continuous; if it

Fig. 7.13

only exists beginning with a certain critical radius B_{cr}, then the curve $A_B(B)$ begins with a certain finite ordinate.

2. In the analytic method one can separate the real and the imaginary quantities for the numerator and the denominator of (7.151) to express the equality between the absolute values and the arguments of both sides of (7.151); this gives

$$A_e{}^2 \frac{X^2(A_e,\Omega_e) + Y^2(A_e,\Omega_e)}{X_s{}^2(\Omega_e) + Y_s{}^2(\Omega_e)} = B^2 \tag{7.153}$$

$$\varphi = - \arctan \frac{Y(A_e,\Omega_e)}{X(A_e,\Omega_e)} + \arctan \frac{Y_s(\Omega_e)}{X_s(\Omega_e)} \tag{7.154}$$

where X and Y are the real and the imaginary parts of the numerator in (7.151) and X_s and Y_s are similar parts of the denominator, that is, $S(j\Omega_e)$. The quantities X and Y correspond to the left-hand side of (7.138), whereas X_s and Y_s correspond to the right-hand side of (7.138). From (7.153) one can determine A_e, after which one calculates φ.

Since there are several parameters, one can select different procedures; for instance, for a given Ω_e (considered as a parameter) one can find a relation between A_e and B. In this case one obtains a family of $B_1 A_e$ curves with Ω_e as a parameter of the family. Likewise the condition of synchronization (that is, B_{cr} as a function of Ω_e) can be determined as the condition for the existence of a real positive value for A_e in Eq. (7.153).

The conditions of stability can be obtained in the same way that they were previously.

7.11 CONCLUDING REMARKS

We have attempted in this chapter to give a brief survey of the applied part of the Popov-Pal'tov theory, which was called by them the method of harmonic linearization; the theoretical fundamentals of the method were outlined in Chap. 3. This outline is only a small part of Popov and Pal'tov's treatise, and for that reason we had to omit a number of topics, some of which are of considerable importance.

Among these topics is the adaptation of the method for investigations of transient conditions in control systems; in this connection some difficulties are encountered.

It is well known that in the theory of nonlinear oscillations the analytical solutions are sought in the form of series expansions; these expansions relate to *stationary periodic solutions*. If, however, one tries to apply these methods to the *transient* intervals, a difficulty appears, since the solution cannot be used in the classical form $x = a_0 \sin \omega_0 t$ but must be sought in the form

$$x = a_0 e^{\xi_0 t} \sin \omega_0 t \tag{7.155}$$

This means that the existing theory of nonlinear oscillations (at least in its asymptotic form, as given by Krylov and Bogoliubov) must be changed in order to take this circumstance into account. Because of lack of space we shall indicate here only the principal point in Popov and Pal'tov's treatise [4, Chap. 7]. In this approach the variable x is sought in the form

$$x = ye^{-bt} \tag{7.156}$$

The constant b requires an explanation. Instead of the regular series, of the Krylov-Bogoliubov theory (Bogoliubov and Mitropolsky [2]), the authors introduce expansions of the form

$$\frac{da}{dt} = -ba + \mu A_1(a) + \mu^2 A_2(a) + \cdots$$
$$\tag{7.157}$$
$$\frac{d\psi}{dt} = \omega_0 + \mu B_1(a) + \mu^2 B_2(a) + \cdots$$

where a and ψ are the amplitude and the phase, respectively.

The difference is that the first approximation for da/dt contains a *finite term*, $-ba$, instead of the expression $da/dt = \mu A_1(a)$, which is used in the classical theory.

The purpose of this change is to be able to investigate the strongly damped (or strongly increasing) oscillations while still being within the scope of the classical (small-parameter) theory. The idea seems to be clear and logical, but requires a complete change in the existing theory—including the theory of linearization.

The importance of this step can be appreciated if one realizes that instead of the classical development of the solution in a Fourier series in terms of a single variable ψ, in this new theory the unknown function

$$f[a(t) \sin \psi, a(t)\omega_0 \cos \psi - ba(t) \sin \psi]$$

is developed *in the plane* of two variables ψ and t according to the trigonometric functions of ψ.

This suggestion is heuristic, and the actual modification of the classical theory has not been attempted, although it seems to be plausible on physical grounds. Apparently this was a point at which physical intuition allowed a "jump forward," which must be justified by mathematicians later.

Another point which we did not attempt in this exposition is of a rather negative nature. It consists in showing that the negation of the "filter hypothesis" (of Aiserman) leads to complications of such a nature that the method of harmonic linearization becomes impracticable. Readers interested in this subject will find it in Popov and Pal'tov [4, Chap. 8]. Calculations become so hopelessly complicated even in the case in which only one additional (third) harmonic is considered, that it is doubtful whether this extension of the method can ever be used. It seems, however, that a purely harmonic version of the method, which we have attempted to outline in this chapter, may turn out to be a reasonably well-codified theory for nonlinear control systems (again, all this is true only if the "filter hypothesis" is fulfilled).

If, however, this hypothesis is not fulfilled, it is probably more reasonable to give up the methods of linearization entirely and to proceed boldly along the road traced by Aiserman (Chap. 8), that is, to definitely adopt the method of *exact solutions* in the form of infinite Fourier series.

At present this "piecewise linear" method is handicapped by the computational difficulties that arise from the transcendental character of the problem. (This happens also in the topological approach to the problem investigated in Chap. 9.)

It would seem, however, that a difficulty of this nature will not remain essential in the "age of computers." If so, one may expect that each of these two major developments will find its proper place in modern control engineering. Whenever the nearly linear character of the problem exists, the method of linearization outlined in this chapter is probably sufficiently broad to cover practically everything which is needed for use with control theory. However, the above-mentioned limitation—connected with "near linearity" or the "filter hypothesis"—is, at present, essential.

If one is interested in entirely discontinuous problems (to which the "filter hypothesis" does not apply), then the new methods outlined in Chap. 8 seem to be definitely indicated. However, at least for the time being, the computational problems connected with these transcendental problems remain, practically, unsurmountable.

REFERENCES

1. Aiserman, M. A.: "Lectures on the Theory of Automatic Regulation," Fizmatgiz, Moscow, 1958.
2. Bogoliubov, N. N., and Y. A. Mitropolsky: "Asymptotic Methods in the Theory of Non-linear Oscillations," Moscow, 1958.
3. Minorsky, N.: "Non-linear Oscillations," D. Van Nostrand, Inc., New York, 1962.
4. Popov, E. P. and I. P. Pal'tov: "Methods of Approximations in the Theory of Non-linear Control Systems," Fizmatgiz, Moscow, 1960.

CHAPTER EIGHT
PIECEWISE
LINEAR METHODS

8.1 INTRODUCTORY REMARKS

In Chap. 6, which concerned relay control systems, we first reviewed elementary theory and in later sections outlined the problem of stability of equilibrium. The difficulty here, as was mentioned already, is that all classical concepts of equilibrium are generally associated with the idea of continuity, and in the case of relay systems the concept of continuity is not available.

There is another difficulty, which we have not investigated so far, and that concerns the question of self-excited oscillations. The limited number of conclusions obtained in Secs. 6.13 and 6.14 are merely a consequence of the *assumption* that the periodic state exists; this does not mean at all that we have covered the question of periodic solutions in systems with relays. This will be done however in Chap. 9, in which a topological approach to this problem is outlined—an approach which is still too remote from the quantitative problems of control theory.

We shall, therefore, continue the argument of the preceding chapter, since it deals with definite engineering problems found in relay control systems.

Before attempting to outline the present state of these studies, it is useful to mention briefly why they are important. From the standpoint of the general theory of nonlinear control systems the phenomenon of self-excited oscillations is generally objectionable; in the theory of relay control systems, however, these oscillations are desirable, since they appear as a carrier for useful signals (as discussed in Chap. 7). In view of this, the theory of self-excited oscillation merits particular attention in relay control systems.

In Chap. 1 we studied these questions in some detail and saw that the real reason for these oscillatory phenomena lies in the *nonanalytic* character of the nonlinearities in control systems. In view of this, there would seem to be no special reason to study relay systems in order to explain the appearance of self-excited oscillations; in fact, such oscillations may be caused by many other effects, such as backlash, saturation, and so on. It is, however, preferable to begin the study of oscillations from a consideration of relay control systems, and this is because of the facility with which the argument can be conducted in connection with this best-studied of nonlinear control elements—the relay.

In all studies of relay control systems one splits the whole system into two component parts: the linear part L and the nonlinear one; the latter is, in this case, a relay R (Fig. 8.1).

Let us try and form first an intuitive grasp of these phenomena.

Assume first that the input $x(t)$ to the relay R is sinusoidal: $\tilde{x}(t) = x_0 \sin \omega t$. To simplify the matter further we assume that the characteristic of R is the simple "ideal" (Fig. 6.4a) characteristic. In such a case the output $y(t)$, in the form of a rectangular Fourier series, will correspond to the sinusoidal input to R. In other words, the relay acts as a *functional transformer*,[1] that is, it transforms a sinusoidal signal into a more complicated signal represented by a certain Fourier series $y(t) = F_1$. This signal F_1, going through the linear part L, will be "smoothed out" to some extent; in other words L generally acts as a *filter*, so that the output $z(t)$ will be less rich in harmonics than $y(t)$.

Assume for the moment that L acts as a *perfect filter*, so that $z(t)$ is the fundamental harmonic of F_1. Suppose that with the open switch S one adjusts the filter L, as just explained, and, moreover, adjusts the phase of $z(t)$ to coincide with that of $x(t)$. Then it is reasonable to expect that on closing the switch S nothing will be changed in this theoretical scheme, and the oscillatory phenomenon will maintain itself if the condition of stability is fulfilled.

We have intentionally simplified many things and introduced implicitly a number of hypotheses in order to approach the study of these complicated phenomena from the physical standpoint.

---

[1] See Chap. 10.

The first obvious conclusion is this. The linear part L must work as a perfect filter, since in this case one may have the fundamental condition $\overrightarrow{x(t)} = \overrightarrow{z(t)}$ fulfilled vectorially, that is, both with regard to amplitudes ($x_0 = z_0$) and to the phases. The equality of phases [in $x(t)$ and $z(t)$] means naturally that they are of the same frequency. To this we add another hypothesis: that of the stability of this theoretical phenomenon.

Let us assume for the moment that the stability condition is fulfilled. If our "filter hypothesis" is also fulfilled, there is no reason at all why a scheme of this kind should not work as an *oscillator*, that is, as a generator of self-excited oscillations.

As a matter of fact, such schemes, as well as their various modifications, occur in great variety in control schemes—and not just in *relay* control systems. In other words, the difficult part is not to *produce* a generator of oscillations of this kind in control systems but rather to *understand* its occurrence. This subject was discussed at length in Chap. 6, and we shall limit ourselves to the points which have not been touched previously.

In the discussion of the above theoretical experiment we have been led to assume that L acts as a perfect filter; in such a case there is no difficulty in understanding *why* oscillations appear in such relay control systems.

This point is generally referred to as the "filter hypothesis" of Aiserman [1], and may be regarded as a necessary cornerstone in the theory of relay control systems. In fact, if one tries to produce artificially something of this nature, one is never certain that such a system will oscillate until the filter hypothesis becomes reality; when this occurs, feedback action with a frequency of the fundamental harmonic becomes possible.

In fact this filter hypothesis is identical with the concept of the feedback action in relay control systems. (We shall return to this important question in Sec. 8.2.) The best way to see this point is to assume the contrary, namely that the output $z(t)$ of L has certain harmonics in addition to the fundamental harmonic; we call this "residual Fourier series" F_2, so that $z(t) = F_2$. If the switch S is closed, clearly $x(t) = z(t)$, so that the Fourier series F_2 will also appear at the input $x(t)$ of R, and a new (rectangular) Fourier series F_2' will appear on its output, which, upon the filtration by L will result in a new Fourier series F_2'', and so on, ad infinitum.

The difficulty here is that this mental process, by which we have attempted to replace the real process, tends to transcend the power of our analysis, since what we want to do is to find a *Fourier series which is a nonlinear function of another Fourier series.*   Unfortunately, this is beyond the reach of our present methods.

M. A. Aiserman not only ascertained this basic difficulty but suggested two fundamental issues. The first issue occurs when Aiserman's filter hypothesis *is fulfilled.* The second issue occurs when the "filter hypothesis" *is not* fulfilled. The situation in the second case is far more complicated, and although a mathematical algorithm has been found, the computational difficulties are still too great for us to be able to use this procedure in engineering practice at present.

In the following section we analyze the first case, which is relatively simple.   The second case is discussed in Secs. 8.3 to 8.14.

8.2   FILTER HYPOTHESIS; AUTORESONANCE

If the linear part L acts as a perfect filter and if the system works as an oscillator in the manner analyzed in the preceding section on the basis of a more or less intuitive argument, it is clear that we can treat a case of this nature on the basis of the general theory outlined in Chap. 1.   First, however, some difficulties must be removed, which we shall proceed to discuss.

We consider again the scheme of Fig. 8.1 and assume that

$$x(t) = A \sin \omega_0 t$$

Since $y(t)$ is a Fourier series, we have

$$y(t) = f(A \sin \omega_0 t) = y_0 + \sum_{k=1}^{\infty} A_k \sin (k\omega_0 t + \varphi_k) \tag{8.1}$$

If $y = f(x)$ is odd, all terms containing even harmonics are absent, and the Fourier series will contain only odd harmonics.   We note that the nonlinear function here is

$$y(t) = f[x(t)] = f(A \sin \omega_0 t) = \sum_{k=1}^{\infty} A_k \sin k\omega_0 t \tag{8.2}$$

This Fourier signal $y(t)$ going through the linear part L will be governed by the principle of superposition, and the output $z(t)$ of L will have the form of (8.1).

Note that since the input $x(t)$ is sinusoidal and the output $y(t)$ is representable by a Fourier series, which, in the case in which the filter hypothesis is fulfilled, becomes merely the fundamental harmonic, the situation resembles that which was analyzed in Sec. 3.5.   In that section, we dealt with the Krylov-Bogoliubov method, where only the fundamental harmonic of the Fourier series was considered as the first-order solution of the differential equation.

There is, however, a formal difference between the analytic case which has just been cited (Sec. 3.5) and the present one; in the first case the nonlinear term appeared with a small parameter μ (and for that reason this type of differential equation was called "nearly linear"), whereas here no parameter is involved. For a number of years this constituted a serious difficulty in the further progress of this problem. It was finally ascertained that the form of the sinusoidal solution at the output of L (Fig. 8.1) is an equivalent criterion to that of near linearity and that there is no necessity for invoking any small parameter in the differential equation. In this manner the fact that the "strong non-linearity" (i.e., the Fourier series $y(t)$, Fig. 8.1) exists between the elements R and L of the system has no relation whatever to the nearly linear behavior of the system, provided that the filter hypothesis of Aiserman is fulfilled. The latter thus plays the same role as the small parameter in the classical theory (due to Poincaré).

We shall accept this proposition and elaborate conclusions on this basis.

If one uses the principle of harmonic balance (Chap. 3) and substitutes the periodic solution of the form

$$x = A \sin \omega t \tag{8.3}$$

into the nonlinear function $y = f(x)$, the result can be written as

$$f(x) = f(A \sin \omega t) = B_1 \sin \omega t + C_1 \cos \omega t \tag{8.4}$$

where

$$B_1 = \frac{1}{\pi} \int_0^{2\pi} f(A \sin x) \sin x \, dx \qquad C_1 = \frac{1}{\pi} \int f(A \sin x) \cos dx \tag{8.5}$$

On the other hand, the basic differential equation corresponding to the general scheme shown in Fig. 8.1 can be written as

$$A D(p) \sin \omega t = [B_1(A)K(p)] \sin \omega t + [C_1(A)K(p)] \cos \omega t \tag{8.6}$$

(For derivation of this equation see Aiserman [1, pages 357–359]). In this form, the left-hand side of Eq. (8.6) is linear, and the right-hand side is nonlinear but appears here as *linearized* on the basis of the Krylov-Bogoliubov theory.

With some additional transformations (Aiserman [1, pages 363–367]) one ultimately obtains the relation

$$I(i\omega) = R(A) \tag{8.7}$$

where $I(i\omega) = D(i\omega)/K(i\omega)$, $D(p)$ and $K(p)$ being the polynomial operators of the linear theory and

$$R(A) = \frac{B_1(A)}{A} + \frac{iC_1(A)}{A} = B(A) + iC(A) \qquad i = \sqrt{-1}$$

This operator $R(A)$ relates to the linearized quantity (that is representing the nonlinear quantity).

We shall not outline this theory here (for details see Aiserman [1, Chap. 5A]) and merely mention that Eq. (8.7) is obtained by constructing two hodographs. The first, $I(i\omega)$, is the usual hodograph of the linear theory and the second, $R(A)$, is constructed knowing the explicit form of the operator $R(A)$. It is clear that the intersection point of the two hodographs gives the desired solution, since in this manner both frequency ω and amplitude A are determined by the nonlinear differential equation.

We mention this graphical procedure as an example of the case in which the first-order solution of the nonlinear problem can be easily obtained on the basis of the fulfillment of the filter hypothesis. In fact, if this hypothesis were not fulfilled, one could not use (8.3) as the periodic solution for $x(t)$.

It is thus seen that Aiserman's filter hypothesis is a kind of bridge which connects the analytic method of Krylov-Bogoliubov with the basic problem of a relay control system as shown in Fig. 8.1. The

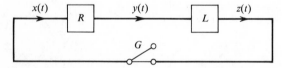

Fig. 8.1

difference in the treatment, as we mentioned, is that the Krylov-Bogoliubov theory is a regular analytic theory (following the small-parameter method of Poincaré), whereas the filter hypothesis is a kind of "short cut" in control theory by which one accomplishes the same thing as with the analytic theory without introducing the concept of a small parameter. We mention in passing that the important theory of harmonic linearization (Chap. 7) starts precisely from this point, that is, when the filter hypothesis *is* fulfilled. In the case in which it *is not* fulfilled, the computational difficulties are so great that the above theory loses its practical meaning.

Another point in Aiserman's theory concerns the so-called auto-resonance. This again may be considered as an attempt to establish a connection between the theory of oscillations and nonlinear control theory. In this connection, we have mentioned one conclusion made on the basis of the filter hypothesis. That is, the fact that there may be manifestations of strong nonlinearities somewhere in a control system does not mean that the nearly linear methods cannot be used for its analysis; in fact, the essential thing that determines whether or not the system is *nearly linear* is the fulfillment of the filter hypothesis.

Similarly, in the autoresonance method an analogous conclusion exists. In fact, there may occasionally be considerable amplitudes in a nonlinear system without disturbing its fundamental property of *near linearity*. Consider the differential equation

$$\ddot{x} + (rx - y) = 0 \qquad y = f(x) \tag{8.8}$$

Written differently this differential equation is

$$\ddot{x} + rx = y \tag{8.9}$$

and it is seen that the amplitude characteristic $A = 1/(r - \omega^2)$ will have an infinite peak if $\omega = \sqrt{r}$. However the system will still be "nearly linear" so long as $|f(x)|$ is sufficiently small. It is convenient, therefore, to consider the nonlinear function $f(x)$ in the form

$$f(x) = rx + \mu\varphi(x) \tag{8.10}$$

where μ is a small parameter and $\varphi(x)$ is a nonlinear function of x. One recognizes in this form the fundamental idea of the method of Poincaré in which the "pure nonlinearity" must be affected by a small multiplier μ.

From this point of view the second formulation of nonlinear control problems—in terms of *autoresonance*—requires:

1. There should be a high peak in the purely linear part, which requires that $D(p) - rK(p) = 0$;[1] this condition means that there are roots situated to the left of the imaginary axis and that a pair of conjugate complex roots are very near to it.
2. The multiplier μ must be small.

Clearly the hypothesis of the filter and the hypothesis of auto-resonance are merely two different formulations of the same basic

---

[1] This operator appears here in connection with the $D(p)A \sin \omega t = K(p)f(A \sin \omega t)$.

fact—that is, the system is *nearly linear* in the sense of Poincaré, although the classical theory of oscillations cannot be used formally in control theory, since the differential equations of control systems do not contain any "small parameter" by which the junction between the two theories could be effected.

Similar considerations have been encountered already in Chap. 7, but the arguments are different. In Chap. 7 the argument leads to an approximation of the process by the first harmonic only (as in all methods of linearization). Here, on the contrary, the method ultimately aims at the *exact* solution (the whole Fourier series). In order to be able to discuss this, one is obliged to retain the idea of *near linearity*, and this, in turn, requires that the filter hypothesis be fulfilled; if it is not, one encounters the difficulty mentioned at the end of Sec. 8.1.

8.3 METHOD OF EXACT SOLUTIONS; PRELIMINARY REMARKS

It is noted in the preceding section that the approximate methods have a limited validity. If we leave out the theory of autoresonance, which is seldom encountered in control problems, and speak only about the filter hypothesis, the method holds if the linear part M (see Fig. 8.1) acts as a very good filter. This permits us to deal with the fundamental harmonic only and not with the Fourier series itself. If the condition is not fulfilled, the method becomes impractical, as we showed intuitively in Sec. 8.1. A more detailed argument can be found in Popov-Pal'tov [4, Chap. 30].

In view of these difficulties Aiserman attempted to use the *entire* (infinite) Fourier series as the solution of the problem instead of adding a few harmonics to the fundamental, which had been done previously.

At this point we must note that the search for solutions in the form of Fourier series leads to solutions with entirely different properties from those which are obtained by power series of the parameter μ of the form $x(t) = x_0(t) + \mu x_1(t) + \mu^2 x_2(t) + \cdots$.

It is known from the general theory of oscillations that the latter solutions are analytic; this greatly simplifies the problem, which may be considered as analytic (at least with a certain degree of approximation). On the other hand, the same polynomial approximation becomes useless when the system is acted on by impulsive disturbances that can be described as mathematical discontinuities of the first kind. From that point of view the approximation by the Fourier series is more adequate, since discontinuities of this kind can fit easier into a Fourier-series analysis.

The drawback of the Fourier analysis is that the familiar feature of approximations (in the analytic domain) does not hold here. In other words, in the analytic domain, the first approximation:

$$x(t) = x_0(t) + \mu x_1(t)$$

can be definitely improved by the second approximation:

$$x(t) = x_0(t) + \mu x_1(t) + \mu^2 x_2(t)$$

The approximation procedure is correctly followed. Nothing can be said in this respect if one uses the Fourier procedure; thus, for example, it is impossible to say whether adding the third harmonic to the fundamental will make things "better" than with the fundamental alone. In fact there is no "yardstick" by which such a comparison could be effected.

The only thing which is *certain* is that by taking the *whole* (*infinite*) *Fourier series, one obtains the exact solution.* This almost obvious idea is the one which Aiserman adopted in his work [1] and the one which was carried out by him in collaboration with Gantmacher in a series of important papers [2].

We must first discard an obvious impossibility. That is, it is impossible to apply a method of this kind in the usual analytic sense, since this would amount to the determination of an infinite Fourier series, which would be a *nonlinear function* of another such series.

Discarding this practically impossible case, there is yet a possibility of doing something with this concept if one agrees to replace a nonlinear function by a *piecewise linear function*. Experience with non-analytic nonlinearities (Chap. 1) shows that a periodic phenomenon can always be approximated by "pieces" of linear phenomena with the "nonanalytic" junctions (see Chaps. 1 and 2).

Hence if one tries to follow this procedure, the situation, while difficult, is not altogether hopeless.

In fact, suppose that we follow a segment (or stretch) AB (in some phase space); during this interval of time we have some Fourier series, say F_1. On arriving at the point B, we encounter a nonanalytic point (a point either with two distinct tangents or with two different radii of curvature, etc.).

It is known (Sec. 1.4) that at such nonanalytic points there are generally impulsive exchanges of energy between the system and an external source. In other words, the original Fourier series F_1 (on

AB) undergoes an impulsive perturbation on arrival at *B* so that on the following stretch *BC* there will be some other series F_2, and so on.

One can question if it is possible to determine the phenomenon (that is, the impulsive actions) in such a way that the ultimate piecewise linear trajectory *ABC* · · · *A* will become closed in the phase space, and the phenomenon will be thus periodic.

It turns out that in spite of the great complexity, the problem is still possible—on the condition (and this is the most difficult condition) that one determines that the instants $t_1, t_2, \ldots, t_n$, at which the representative point *R* passes from one linear "piece" to the other, are not arbitrary but quite definite.   This must be done in order to obtain periodicity.

In other words, if one manipulates these transitions (from *AB* to *BC*, from *BC* to *CD*, etc.), at *very definite instants* $t_1, t_2, \ldots, t_n$, the piecewise linear trajectory *may close*, and the phenomenon will become then periodic.

We have just tried to make a rough sketch of the immensely difficult problem of Aiserman; we noted the following topics:

1. Modification of the infinite Fourier series by discontinuities of the first kind
2. Determination of discontinuities
3. Determination of the instants at which discontinuities must be released in order to obtain periodicity

Topics 1 and 2 do not present any particular difficulty once the method of a certain "coexistence" between the Fourier series and the corresponding discontinuities is ascertained.

The difficult point is 3, which is transcendental at this point and, hence, does not admit any easy solution except, possibly, through the use of computers.

8.4   THE GENERAL FORM OF OPERATIONAL EQUATIONS

Practically all control systems using relays have only one relay element associated with the linear system.   This permits reducing somewhat the generality of the problem and in this manner obtaining more definite results: we shall indicate by subscript 1 the degree of freedom in which the nonlinearity (e.g., the discontinuous action of a relay) occurs. For the sake of generality we designate by $y = f(x)$ a nonlinear function such as the discontinuous characteristic of a relay, which in this case will be of a nonanalytic type.

The differential system under these assumptions will be

$$\dot{x}_1 = \sum_{j=1}^{n} a_{1j}x_j + f(x_k) \qquad \dot{x}_i = \sum_{j=2}^{n} a_{ij}x_j \qquad i = 2, \ldots, n \qquad (8.11)$$

The first equation (8.11) is the one in which the nonlinearity $f(x_k)$ exists; the remaining $n-1$ equations are linear. If one assumes further that $f(x_k)$ is sufficiently well behaved (i.e., is continuous with a certain number of continuous derivatives), one can eliminate between equations (8.11) all coordinates except one: $y = f(x_k)$ and x_k. After this, one can drop the index k and can write (8.11) as

$$\sum_{j=1}^{n} a_{1j}x_j = \dot{x}_1 - y \qquad \dot{x}_1 = \frac{dx_1}{dt} \qquad (8.12)$$

Differentiating this equation with respect to t, one has

$$a_{11} \sum_{j=1}^{n} a_{1j}\dot{x}_j + a_{11}y + \sum_{j=2}^{n} a_{1j} \sum_{j=1}^{n} a_{jl}x_l = \ddot{x}_1 - \dot{y}$$

This, after rearranging, can be written as

$$\sum_{j=1}^{n} a_{1j}^{(1)}x_j = \ddot{x}_1 - a_{11}y - \dot{y} \qquad (8.13)$$

where $a_{1j}^{(1)}$ are constants.   Differentiating once more, one gets

$$\sum_{j=1}^{n} a_{1j}^{(2)}x_j = \dddot{x}_1 - a_1^{(1)} - a_{11}\dot{y} - \ddot{y} \qquad (8.14)$$

and this again can be ultimately reduced to the form

$$\sum_{j=1}^{n} a_{1j}^{(n-1)}x_j = x_1^{(n)} - a_{11}^{(n-2)}y - a_{11}^{(n-3)}\dot{y} - \cdots - a_{11}y^{(n-2)} - y^{(n-1)}$$

where

$$x_1^{(n)} = \frac{d^n x_1}{dt^n} \qquad y^{(n-2)} = \frac{d^{n-2}y}{dt^{(n-2)}}, \ldots$$

Since $x_1, \ldots, x_n$ enter linearly in Eqs. (8.13), (8.14), $\ldots$, one can solve then with respect to x_1. Setting $x_1 = x$, one obtains finally the differential equation

$$a_0 x^{(n)} + a_1 x^{(n-1)} + \cdots + a_n x = b_0 y^{(m)} + b_1 y^{(m-1)} + \cdots + b_m y \qquad (8.15)$$

where $a_0, \ldots, a_n, b_0, \ldots, b_m$ are constants and $m \leqslant n - 1$.

If one sets now

$$D(p) = a_0 p^n + a_1 p^{n-1} + \cdots + a_n \qquad K(p) = b_0 p^m + b_1 p^{m-1} + \cdots + b_m \qquad (8.16)$$

Eq. (8.15) can be written in the operational form

$$D(p)x = K(p)y \qquad p = \frac{d}{dt} \qquad y = F(x) \tag{8.17}$$

This is a convenient form for the investigation of system (8.11), and we shall be continuously concerned with (8.17) in what follows.

8.5   GENERALIZED DERIVATIVES[1]

We shall designate by $PF(t)$ an ordinary derivative of the function $F(t)$; this derivative exists everywhere where $F(t)$ is continuous.   At the points t_q of the discontinuities, $PF(t)$ has no meaning, and one has to introduce a new definition, since to the right and to the left of it the ordinary derivatives $PF(t)$ exist, but, since there is no continuity at $t = t_q$, there may also be a discontinuity in the derivative.   We shall use the notations $t = t_q + 0$ and $t = t_q - 0$ instead of the words "to the right" and "to the left" and introduce the following definition of the *generalized derivative* $P^*F(t)$ (Aiserman [1])

$$P^*F(t) = PF(t) + \sum_q \xi_{0q}\delta(t - t_q) \tag{8.18}$$

where t_q are the instants at which F undergoes discontinuities; δ is the Dirac function, and ξ_{0q} is the magnitude of the discontinuity defined by the relation

$$\xi_{0q} = F(t_q + 0) - F(t_q - 0) \tag{8.19}$$

The sign of summation is extended over all points of discontinuities.
It is clear that if F is continuous, one has: $PF(t) = P^*F(t)$.   The higher-order derivatives such as P^{*2}, P^{*3}, . . . , follow the ordinary rules of differentiation, but one has to take into account the derivatives of the δ function.
The operational polynomial $D(P^*)$ can be written as

$$\begin{aligned}
D(P^*) = {} & a_0 P^n F(t) + \sum_q [a_0 \xi_{0q}\delta^{(n-1)}(t - t_q) + a_0 \xi_{1q}\delta^{(n-2)}(t - t_q) + \cdots \\
& + a_0 \xi_{n-1,q}\delta(t - t_q)] + a_1 P^{n-1}F(t) + \sum [a_1 \xi_{0q}\delta^{(n-2)})(t - t_q) + \cdots \\
& + a_1 \xi_{n-2,q}\delta(t - t_q)] + \cdots + a_{n-2}P^2 F(t) + \sum_q [a_{n-2}\xi_{0,q}\delta^1(t - t_q) \\
& + a_{n-2}\xi_{1,q}\delta(t - t_q)] + a_{n-2}PF(t) + \cdots + \sum
\end{aligned} \tag{8.20}$$

---

[1] We use the notation of Aiserman.

where $\xi_{0q}, \xi_{1q}, \ldots, \xi_{nq}$ are discontinuities in $F(t), PF(t), \ldots, P^{n-1}F(t)$ at the instants $t = t_q$, and the symbols $\delta', \delta'', \ldots, \delta^{n-1}$ are the subsequent derivatives of the function δ.

If one applies the procedure of elimination of the intermediate variables, as in Sec. 8.4, one again obtains Eq. (8.17) in the form

$$D(P^*)x_1 = K(P^*)y \qquad y = f(x_1) \tag{8.21}$$

This now holds for functions undergoing discontinuities at the instants $t = t_q$—supplemented for each t_q by the following *conditions of jumps*:

$$a_0\xi_0 = b_0\eta_0$$
$$a_0\xi_1 + a_1\xi_0 = b_0\eta_1 + b_1\eta_0 \tag{8.22}$$
$$a_0\xi_{n-1} + \cdots + a_{n-1}\xi_0 = b_0\eta_{n-1} + \cdots + b_{n-1}\eta_0$$

In these notations $\xi_0, \xi_1, \ldots, \xi_{n-1}$ are the discontinuities of x_1, $Px_1, \ldots, P^{n-1}x_1$.

The quantities $\eta_0, \eta_1, \ldots,$ can be calculated from their very definition; that is,

$$\eta_0 = f[x_1(t_q + 0)] - f[x_1(t_q - 0)]$$
$$\eta_1 = Pf[x_1(t_q + 0)] - Pf[x_1(t_q - 0)] \tag{8.23}$$
$$= \frac{d}{dx_1}f(x_1)\bigg|^+ \dot{x}_1^+ - \frac{d}{dx_1}f(x_1)\bigg|^- \dot{x}_1^-$$

where the symbols $(+)$ and $(-)$ mean the substitution of the arguments $t_q + 0$ and $t_q - 0$, respectively, in x_1.

Theorem   *The initial system* (8.11) *is equivalent to one symbolic equation* (8.21) *supplemented by* (8.22).

8.6   EQUATION OF PERIODS

If $x_1, Px_1, \ldots, P^{n-1}x_1$ are known for $t = t_1 + 0$, and if one takes these values as the initial conditions, one can carry out the integration of (8.21) by replacing $f(x_1)$ by $S_1x_1 + g_1$, that is, by introducing a linear relation

$$f(x_1) = S_1x_1 + g_1 \tag{8.24}$$

S_1 and g_1 being appropriate constants for the first interval $t_1 < t < t_2$. As the result of this integration one determines x_1 in $(t_1 < t < t_2)$, and, knowing x_1, one determines Px_1, P^2x_1, ..., $P^{n-1}x_1$, $f(x_1)$, $Pf(x_1)$, ..., $P^{n-1}f(x_1)$, known for $t_2 - 0$.

These values cannot be considered as the initial conditions for the following interval (t_2, t_3), since x_1, as well as the derivatives, undergo discontinuities. If, however, one *supplies* the jumps determined by (8.22), in addition to the values of x_1, Px_1, ..., $P^{n-1}x_1$, $f(x_1)$, $Pf(x_1)$, ..., $P^{n-1}f(x_1)$, one obtains the quantities x_1, Px_1, ..., $P^{n-1}x_1$ etc., for the next interval beginning at the time $t = t_2 + 0$ and valid from $t_2 + 0$ up to $t_3 - 0$, and so on.

This method is sometimes called the *method of supply*,[1] since it is based on the *supply* of additional information at the points at which discontinuities appear.

The idea of the method should be sufficiently clear, but there are certain additional conditions to be considered.

Monotonicity   The method presupposes that the operation of the relay always occurs in the direction in which the characteristic is traversed monotonically—with the exception of two points in the cycle, in which $\dot{x}$ changes its sign.   Figure 8.2, which represents the ideal characteristic

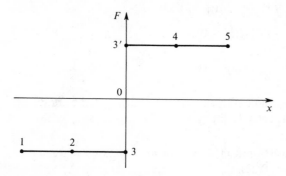

Fig. 8.2

of the relay, permits grasping this point.   Assume that the independent variable x varies between points 1 and 5, at which $\dot{x}$ changes its sign. Between these two "switchings" the coordinate x varies monotonically. This is called the *normal switching*.

An example of *abnormal switching* (which we wish to exclude) would be the case in which x, having reached point 5, reaches 4 on the return and reverses the motion again in the direction of 5.

---

[1] Sometimes the term "method of sewing" is also used, since expressions (8.22) act as the "sewing" of one interval to the other.

The condition of "correct switchings" can always be assured by the requirement that $\dot{x}$ reverse *only* at the ends of the interval.

Transcendental character of the problem Unfortunately this difficulty can not be surmounted, and one can merely ascertain it. It constitutes the principal obstacle to this problem. In fact, it follows from the preceding that the *normal* stretches are those in which there are no discontinuities. Thus $(t_1 + 0, t_2 - 0)$; $(t_2 + 0, t_3 - 0), \ldots$, are the normal stretches, and one can operate with $P(t)$ [without involving $P^*(t)$ plus conditions (8.22) for the jumps]. One can write, therefore, for such a normal stretch

$$x_1(t_1 + 0) = \sum_{j=1}^{n} C_j \, e^{\lambda_j t'}$$

$$x_1(t_1 - 0) = \sum_{j=1}^{n} C_j \, e^{\lambda_j t''}$$

(8.25)

since on each stretch one uses a linear approximation. If there are, for instance, n stretches approximating a closed nonlinear trajectory, there will be n equations. In this equation the unknown constants C_j enter *linearly*, but the times $t', t'', \ldots$, on the contrary, enter *non-linearly* (more precisely in $e^{\lambda_j t'}$ and $e^{\lambda_j t''}$). It follows, therefore, that if one wishes to determine the instants t', t'', one has to solve a system of *transcendental equations*. The equations which determine these instants and for which the piecewise linear solution becomes closed (hence periodic) is called the *equation of periods*.

The term is probably not very fortunate, since instead of *one* equation, there is always a system of such transcendental equations to be solved. This is the reason that this method has been seriously handicapped—because of the computational difficulties that arise in this case. We should mention in passing that the point-transformation method (Chap. 9), which is based on an entirely different principle, has the same difficulty, since, ultimately, it also leads to a system of transcendental equations and, hence, to the same computational difficulties.

The method of "supply" is occasionally used, but the above difficulties seriously limit its more general use.

8.7 EXACT SOLUTIONS (Aiserman)

We have mentioned already that the idea of this method is to use the entire (infinite) Fourier series both for x_1 and $y = f(x_1)$.

Let us assume therefore that x_1 and $y = f(x_1)$ are represented by two such series

$$x_1(t) = \sum_{r=-\infty}^{\infty} \alpha_r e^{ir\omega t}$$

and   (8.26)

$$y(t) = \sum_{r=-\infty}^{\infty} \beta_r e^{i\omega r t}$$

where $i = \sqrt{-1}$ and $y = f(x_1)$.

It is clear that, since y is a certain nonlinear function of x_1, there must be relations between the two infinite sequences of constants $\{\alpha_r\}$ and $\{\beta_r\}$.

Recall that if $y = f(x_1)$ is *any* nonlinear function, the problem is very difficult, since in order to determine y one must determine a nonlinear function of another infinite Fourier series.

However with the piecewise linear approach the matter becomes easier, since for each *stretch* a linear approximation can be used. The ultimate difficulty is in the problem of how to combine these linear stretches in order to obtain a closed polygon and thus a *periodic solution*.

It will be seen that the essence of this method is the same as that of the point-transformation method (Chap 9); the only difference between the two is that the latter method leads to topological results (existence of the fixed point of the transformation, etc.), whereas here one proceeds on the basis of "piecewise" analysis without involving any topological concepts.

Unfortunately, the fundamental difficulty—that resulting from the transcendental nature of the problem—cannot be avoided, as will be shown later.

Returning now to Eqs. (8.26), note that if

$$f(t) = \sum_{r=-\infty}^{\infty} \gamma_r e^{ir\omega t}$$ (8.27)

is a periodic function, then its derivative

$$f'(t) = \sum_{r=-\infty}^{\infty} ir\omega\gamma_r e^{ir\omega t}$$ (8.28)

determines the function $P^*f(t)$ *and not $Pf(t)$*. We shall assume this conclusion without proof.

8.8 DETERMINATION OF PERIODIC STATES IN RELAY CONTROL SYSTEMS

We shall consider again the basic equation (8.21) and assume that $f(x_1)$ is the ideal characteristic of the relay (Fig. 8.2). We shall try to determine the simplest case—that is, when the relay operates at instants $T/2, T, 3T/2, \ldots , T$ being the period. This operation is shown in Fig. 8.3. The problem is to determine the instants of switchings separated by $T/2$, assuming that $x_1(t)$ is a simple harmonic function and

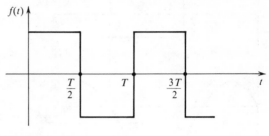

Fig. 8.3

that $y(t) = f[x_1(t)]$ is a nonlinear function of $x_1(t)$. From the elementary theory of relays, one has the following obvious conditions.

1. $y(t) = \begin{cases} +k_p & \text{for } 0 < t < \dfrac{T}{2} \quad T < t < \tfrac{3}{2}\,T, \ldots \\[2ex] -k_p & \text{for } \dfrac{T}{2} < t < T \quad \tfrac{3}{2}\,T < t < 2T, \ldots \end{cases}$

2. $x_1(0) = +k$ \hfill (8.29)

3. $x_1(t) > -k \quad \text{for } 0 < t < \dfrac{T}{2} \quad T < t < \dfrac{3T}{2}, \ldots$

$\quad\;\; x_1(t) < k \quad \text{for } \dfrac{T}{2} < t < T \quad \dfrac{3T}{2} < t < 2T, \ldots$

We look for the periodic solution in the form of (8.26).

If one substitutes $x_1(t)$ and $y(t)$ into (8.21), one obtains

$$\sum_{r=-\infty}^{\infty} \alpha_r D(ir\omega)e^{ir\omega t} = \sum_{r=-\infty}^{\infty} \beta_r K(ir\omega)e^{ir\omega t} \tag{8.30}$$

We thus have the relations between the Fourier coefficients

$$\alpha_r = \beta_r \frac{K(ir\omega)}{D(ir\omega)} = \beta_r W(ir\omega) \tag{8.31}$$

where $W(ir\omega)$ is the frequency characteristic of the linear part L of the relay control system.

One replaces series (8.26) in the nonlinear characteristic $y = f(x_1)$; it is to be observed that it will be satisfied if the previously mentioned conditions (Sec. 8.6) are fulfilled. They are: (1) monotonicity; (2) equation of periods (i.e., transcendental character); and (3) determination of the roots of the characteristic equation.

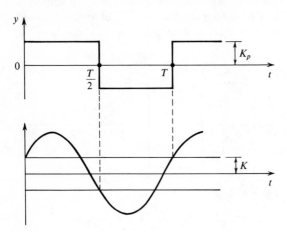

Fig. 8.4

The periodic function shown in Fig. 8.4 is expressed by the Fourier series

$$y = \frac{4k_p}{T} \sum_{r=-\infty}^{\infty} \frac{e^{ir\omega t}}{ir\omega} \tag{8.32}$$

and the periodic solutions have coefficients

$$\beta_r = \frac{4k_p}{ir\omega T} \qquad \alpha_r = \beta_r \frac{K(ir\omega)}{D(ir\omega)} \tag{8.33}$$

It is noted that the coefficients α_r are expressed through one single unknown, $T = 2\pi/\omega$.

So far only condition 1 of (8.29) has been fulfilled; it is thus necessary to impose also the condition:

$$x_1(t) = \sum_{r=-\infty}^{\infty} \alpha_r e^{ir\omega t} = \frac{4k_p}{T} \sum_{r=-\infty}^{\infty} \frac{K(ir\omega)}{ir\omega D(ir\omega)} e^{ir\omega t} \tag{8.34}$$

From condition 2 of (8.29) we have

$$k = \frac{4k_p}{T} \sum_{r=-\infty}^{\infty} \frac{K(ir\omega)}{ir\omega D(ir\omega)} \tag{8.35}$$

and this is the *equation of periods.*

If $T = T^*$ is its root, one clearly obtains

$$x_1 = \frac{4k_p}{T^*} \sum_{r=-\infty}^{\infty} \frac{K(ir\omega^*)}{ir\omega^* D(ir\omega^*)} e^{ir\omega^* t} \tag{8.36}$$

$$y = \frac{4k_p}{T^*} \sum_{r=-\infty}^{\infty} \frac{e^{ir\omega^* t}}{ir\omega^*} \qquad \omega^* = \frac{2\pi}{T^*} \tag{8.37}$$

These series satisfy the basic equation (8.21) and the first two conditions of (8.29); in order to see whether the third equation in (8.29) is fulfilled, it is necessary to build the function (8.36) over the period.

The transcendental character of the problem is seen directly from Eqs. (8.36) and (8.37); in fact $T = T^*$ (or, which is the same, $\omega = \omega^*$) enters into the whole infinite series, and for that reason the problem of the determination of T^* is not algebraic.

Aiserman stresses that the third condition of (8.29) is the most important one.

When $k = 0$ [in (8.35)], condition 3 requires (this is a necessary but not a sufficient condition) that $\dot{x}_1 \big|_{t=0} > 0$; from (8.36) one obtains

$$\dot{x}_1 = \frac{4k_p}{T^*} \sum_{r=-\infty}^{\infty} \frac{K(ir\omega^*)}{D(ir\omega^*)} e^{ir\omega^* t} \tag{8.38}$$

Setting $t = 0$, one obtains the condition

$$\sum_{r=-\infty}^{\infty} \frac{K(ir\omega^*)}{D(ir\omega^*)} > 0 \tag{8.39}$$

This inequality permits making the selection of the roots which do not satisfy the equation of period for $k = 0$. The roots which do not satisfy (8.39) must be rejected, since they do not satisfy equation 3 of (8.29).

8.9 PERIODIC SOLUTIONS OF PIECEWISE LINEAR SYSTEMS

We consider now piecewise linear systems of a more general type than the relay with which we have been concerned so far—namely, those amenable to the differential equation

$$\dot{x}_j = \sum_{k=1}^{n} a_{jk} x_k + \lambda_j f(x_1) + F_j(t) \qquad j = 1, 2, \ldots, n \tag{8.40}$$

where a_{jk} and λ_j are constants (some of which may be zero); $f(x_1)$ is a piecewise linear function, as before; and $F_j(t)$ is a sufficiently well-behaved function of t (that is, continuous with a certain number of continuous derivatives). Some of $F_j(t)$ may be zero. System (8.40) is thus a nonautonomous system, the autonomous features of which have been previously studied.

It is proposed to determine the periodic solution of (8.40) assuming that $F_j(t)$ are periodic functions with the same period T. If all $F_j(t)$ are constant, one has again the autonomous case of self-excitation; if at least one of $F_j(t)$ is not constant, one will be interested in determining a periodic solution with period T of the function $F_j(t)$.

If one follows the same procedure as outlined in Sec. 8.4 and eliminates all variables except x_1 (which relates to the degree of freedom in which there is nonlinearity), the reduced system can be written as

$$D(P^*)x_1 = k(P^*)y_1 + \Phi(t) \qquad y_1 = f(x_1) \tag{8.41}$$

In the process of elimination of $x_2, \ldots, x_n$, the function $\Phi(t)$ has been obtained from $F_j(t); j = 1, \ldots, n$ by the operations of differentiation, multiplication by constants, and addition, so that $\Phi(t)$ has the same period T as do all other functions $F_j(t)$.

If all $F_j(t) \equiv$ const, then $\Phi(t) \equiv$ const, but, in general, $\Phi(t) \neq$ const if at least one of $F_j(t) \neq$ const.

We shall investigate a case which has applied significance—that is, the case in which $f(x_1)$ consists of two given straight lines which need not be parallel (otherwise, we would be back to the theory of relay control systems, which have already been studied). The coordinate x_1 is continuous, but $y = f(x_1)$ may have discontinuities as the representative point R passes from one straight line to the other, since these passages are generally not limited to the points at which the straight lines L_1 and L_2 intersect.

One can specify the problem as follows. The motion of R begins at the point P of the line L_1 (Fig. 8.5) and follows it up to the point Q at which R passes on the other line L_2 at the point Q'. After this the motion follows L_2, but in the opposite direction, until the point P' is reached; then the passage $P'P$ occurs, and from that point the phenomenon reproduces itself again.

For the time being we assume this simple representation as a mathematical model of a closed trajectory in the presence of discontinuities of the first kind.   Equations of lines L_1 and L_2 are $y_1 = k_1 x_1 + h_1$ and $y_2 = k_2 x_1 + h_2$, respectively.

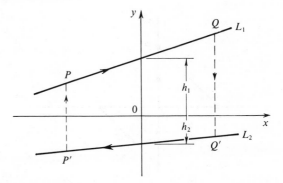

Fig. 8.5

If $\Phi(t)$ is not constant, the system becomes nonautonomous, and the time origin cannot be changed.

8.10   REDUCTION TO THE COORDINATE AXES

For the subsequent analysis it is convenient to transform the system so that the continuous motions of R occur only along the coordinate axes x and y, and the discontinuities take place between these axes.   This can be accomplished by means of the linear transformation of variables:

$$x_1 = \alpha x + \beta y + k$$
$$(\alpha\delta - \beta\gamma) \neq 0 \tag{8.42}$$
$$y_1 = \gamma x + \delta y + \lambda$$

With this change of variables, instead of the motion shown in Fig. 8.5, the representation of the same motion is shown in Fig. 8.6.   The discontinuous transitions QQ' and $P'P$ occur now between the axes x and y, whereas the continuous motion takes place only along the axes x and y.

For this transformation one must set

$$\gamma = k_1\alpha \qquad \delta = k_2\beta \qquad k = \frac{h_1 - h_2}{k_2 - k_1}$$

$$\lambda = \frac{k_2 h_1 - k_1 h_2}{k_2 - k_1} \tag{8.43}$$

where h_1 and h_2 are the intercepts of the lines L_1 and L_2 on the y axis, which is seen from Fig. 8.5.

The constants α and β can be chosen arbitrarily so long as the two relations of (8.43) are fulfilled.

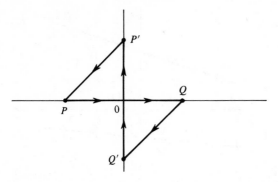

Fig. 8.6

Equation (8.41) becomes then

$$L(P^*)x = M(P^*)y + \Psi(t) \tag{8.44}$$

This holds if $k_2 \neq k_1$, that is, if the straight lines L_1 and L_2 *are not parallel.*

Owing to this transformation of variables, the piecewise linear process is represented in Fig. 8.7, which is self-explanatory. The motion of R starts at point P, Fig. 8.7a, and moves along the x axis to point Q; the motion along the continuous trajectory PQ, Fig. 8.7a, corresponds to this. At the point Q there appears a discontinuity; however, after Q', the motion again becomes continuous (along the y axis), and this part of the motion is shown in Fig. 8.7b between points Q' and P'.

For the quantitative part of the problem one proceeds as previously; that is, one looks for the solutions for x and y in the form of the two Fourier series:

$$x = \sum_{r=-\infty}^{\infty} \alpha_r e^{ir\omega t} \qquad y = \sum_{r=-\infty}^{\infty} \beta_r e^{ir\omega t} \tag{8.45}$$

If one replaces these series into (8.44), in which

$$L(P^*) = \alpha D(P^*) - \gamma K(P^*) = a_0 P^{*n} + a_1 P^{*n-1} + \cdots + a_n$$

$$M(P^*) = \delta K(P^*) - \beta D(P^*) = b_0 P^{*m} + b_1 P^{*m-1} + \cdots + b_m \tag{8.46}$$

$$\psi(t) = \sum_{r=-\infty}^{\infty} \epsilon_r e^{ir\omega t} \qquad f(\alpha x + \beta y + k) = \gamma x + \delta y + \lambda$$

one obtains

$$L(ir\omega)\alpha_r = M(ir\omega)\beta_r + \epsilon_r \tag{8.47}$$

Let μ_r^* be the Fourier coefficients of the periodic function $M(P^*)y$; that is, $\mu_r^* = M(ir\omega)\beta_r$. In this case one clearly has the relations

$$\alpha_r = \frac{\mu_r^* + \epsilon_r}{L(ir\omega)} \qquad \beta_r = \frac{\mu_r^*}{M(ir\omega)} \tag{8.48}$$

On the other hand, one can repeat this argument with respect to the periodic function $M(P)y$ with the same period T, where P is the "ordinary" (not "generalized") derivative. In this case one obtains the coefficients μ_r.

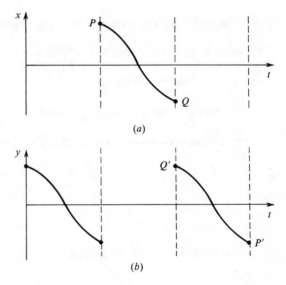

Fig. 8.7

It can be shown (we refer to Aiserman [1, page 416] for the proof) that between μ_r and μ_r^* the following relation exists.

$$\mu_r^* = \mu_r + \frac{1}{T}\left[e^{-ir\omega t_1}\sum_{k=0}^{n-1}\eta_k^1 m_k(ir\omega) + e^{-ir\omega t_2}\sum_{k=0}^{n-1}\eta_k^2 m_k(ir\omega) + \cdots\right] \tag{8.49}$$

where η_k^1 and η_k^2 are the *magnitudes* of discontinuities of the kth derivative of y at the instants $t_1, t_2, \ldots$, and

$$m_k(S) = b_{n-k-1} + b_{n-k-2}S + \cdots + b_n S^{n-k-1} \tag{8.49a}$$

The number of terms [in the square brackets of (8.49)] is equal to the number of discontinuities per period.   In the case considered here, there are only two such points (one for $t = t_1$ and the other for $t = t_2$). Hence, only the written terms in (8.49) are to be considered.

As regards the coefficients μ_r [of the Fourier series $M(p)y$], they are determined by the usual Fourier procedure

$$\mu_r = \frac{1}{T} \int_{t_0}^{t_2} M(P)ye^{-ir\omega t}\, dt = \frac{1}{T}\left[\int_{t_0}^{t_1}(\ )\, dt + \int_{t_0}^{t_2}(\ )\, dt \right] \qquad (8.50)$$

where the parentheses (   ) contain the same integrands.

8.11   FORMATION OF EQUATIONS OF PERIODS

For calculations of the integrals in (8.50) one substitutes the values of $\Psi(t)$ into (8.44) and for intervals (stretches) *without* discontinuities, one uses P (instead of P^*).   This gives

$$L(P)x = M(P)y + \Phi(t) + \lambda K(0) - kD(0) \qquad (8.51)$$

For the periodic process shown in Fig. 8.7 one has

$$y = 0 \qquad \text{for } t_0 < t < t_1$$

and

$$x = 0 \qquad \text{for } t_1 < t < t_2$$

On the other hand the condition $y = 0$ is equivalent to

$$M(P)y = 0 \qquad (8.52)$$

$$y(t_1 - 0) = y^1(t_1 - 0) = \cdots = y^{(n-1)}(t_1 - 0) = 0 \qquad (8.53)$$

Likewise $x = 0$ is equivalent to

$$L(p)x = 0 \qquad (8.54)$$

$$x(t_2 - 0) = x^1(t_2 - 0) = \cdots = x^{(n-1)}(t_2 - 0) = 0 \qquad (8.55)$$

One notes from (8.52) that

$$\int_{t_0}^{t_1} M(P)ye^{-ir\omega t}\, dt = 0 \qquad (8.56)$$

Similarly (8.54) can be used in (8.51); in view of (8.54), it becomes

$$M(P)y = -\Phi(t) - \lambda K(0) + kD(0) \qquad t_1 < t < t_2 \qquad (8.57)$$

so that (8.50) becomes

$$\mu_r = -\frac{1}{T}\int_{t_0}^{t_1} [\Phi(t) + \lambda K(0) - kD(0)] e^{-ir\omega t}\, dt \qquad (8.58)$$

This permits calculating μ_r if one knows $\Phi(t)$. From (8.48) and (8.49) one obtains

$$\alpha_r = \frac{\mu_r + \epsilon_r}{L(ir\omega)} + \frac{1}{TL(ir\omega)}\left[e^{-ir\omega t_1}\sum_{k=0}^{n-1}\eta_k^1 m_k(ir\omega) + e^{-ir\omega t}\sum_{k=0}^{n-1}\eta_k^2 m_k(ir\omega)\right]$$

$$(8.59)$$

$$\beta_r = \frac{\mu_r}{M(ir\omega)} + \frac{1}{TM(ir\omega)}\left[e^{-ir\omega t_1}\sum_{k=0}^{n-1}\eta_k^1 m_k(ir\omega) + e^{-ir\omega t_2}\sum_{k=0}^{n-1}\eta_k^2 m_k(ir\omega)\right]$$

If one replaces these values for α_r and β_r in the Fourier series for x and y and collects terms with like η, one obtains

$$x = \sum_{k=0}^{n-1}[R_k(t - t_1)\eta_k^1 + R_k(t - t_2)\eta_k^2] + R(t) \qquad (8.60)$$

$$y = \sum_{k=0}^{n-1}[S_k(t - t_1)\eta_k^1 + S_k(t - t_2)\eta_k^2] + S(t) \qquad (8.61)$$

where $\eta_k^1, \eta_k^2, \ldots$, are the values of discontinuities of the kth derivatives ($k = 0, 1, \ldots, n - 1$) of the functions R_k, S_k, R, and S, which are convergent Fourier series.

$$R_k = \frac{1}{T}\sum_{r=-\infty}^{\infty}\frac{m_k(ir\omega)}{L(ir\omega)}e^{ir\omega t}$$

$$(8.62)$$

$$S_k = \frac{1}{T}\sum_{r=-\infty}^{\infty}\frac{m_k(ir\omega)}{M(ir\omega)}e^{ir\omega t}$$

$$R = \sum_{r=-\infty}^{\infty}\frac{\mu_r + \epsilon_r}{L(ir\omega)}e^{ir\omega t}$$

$$(8.63)$$

$$S = \sum_{r=-\infty}^{\infty}\frac{\mu_r}{M(ir\omega)}e^{ir\omega t}$$

Returning to conditions (8.53) and (8.55), we require that x and y given by (8.60) and (8.61) should also satisfy these conditions. This ultimately results in the system of equations

$$\sum_{k=0}^{n-1} [R_k(t_2 - t_1 - 0)\eta_k^1 + R_k(-0)\eta_k^2] + R(t_2 - 0) = 0$$

$$\sum_{k=0}^{n-1} [R_k^1(t_2 - t_1 - 0)\eta_k^1 + R_k^1(-0)\eta_k^2] + R^1(t_2 - 0) = 0$$

$$\cdot \cdot \cdot \cdot \cdot \cdot \cdot \cdot \cdot \cdot \cdot \cdot \cdot \cdot \cdot \cdot \cdot \cdot \cdot \cdot \cdot \cdot \cdot \cdot \cdot \cdot \cdot \cdot \cdot \cdot \cdot \cdot \cdot \cdot \cdot \cdot \cdot \cdot \cdot \cdot$$

$$\sum_{k=0}^{n-1} [R_k^{(n-1)}(t_2 - t_1 - 0)\eta_k^1 + R_k^{(n-1)}(-0)\eta_k^2] + R^{(n-1)}(t_2 - 0) = 0$$

$$\sum_{k=0}^{n-1} [S_k(-0)\eta_k^1 + S_k(t_1 - t_2 - 0)\eta_k^2] + S(t_1 - 0) = 0 \tag{8.64}$$

$$\sum_{k=0}^{n-1} [S_k^1(-0)\eta_k^1 + S_k^1(t_1 - t_2 - 0)\eta_k^2] + S^1(t_1 - 0) = 0$$

$$\cdot \cdot \cdot \cdot \cdot \cdot \cdot \cdot \cdot \cdot \cdot \cdot \cdot \cdot \cdot \cdot \cdot \cdot \cdot \cdot \cdot \cdot \cdot \cdot \cdot \cdot \cdot \cdot \cdot \cdot \cdot \cdot \cdot \cdot \cdot \cdot \cdot \cdot \cdot$$

$$\sum_{k=0}^{n-1} [S_k^{(n-1)}(-0)\eta_k^1 + S_k^{(n-1)}(t_1 - t_2 - 0)\eta_k^2] + S^{(n-1)}(t_1 - 0) = 0$$

These equations contain the unknown instants t_1 and t_2, as well as the unknowns η entering *linearly*. Hence, *if one fixes* the values t_1 and t_2, one can determine all discontinuities η_k^1 and η_k^2 (since they are given by linear equations whose number is equal to the number of these unknowns). If the values of η_k^1 and η_k^2 are substituted into (8.60) and (8.61), one obtains $x(t)$ and $y(t)$, which will satisfy the basic equation (8.44).

This means that for $t_0 < t < t_1$ the motion along the x axis ($y = 0$) is guaranteed and for $t_1 < t < t_2$ it is guaranteed along the y axis ($x = 0$). However the transitions $Q \to Q^1$ and $P^1 \to P$ are not yet specified. For this, one must have additional conditions

$$y(t_1 + 0) = y_1 \qquad y(t_2 - 0) = y_2$$

where

$$y_1 = \frac{\sigma - (h_1 - h_2)/(k_2 - k_1)}{\beta} \qquad y_2 = \frac{\sigma_2 - (h_1 - h_2)/(k_2 - k_1)}{\beta}$$

$$\tag{8.65}$$

This follows from Fig. 8.6 and from the definitions

$$\eta_0^1 = y(t_1 + 0) - y(t_1 - 0) \qquad \eta_0^2 = y(t_2 + 0) - y(t_2 - 0)$$

as well as from conditions

$$y(t_1 - 0) = y(t_2 + 0) = 0$$

Equations 8.65 can be written as

$$\eta_0^1 = y_1 \qquad \eta_0^2 = -y_2 \tag{8.66}$$

If the determinant $\Delta(t_1,t_2) \neq 0$, system (8.64) can be solved with respect to η_0^1 and η_0^2. Suppose then that we have obtained these solutions in the form

$$\eta_0^1 = f(t_1,t_2) \qquad \eta_0^2 = f_2(t_1,t_2) \tag{8.67}$$

In such a case, in view of (8.67) one also has

$$f_1(t_1,t_2) = y_1 \qquad f_2(t_1,t_2) = -y_2 \tag{8.68}$$

which can be used for the determination of t_1 and t_2. This can be done (for instance, graphically, Fig. 8.8) by constructing two curves $y_1 = f_1(t_1,t_2) = 0$ and $-y_2 = f_2(t_1,t_2) = 0$ in the (t_1,t_2) plane and determining

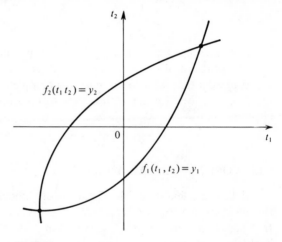

Fig. 8.8

by the point of their intersection the values t_1 and t_2 in which we are interested. Once these values have been found, it is necessary to check to see whether they satisfy the two other conditions. These are: (1) $0 < t_1 < t_2$; and (2) there are no other switchings within one period T besides t_1 and t_2. These conditions can also be verified graphically. For instance, for (1) one constructs the bisector of the (t_1,t_2) plane (the first quadrant). If the point S of intersection of f_1 and f_2 (Fig. 8.8) is in the shaded area of Fig. 8.9, such a point is to be rejected. For the fulfillment of condition (2), it is necessary for the points t_1 and t_2 in question to determine [from (8.64)] the values of η. Substitute them into (8.60) and (8.61) and construct the solution for one period. If in the solution so constructed x_1 is reached for $t \neq t_1$ and y_2 is reached for $t \neq t_2$, then such a solution does not fulfill condition (2) and must be rejected.

There may be special cases when $\Delta(t_1,t_2) = 0$, but we shall not try to examine these details.

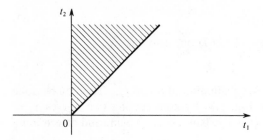

Fig. 8.9

It can be seen from what has been outlined in the last nine sections that the problem of exact solutions is a very difficult one; one cannot say at present that it has been mastered completely. We shall develop the subject a little further with a view to obtaining at least some conclusions.

8.12   COMPUTATIONAL WORK

In all transcendental problems the most difficult part is in carrying through the calculations necessary before any conclusion can be formed. In Chap. 9 we shall examine a situation of this nature, in which the problem is transcendental and the existence of a periodic solution depends on the existence of the fixed point of the transformation. Here the matter hinges on the solution of the "equation of periods," which is transcendental in terms of the instants t_1, t_2, ... at which reversals of relay (or, more generally, transitions from one "stretch" to the other in the piecewise linear problem) must occur.

There are a number of such computational details; we shall mention them only briefly, since this is beyond our immediate task, which is to outline the *method* but not the numerical part of these long and tedious calculations.

The first problem is to organize the computational procedure in connection with system (8.63), which is basic in this problem. Note that the determination of the periodic solutions of system (8.44) under the existing handicap (of transcendentality) is reduced to a determination of a multiple solution of the system of linear equations (8.64). The term "multiple" indicates that a solution found for some arbitrary sequence $t_1, t_2, \ldots, t_n$ is not yet the *solution* but only a "candidate" for the solution (using the pictorial term of Aiserman). In order to justify this "candidacy," as we saw, a number of additional conditions must be fulfilled; if even one of them is not fulfilled, the "candidacy" of a solution for being the ultimate periodic solution is destroyed.

All this makes the procedure very complicated and tedious, but there is no other choice if one wants to pursue the search for an *exact solution*.

It is noted that the functions $R(t)$, $S(t)$, $R_k(t)$, and $S_k(t)$, as well as their derivatives up to the $(n-1)$st order, are coefficients of these linear equations. These functions *become constants if the instants* $t_1, t_2, \ldots, t_n$ *are fixed*. It is seen from that that the time enters implicitly in a very complicated manner to fix the form of the linear system which in itself is not difficult to solve. The difficulty lies in the selection of those instants for which the linearly determined variables $\eta_k{}^j$ determine the periodic solution.

There is one detail worth mentioning. In addition to the above-mentioned functions $R(t)$, $S(t)$, ..., etc., one must also investigate the accuracy which can be obtained by using them. These functions are determined by their developments in a Fourier series, and, according to this method, it is necessary to differentiate these series $(n-1)$ times, which often reacts on their convergence. In order to avoid this difficulty, use is made of an old procedure of A. N. Krylov[1] (not to be confused with N. M. Krylov of the Krylov-Bogoliubov team) for improving the convergence of Fourier series by a special method, the essence of which is as follows.

Assume that we have an R_k function given by its Fourier series

$$R_k = \frac{1}{T} \sum_{r=-\infty}^{\infty} \frac{m_k(ir\omega)}{L(ir\omega)} e^{ir\omega t} \qquad (8.69)$$

where

$$m_k(S) = b_{n-k-1} + b_{n-k-2}S + \cdots + b_0 S^{n-k-1}$$

Let l be an arbitrary positive integer. Divide the polynomial $S^{k+l}m_k(S)$ by $L(s)$ and designate the quotient by $\gamma_0 S^{l-1} + \gamma_1 S^{l-2} + \cdots + \gamma_{l-1}$ and the remainder by $c_0 S^{n-1} + c_1 S^{n-2} + \cdots + c_n$.

---

[1] For many years A. N. Krylov was Professor of the Naval Academy in Petrograd (now Leningrad).

Then one can write (after an intermediate step)

$$\frac{m_k(S)}{L(S)} = \frac{\gamma_0}{S^{k+1}} + \frac{\gamma_1}{S^{k+2}} + \cdots + \frac{\gamma_{l-1}}{S^{k+l}} + \frac{c_0 S^{n-1} + c_1 S^{n-2} + \cdots + c_{n-1}}{S^{k+l} L(s)}$$

(8.70)

Using this identity, the Fourier series for R_k can be replaced by the sum of Fourier series

$$R_k = \frac{C_{n-k-1}}{a_n} + \gamma_0 H_{k+1}(t) + \gamma_1 H_{k+2}(t) + \cdots + \gamma_{l-1} H_{k+l}(t) + R_k^*(t)$$

(8.71)

where

$$H_j(t) = \frac{1}{T} \sum_{r=-\infty}^{\infty} \frac{1}{(ir\omega)^j} e^{ir\omega t}$$

(8.72)

where $j = k + 1, k + 2, \ldots, k + l$,

$$R_k^*(t) = \frac{1}{T} \sum_{r=-\infty}^{\infty} \frac{c_0 (ir\omega)^{n-1} + c_2 (ir\omega)^{n-2} + \cdots + c_{n-1}}{(ir\omega)^{k+l} L(ir\omega)}$$

(8.73)

and Σ' means the sum in which the term $r = 0$ is omitted.

The series $R_k^*(t)$ has the advantage [as compared with $R_k(t)$], since all series obtained by subsequent differentiations up to the $(n - 1)$st order converge.   Moreover, the larger l is, the better is the convergence of the series so obtained.

8.13   CALCULATION OF THE FOURIER SERIES

The procedure of A. N. Krylov gives a convenient algorithm for the calculation of the functions $R_k(t)$ appearing in (8.64).

Consider a function $H_j(t)$; we note that

$$H_j(t) = \frac{1}{\omega T} h_j(\omega t) \quad \text{where} \quad h_j(z) = \sum_{r=-\infty}^{\infty} \frac{1}{(ir)^j} e^{irz}$$

(8.74)

Differentiating $h_j(z)$, one has

$$h_j^{1}(z) = \sum_{r=-\infty}^{\infty} \frac{1}{(ri)^{j-1}} e^{irz} = h_{j-1}(z)$$

(8.75)

that is,

$$h_j(z) = \int h_{j-1}(z) \, dz + C$$

(8.76)

This is a recursive formula in which the constant C is determined from the following conditions:

1. For j even,

$$\int_0^\pi h_j(z)\, dz = 0$$

2. For $j > 1$ and odd, $h_j(0) = 0$

The first condition follows from the fact that h_j (for j even) is an even function which has no constant term in its decomposition in the Fourier series; the second follows from the fact that h_j for j odd and greater than one is a continuous odd function.

It is noted that

$$h_1(z) = \sum_{r=-\infty}^{\infty}{}' \frac{1}{ir} e^{irz} = 2 \sum_{n=1}^{\infty} \frac{\sin nz}{n} \tag{8.77}$$

is a periodic function with period 2π, which for $0 < z < 2\pi$ is given by

$$h_1(z) = \pi - z \tag{8.78}$$

Substituting this value into (8.76), one gets

$$h_2(z) = \int (\pi - z)\, dz + C = \pi z - \frac{z^2}{2} + C \tag{8.79}$$

in which C is determined from the condition

$$\int_0^\pi h_2(z)\, dz = \left(\frac{\pi z^2}{2} - \frac{z^3}{6} + Cz \right)\Big|_0^\pi = 0 \tag{8.80}$$

which yields

$$C = -\frac{\pi^2}{3} \quad \text{and} \quad h_2(z) = \pi z - \frac{z^3}{2} - \frac{\pi^2}{3} \tag{8.81}$$

The process can obviously be continued. Aiserman [1] has calculated the functions h_j up to the 11th order, which results in rather complicated numerical formulas with which one can carry out the calculation of $R_k(t)$ and its derivatives up to the $(n - 1)$st order with a degree of accuracy, but we shall not continue this subject further.

8.14   CONCLUDING REMARKS

The theory of Aiserman, with its numerous ramifications for both theoretical and applied topics, is perhaps the most ambitious in its philosophical implications of everything that has been done to date in this field.

It aims directly at establishing a "coexistence" of some kind between the continuous methods of analysis and the discontinuous ones. The first are by far more numerous and more developed than the second.

It so happens that modern developments in control theory lead inevitably toward such a "coexistence" of those two attitudes, which seemed previously to exclude one another but which, in reality, coexist and interact in a complicated fashion which escaped the standard methods of analysis.

The value of the material in this chapter will vary according to the attitude of different readers. In Sec. 8.2, we presented in abridged form two developments of Aiserman. The importance of these, however, was emphasized in Chap. 7, which dealt with the question of harmonic linearization, which has been a very interesting subject in recent years for engineering applications. Because of this, Sec. 8.2 (and the introduction) will probably be the only part of this chapter of more or less *immediate* interest from the point of view of applications. (Remember that Chap. 7 is directly connected with Sec. 8.2.)

However, the principal importance of this chapter lies in the presentation of the method of *exact solutions*, which begins with Sec. 8.3. From the point of view of *immediate* applications, this part is still in a somewhat unfinished form but the importance of the philosophical implications of these developments is far greater than its immediate contributions to today's engineer. The term "philosophical" is perhaps more appropriate than the term "mathematical," since for the time being the direction in which the mathematical analysis will have to proceed is not yet certain, and some new extensions in the mathematical methods themselves may be necessary in order to simplify the extraordinary complexity of calculations necessary in the case in which one follows the standard theory. The outcome of these questions cannot even be approximately predicted at present, but it usually happens that new applied problems start new developments in mathematical methods. Thus the enormous difficulties which begin to appear in Sec. 8.3 merely show that one is in the midst of a new "offensive"; it is too early to try and forecast the result.

8.15 REMARKS

The introduction of piecewise linear notations may appear somewhat confusing to readers who are primarily interested in the applied significance of these notations. In this connection the argument (of Aiserman and Gantmacher) used in this chapter may lead to the following question: How can a travel of the representative point alternatively on one or the other line in Fig. 8.5 be realized? In fact, the authors leave out all physical considerations in order to follow a purely mathematical argument, which is broad enough to cover many physical realizations. As an example, consider Fig. $A8.1$, which shows a certain nonlinear characteristic $y = f(x)$ of the form indicated. If the representative point R for $t = t_0$ begins to follow the upper branch AFB, it cannot go beyond the point B at which the two branches AFB and $B'B$ join; the result is that there are no points on either of these two branches (to the right of B). It follows, therefore, that for $x = x_B$ the point R will jump on the lower branch (point C), which is traversed from C in the direction of D if $x > x_B$. If, however, the variable begins to decrease (from $x \geqslant x_B$), the branch DCE will be followed until the point $x = x_E$ is reached, where another jump $E \to E''$ will take place, bringing R again on the upper branch.

These considerations were introduced by Poincaré [3] in his theory of bifurcations; in this he says: "the conditions of equilibrium always disappear (or appear) in pairs" (one point of stable equilibrium combines with another point of unstable equilibrium), after which the jump becomes possible (see Chap. 1), since there remains no equilibrium point after this confluence.

Clearly, this physical argument can be conveniently replaced by a mathematical idealization of two lines AFB and DCE with the passages of R from one line to the other for $x = x_B$ and $x = x_E$. One can conceive a great variety of possible ramifications if one follows this argument further, for example, by introducing a parameter owing to which the form of the characteristic is changed, etc.

Referring again to system (8.64), it was said that the problem of determining η_x^1 and η_k^2 is not difficult if t_1 and t_2 are fixed to some values. However η_x^1 and η_k^2 so determined will not, in general, yield a periodic solution. In order to obtain this result, it is necessary to carry out a number of such solutions (for η_k^1 and η_k^2), rapidly changing the subsequent instants $t_2, t_3, \ldots, t_n$ of the manifold $(t_1, t_2, \ldots, t_n)$ until a point of this manifold is reached at which the solution becomes periodic. If the piecewise linear approximation limits itself to a relatively small number of "pieces" (say two or three, as will be seen in the following chapter), the problem is probably within the reach of modern computer techniques and will consist in sweeping the manifold in a certain predetermined order (the t sweep) and after each sweep (and the incidental solutions η_k^1 and η_k^2) observing whether one comes nearer to the periodic solution.

In Sec. 10.10 a computer which could yield the solutions of Fredholm's equation by approximations is described. This would consist in rapidly adjusting (for each approximation) the value of the kernel of the integral equation. In this case the problem is simpler, since the "manifold" to be swept is nondimensional. The present problem is more difficult, since it always involves a multidimensional manifold $(t_1, t_2, \ldots, t_n)$; however, if t is a relatively small number, say two or three, it is possible that a similar procedure can be attempted here. For the time being, however, this problem remains open.

REFERENCES

1. Aiserman, M. A.: "Lectures on the Theory of Automatic Regulation," Fizmatgiz, Moscow, 1958.
2. Aiserman, M. A., and F. R. Gantmacher: *Avtomatika i Tell.*, nos. 2 and 3, 1957.
3. Poincaré, H.: *Acta Math.*, vol. 7, 1885.
4. Popov, E. P., and I. P. Pal'tov: "Methods of Approximations in the Theory of Non-linear Control Systems," Fizmatgiz, Moscow, 1960.

CHAPTER NINE
POINT-
TRANSFORMATION
METHOD

9.1 INTRODUCTORY REMARKS

In this chapter we cover the same subject covered in Chap. 8, but from the standpoint of point-transformation theory. The realization of piecewise linear effects in the theory of analog and functional trans-formers (Chap. 10) consists in replacing a nonlinear characteristic (Fig. 9.1) by a number of rectilinear stretches DA, AB, BC, . . . , on which

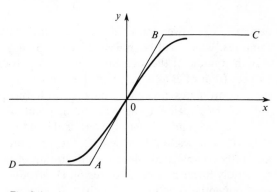

Fig. 9.1

the motion of the representative point R is governed by a linear differen-tial equation. In control theory these piecewise linear features appear in a somewhat different manner.

Suppose we have a system controlled by a relay (or a similar device).   A relay may close either one contact, say a, or another, say b, or may keep them both open.   One thus has three different laws of control, and hence three different differential equations; as a result, the motion of the representative point R will be somewhat complicated as it passes from one region to the other and returns to the starting point (if this is possible).   For the time being we shall not specify the problem in more detail but shall assume that in the phase plane there are three different regions—I, II, and III—separated by the semiaxes AS, AS_3 (between regions I and III), and BS_1, BS_2 (between I and II) (see Fig. 9.2).   Suppose that the point R initially ($t = t_0$) is at a point s of the

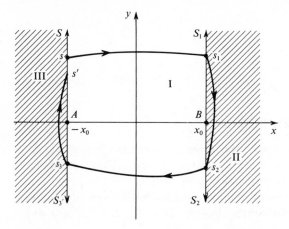

Fig. 9.2

semiaxis S (a lowercase s will designate the ordinates measured on the semiaxes, which will be indicated by a capital S).   Say that the origin is in the middle of the segment A, B and the abscissa of A is designated as $-x_0$ (that of B as $+x_0$); with these notations the initial point s will have coordinates $(-x_0, s)$.   Starting with the point s the trajectory will occur in region I and will end at point s_1 of the semiaxis S_1, at which region I ends.   Since the terminal point s_1 has the known abscissa $+x_0$, it is necessary to calculate the ordinate s_1.   Its expression is generally complicated, since the integration of the differential equation (generally linear and valid for region I) introduces either trigonometric or exponential functions (or both).   In any case, when the coordinate s_1 is determined, the coordinates of this point $(+x_0, s_1)$ are known, and it becomes the initial point for the following arc of trajectory in region II, in which another differential equation governs the motion of R. Continuing this procedure, one arrives at the point s_2 on the S_2 semiaxis, at which the same procedure is applied.   At this point R reenters region I and describes an arc S_2S_3 in this region, which ends at the point S_3, after which R again enters region III.   Region III ends at point s'.   The important point of this procedure is to investigate whether the terminal point s' can, under certain conditions, coincide with the initial point s and whether such coincidence is stable.   If this is possible, one has a *stable piecewise periodic phenomenon*.   Experiment shows that, in fact, such oscillations appear very often in control systems; thus the problem is not so much to discover their physical existence but rather to *explain* them theoretically.   In what follows we shall use the so-called *point-transformation theory*, the origin of which is rather remote (Koenigs [4]).   It often happens in applications that old theories acquire new importance in view of new experimental facts.

The first suggestion that point-transformation theory be used for nonlinear control problems was apparently due to Andronov [around 1937], but for a long time this question remained inactive.   Finally some further developments (Geleszov [2]) permitted a generalization of the theory to such a point that applications became possible.   In fact, soon after these additional studies an interesting book (Gorskaya [3]) appeared in which practically all known nonlinear servomechanisms were treated on this basis.

These phenomena occur under a great variety of conditions and are not limited to a relay control only.   Thus, for instance, in Sec. 9.4, we study the case in which oscillation of this nature is due to the saturation phenomenon in electronic circuits.   Many of these phenomena are observed in mechanical systems, and the literature on this subject has been extensive during the last few years.

The only drawback in this method lies in the necessity for graphical constructions, which are inevitable because these methods are of an essentially topological character.   From this standpoint the method of Chap. 8 has the advantage in the sense that it does not depend on the accuracy of graphical constructions; on the other hand, this latter method has not yet reached a stage at which it can be used for solutions of applied problems.

A remark is necessary at this point.   The term "piecewise linear" becomes clear from an inspection of Fig. 9.2.   In fact on the arcs ss_1, s_1s_2, s_2s_3, ..., linear differential equations govern the motion, and it is well known that such systems are unable to produce self-sustained oscillations.   However, in these piecewise linear systems the essence of the performance is in the impulsive energy inputs which occur at the points s, s_1, s_2, s_3, ..., at which appear discontinuities in the derivatives of the integral curve (Minorsky [5]), and it is obvious that the steady state of such a piecewise linear oscillation can be reached when the continuous energy dissipation on the analytic arcs ss_1, s_1s_2, s_2s_3, and s_3s' (with $s' = s$) is compensated for at the "angular points" s_1, s_2, s_3 ($s = s'$), at which the impulsive energy inputs occur. These impulsive energy inputs at the "angular points" permit explaining the apparent paradox that a number of analytic arcs (each of which is the solution of a linear differential equation not capable of exhibiting any limit-cycle feature) joined together, as previously explained in connection with Fig. 9.1, can under certain conditions exhibit the essentially nonlinear feature of a *nonanalytic limit cycle*. This "energy approach" to the description of piecewise linear phenomena is still in an embryonic stage. In view of this, in the following exposition of the theory we shall outline the early theory of Andronov [1], which was supplemented by later developments (Geleszov [2] and Gorskaya [3]). It is first necessary to outline the method.

9.2 POINT-TRANSFORMATION THEORY

One can interpret the migration of the representative point R in the phase plane (Fig. 9.2) in a somewhat formal manner; that is, one can consider a differential equation as an *operator which establishes a certain correspondence* between two points of a plane (the phase plane here). Thus, for instance, in region I this correspondence manifests itself between the position of the representative point R at the point s of the semiaxis AS (for $t = t_0$) and the position of R at the point s_1 of the semi-axis BS_1 (for $t = t_1$).

In this manner one can make a point s_1 of the BS_1 axis correspond to any point s of the AS axis. Since this holds for *any* point, one can say that the operator existing in region I transforms the AS axis into the BS_1 axis; one can write this symbolically as $(S) \rightarrow (S_1)$. One can use this argument for the following transformations. Thus in region II the operator (that is the differential equation in that region) transforms the semiaxis BS_1 into BS_2, which again can be written as $(S_1) \rightarrow (S_2)$ and so on.

This definition is still too general, since arriving at the point S_3 and repeating the argument, we conclude that $(S_3') \rightarrow (S)$. This does not yet give what is desired in connection with the periodic trajectories, since one is interested not so much in the transformation of one line into the other line but rather in the transformation of *one point of one line into another point of the other line*. This may then be called *point transformation*. With the notations used here the matter is simple, and it is sufficient to replace the capital letters S by lowercase letters. We have thus these notations:

Region I: $s \rightarrow s_1$
Region II: $s_1 \rightarrow s_2$
Region III: $s_2 \rightarrow s_3$

Clearly, this is the necessary condition for what we have in mind (the periodic solution), but is not yet sufficient, since what is ultimately needed is the coincidence of s' and s.

This permits specifying the required conditions better. Let us denote the point s_1 as a certain function $\varphi_1(\tau_1)$ of the time τ_1 needed for the traveling of R from s to s_1 (that is, in a clockwise direction). One can also consider the same point s_1 as a function $\psi_2(\tau_2)$ of τ_2, that is, a time to go from s_1 to s_2. Here we are interested in the inverse process (from s_2 to s_1). Formally these subsequent transformations T_i will be:

$$
\begin{aligned}
T_1: \quad & s_1 = \varphi_1(\tau_1) \qquad s = \psi_1(\tau_1) \\
T_2: \quad & s_2 = \varphi_2(\tau_2) \qquad s_1 = \psi_2(\tau_2) \\
T_3: \quad & s_3 = \varphi_3(\tau_3) \qquad s_2 = \psi_3(\tau_3) \\
T_4: \quad & s' = \varphi_4(\tau_4) \qquad s_3 = \psi_4(\tau_4)
\end{aligned}
\tag{9.1}
$$

These relations express the fact that a given point, say s_1, may be regarded as a function of τ, the time of traveling on the arc ss_1; it can also be regarded as a function of τ_2, the time of traveling on the contiguous arc $s_2 s_1$.

It is clear that if the limit cycle (i.e., the periodic solution) exists, one must equate the relations joined by broken lines; for example

$$
s_1 = \varphi_1(\tau_1) = \psi_2(\tau_2); \qquad s_2 = \varphi_2(\tau_2) = \psi_3(\tau_3); \ldots
\tag{9.2}
$$

These are generally transcendental equations, and this constitutes the principal computational difficulty of this problem.

Once the fixed point is determined, its stability (and, hence, that of the piecewise analytic cycle so obtained) is given by the theorem of Koenigs [4]; this is

$$
\frac{ds'}{ds} = \frac{\varphi_1(\bar{\tau}_1)\varphi_2(\bar{\tau}_2)\varphi_3(\bar{\tau}_3)\varphi_4(\bar{\tau}_4)}{\psi_1(\bar{\tau}_1)\psi_2(\bar{\tau}_2)\psi_3(\bar{\tau}_3)\psi_4(\bar{\tau}_4)}
\tag{9.3}
$$

where $\bar{\tau}_i$ means τ_i for the fixed point.

Although the procedure is clear enough, the difficulty is in carrying it through in view of its transcendental character; this is discussed in the following section.

9.3 PIECEWISE LINEAR LIMIT CYCLE OF AN ELECTRONIC OSCILLATOR

As an example of the preceding theory we shall investigate self-excited oscillations of an electron-tube circuit which has its oscillating circuit either in the grid (Fig. 9.3*a*) or in the anode circuit (Fig. 9.3*b*). As usual, one neglects the grid current and the anode reaction in the first approximation.

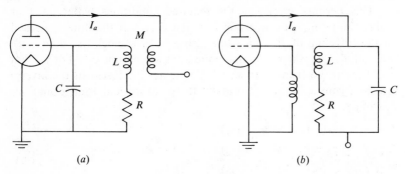

(*a*)   (*b*)

Fig. 9.3

One can obtain the differential equation of such an oscillator starting from the following differential equation

$$LC\frac{d^2v}{dt^2} + RC\frac{dv}{dt} + v = M\frac{dI_a}{dt} \tag{9.3a}$$

of the oscillating circuit in terms of the grid voltage v on which the emf $M\, dI_a/dt$ (injected through the mutual inductance M) from the anode current I_a acts.

Under the above simplifying assumptions the anode current I_a depends only on the grid voltage v, which generally is sufficiently well fulfilled in applications for electron tubes with a large amplification factor (e.g., pentodes).

This can be expressed by the relation

$$S(v) = \frac{dI_a}{dv} \tag{9.4}$$

The nonlinear element in this relation is $S(v) = dI_a/dv$, which expresses the slope of the characteristic $I_a(v)$. In view of (9.4) Eq. (9.3a) can be written as

$$LC\ddot{v} + [RC - MS(v)]\dot{v} + v = 0 \tag{9.5}$$

We shall use a piecewise linear approximation which consists in replacing the actual (nonlinear) characteristic of the electron tube by a broken-line characteristic (shown in Fig. 9.4), which can be expressed by the relations

$$I_a = \begin{cases} 0 & \text{for } v \leqslant -v_0 \\ S(v + v_0) & \text{for } v > -v_0 \end{cases} \tag{9.6}$$

In this idealization, S is constant.

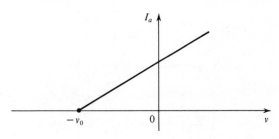

Fig.9.4

Using the dimensionless variables

$$x = \frac{v}{v_0} \qquad t' = \omega_0 t \qquad \omega_0 = \frac{1}{\sqrt{LC}} \tag{9.7}$$

the differential equation will be represented by two equations

$$\begin{aligned} \ddot{x} + 2h_1\dot{x} + x = 0 & \quad \text{for } x < -1 \\ \ddot{x} - 2h_2\dot{x} + x = 0 & \quad \text{for } x > -1 \end{aligned} \tag{9.8}$$

where

$$h_1 = (\omega_0/2)RC \qquad h_2 = (\omega_0/2)[MS - RC] \tag{9.9}$$

In this manner, because of the above piecewise linear approximation, the phase plane $(x, y = \dot{x})$ of the oscillator is divided by the line $x = -1$ into regions I and II, which are shown by different shadings in Fig. 9.5.

The only position of equilibrium $(x = 0; y = 0)$ is situated in region II; it is stable for $h_2 < 0$ (that is, $MS < RC$) and unstable for $h_2 > 0$ ($MS > RC$).

The unstable condition is more interesting, since only in such a case will self-excited oscillation appear; for that reason we shall investigate this case only. This instability at the origin may be either of a focal type (if $0 < h_2 < 1$) or of a nodal type ($h_2 > 1$), but it cannot be of a saddle-point type.   We shall assume that this instability is of a focal-point type, since only in such a case do self-excited oscillations become possible.

Since the differential equations are linear in each region, no closed trajectories situated entirely in each of these two regions are possible. This does not exclude, however, the possibility of a closed trajectory crossing the regions I → II → I (as shown in Fig. 9.5).

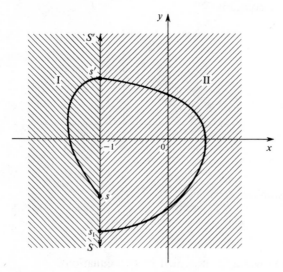

Fig.9.5

We shall introduce the following notations.   For the line $x = -1$ separating the regions I and II, we consider two semiaxes (or semilines): S and S', the lower and the upper, respectively.   On these semilines the ordinates of the points of intersection of the trajectory are indicated by lowercase s, and the semiaxes are indicated by capital letters (S or S').

The semiaxes are obviously without contact with respect to trajectories; more specifically the semiline (or semiaxis) S' is crossed by trajectories from left to right, whereas S is crossed in the opposite direction (from right to left).

Consider a trajectory passing through the point s on the semiline S.   This trajectory will cross the semiline S' at the point s', and, if $h_2 < 1$ (i.e., the trajectories are spirals), the representative point R will ultimately reach the point s_1 (Fig. 9.5).   In this manner one obtains for $0 < h_2 < 1$ a transformation of the semiline S into itself.

The fixed point of the transformation is clearly the point of intersection of the closed trajectory (when s and s' coincide) with the semiline S.

If $h_2 > 1$, the equilibrium point ($x = y = 0$) is an unstable node; in this case there will be branches going to infinity without turning back to the semiline S. This case is therefore of no interest from the standpoint of oscillations, and we consider only the case in which $0 < h_2 < 1$.

Clearly the transformation T of the semiline S into itself can be represented by the product $T_1 T_2$ of two partial transformations. The transformation T_1 transforms the points s of the semiaxis S into the points s' of S', and the transformation T_2 transforms the points s' of S' into s_1 of S.

It is necessary now to express these transformations analytically. In region I ($x < -1$) the trajectories are determined by the first equation in (9.8). Its solution for the trajectory passing at $t = 0$ through the point x_0, y_0 is:

$$x = e^{-h_1 t}\left(x_0 \cos \omega_1 t + \frac{y_0 + h_1 x_0}{\omega_1} \sin \omega_1 t\right) \tag{9.10}$$

$$y = \dot{x} = e^{-h_1 t}\left(y_0 \cos \omega_1 t - \frac{x_0 + h_1 y_0}{\omega_1} \sin \omega_1 t\right) \qquad \omega_1 = +\sqrt{1 - h_1^2}$$

In this case for $t = 0$ the trajectory passes through the point s on the semiaxis S (that is, $x_0 = -1$; $y_0 = -s$; $s > 0$); Eq. (3.8) becomes

$$x = -e^{-h_1 t}\left(\cos \omega_1 t + \frac{s + h_1}{\omega_1} \sin \omega_1 t\right)$$

$$y = \dot{x} = e^{-h_1 t}\left(-s \cos \omega_1 t + \frac{1 + h_1 s}{\omega_1} \sin \omega_1 t\right) \tag{9.11}$$

The representative point R moving along this trajectory will reach the semiline S^1 at the instant $t_1 = \tau_1/\omega_1$ at the point s' ($x = -1$; $y = s' > 0$). Hence

$$-1 = -e^{-(h_1 \tau_1/\omega_1)}\left(\cos \tau_1 + \frac{s + h_1}{\omega_1} \sin \tau_1\right)$$

$$s' = e^{-(h_1 \tau_1/\omega_1)}\left(-s \cos \tau_1 + \frac{1 + s h_1}{\omega_1} \sin \tau_1\right) \tag{9.12}$$

Solving these equations with respect to s and s', one obtains the successor function (of Poincaré) for the transformation T_1 written in the parametric form

$$s = \frac{e^{\gamma_1\tau_1} - \cos \tau_1 - \gamma_1 \sin \tau_1}{\sqrt{1 + \gamma_1^2} \sin \tau_1} \tag{9.13}$$

$$s' = \frac{e^{-\gamma_1\tau_1} - \cos \tau_1 + \gamma_1 \sin \tau_1}{\sqrt{1 + \gamma_1^2} \sin \tau_1} \tag{9.14}$$

where

$$\gamma_1 = \frac{h_1}{\omega_1} = \frac{h_1}{\sqrt{1 - h^2}}$$

The quantity γ_1 increases monotonically from 0 to ∞ when h_1 varies from 0 to $+1$. The expression for s' is obtained from that for s by changing γ_1 to $-\gamma_1$.

The subsequent calculations are simple but very long (Andronov [1, 2d ed., page 511]). We indicate only the different steps in this calculation. One calculates $ds/d\tau_1$ and $ds'/d\tau_1$ as functions of γ_1 and τ_1. This permits constructing the graphs of the successor function for the transformation T_1; this function connects the values of s and s'.

A similar procedure is followed for the transformation T_2, which transforms the points of the semiline S^1 into the points s_1 of the semiline S owing to the trajectories in region II; one considers only the case in which $0 < h_2 < 1$, as was previously explained.

The subsequent calculation follows the same procedure as in the transformation T_1. One obtains thus

$$s_1 = \frac{e^{\gamma_2\tau_2} - \cos \tau_2 - \gamma_2 \sin \tau_2}{\sqrt{1 + \gamma_2^2} \sin \tau_2}$$
$$s' = \frac{e^{-\gamma_2\tau_2} - \cos \tau_2 + \gamma_2 \sin \tau_2}{\sqrt{1 + \gamma_2^2} \sin \tau_2} \tag{9.15}$$

The rest of the calculation is the same as in the case of T_1.

To summarize, the calculation of T_1 establishes the graph of the function $s = f_1(s')$ and that for T_2 establishes a similar graph for $s_1 = f_2(s')$. The ultimate result—the fixed point of the transformation $T = T_1T_2$—is obtained as the point of intersection of the two curves $s = f_1(s')$ and $s_1 = f_2(s')$, as shown in Fig. 9.6. The abscissa s' of the point of intersection of the two curves gives the fixed point of the transformation $T = T_1T_2$ for which the points s_1 and s coincide (Fig. 9.5), thus expressing the condition for the existence of a nonanalytic limit cycle in the two-sheet phase plane of Fig. 9.5.

It should be mentioned that there may be cases in which the two curves have no point of intersection; in this case there is no periodic solution (limit cycle).

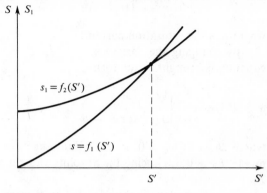

Fig. 9.6

We mention in passing that this procedure is connected with the theory of "successor functions" (le théorie des conséquents) of Poincaré, which makes use of transformation theory.

9.4   ELECTRON-TUBE OSCILLATOR WITH A HIGH-GRID VOLTAGE

In this case the characteristic of the electron tube $i = f(u_g)$, i being the plate current and u_g the grid voltage, approaches the form shown in Fig. 9.7; this is also the usual form of the nonlinearity of the relay type.

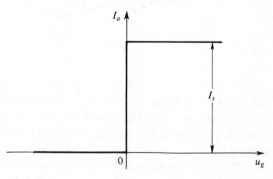

Fig. 9.7

One easily finds that the differential equation of the oscillator in this case reduces to:

$$LC\frac{d^2i}{dt^2} + RC\frac{di}{dt} + i = \begin{cases} I_s & \text{for } u_g > 0 \\ 0 & \text{for } u_g < 0 \end{cases} \qquad (9.16)$$

where I_s is the saturation current.

By changing the variables $x = i/I_s$; $t' = \omega_0 t$; $\omega_0 = 1/\sqrt{LC}$, this equation is brought to the form

$$\ddot{x} + 2h\dot{x} + x = \begin{cases} 1 & \text{for } \dot{x} > b \\ 0 & \text{for } \dot{x} < b \end{cases} \qquad (9.17)$$

where $2h = RC\omega_0 > 0$ is the damping coefficient and $b = E_g/\omega_0 |M| I_{s0} > 0$, $|M|$ being the absolute value of the (negative) coupling M.

The phase plane is thus divided by the straight line $y = b$ into two regions (Fig. 9.8); the upper region, I, is shaded.   On the line $y = b$

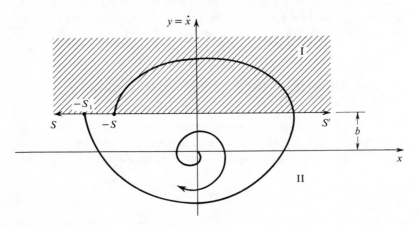

Fig. 9.8

are situated the nonanalytic points (junctions between the trajectories of regions I and II).   If one takes two half-lines S and S' on the line $y = b$, as shown, one can follow the previous argument.   Trajectories leave S' (for t increasing) and go in region I; arriving at S' they pass into region II.

Note that for the semiline S the abscissa is $x = -s$, $s > 2hb - 1$; for s' the abscissa is $s' > -2hb$.

9.5 APPLICATIONS OF THE PIECEWISE LINEAR METHOD TO CONTROL PROBLEMS

A number of control problems with relay characteristics were explored by this method (Andronov and Chaikin [1] and Geleszov [2]).

One of these problems considers a quasidiscontinuous operation of the rudder of a small craft. This application is interesting not so much by itself (since it is generally objectionable to operate the rudder by jerks) but as an illustration of the piecewise linear method.

If φ is the angle of deviation of the craft from her course, the differential equation of the angular motion of yawing is

$$I\ddot{\psi} + H\dot{\varphi} = M \tag{9.18}$$

where I is the moment of inertia of the craft about the vertical through its center of gravity, $H\dot{\varphi}$ is the so-called "resistance to turning," and M is the moment produced by the rudder. This equation is linearized, supposing that φ is very small and neglecting some other hydro-dynamical factors complicating the angular motion.

It is assumed that the rudder can be operated only between angles $+\psi_0$ and $-\psi_0$, giving rise to moments M_0 and $-M_0$, and that rudder changes are rapid enough to permit its idealization by a discontinuous function of the relay type depending on the argument $\sigma = \varphi + b\dot{\varphi}$. Figure 9.9 illustrates this assumed behavior of the rudder. Since the

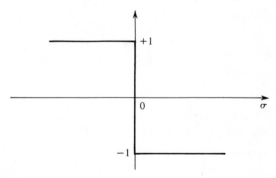

Fig. 9.9

discontinuous function is

$$Z(\sigma) = \begin{cases} -1 & \text{for } \sigma > 0 \\ +1 & \text{for } \sigma < 0 \end{cases} \tag{9.19}$$

the moment of the rudder will be then

$$M = M_0 Z(\varphi_0 + b\dot{\varphi}) \tag{9.20}$$

with variables $\varphi = Ax$; $t = Tt'$. The new differential equation will be of the form

$$\ddot{x} + x = z \qquad z = Z(x + \beta\dot{x}) \tag{9.21}$$

We consider now in the phase plane $(x,\dot{x})$ the line defined by

$$x + \beta\dot{x} = x + \beta y = 0 \tag{9.22}$$

The line divides the phase plane into two regions: I and II (Fig. 9.10);

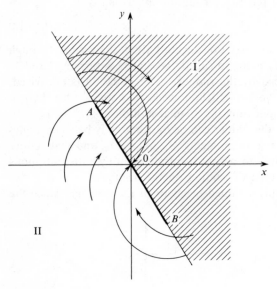

Fig. 9.10

it corresponds to changes in the rudder angle. In regions I and II the following differential equations hold:

In I: $x + \beta y > 0$ $\dot{x} = y$ $\dot{y} = -y - 1$

In II: $x + \beta y < 0$ $\dot{x} = y$ $\dot{y} = -y + 1$ $\qquad(9.23)$

The trajectories are symmetrical with respect to the origin, since the second set of equations is obtained from the first by replacing x and y by $-x$, $-y$.

The line described by (9.22) may be called the "line of switching"; that is, on this line the rudder is changed from one "hard over" position to the other. On this line the second equation in (9.21) does not determine the motion, since for $\sigma = 0$ the rudder may be anywhere in the interval $(-1, +1)$. In order to avoid this uncertainty, we introduce the coordinate

$$\xi = x + \beta y \tag{9.24}$$

Its derivative in the region I is:

$$\dot{\xi} = \dot{x} + \beta \ddot{y} = y - \beta(y + 1) = (1 - \beta)y - \beta \tag{9.25}$$

The isocline $\dot{\xi} = 0$ is $y = \beta/(1 - \beta)$. If $0 < \beta < 1$, the trajectories move away from line (9.22) *above* it; if they are *below* it, they approach line (9.22). In region II the situation is similar. In this way there exists on the "line of switching" a segment (AB in Fig. 9.10)

$$|y| \leqslant \left| \frac{\beta}{1 - \beta} \right| \tag{9.26}$$

toward which trajectories approach *from both sides*. Outside this segment they approach from one side and move away from the other side. A similar situation exists for $\beta > 1$.

This particular orientation of trajectories in the neighborhood of line (9.22) specifies the motion of the representative point as follows:

1. If R arrives on line (9.22) outside the segment AB, it crosses this line from region I to region II.

2. If it arrives on AB, it moves on this segment. The motion in this case is obtained from (9.22) by setting $y = \dot{x}$ and integrating; one obtains

$$x = x_0 e^{-t/\beta} \tag{9.27}$$

This is the so-called "slipping operation," when the regulating element is in the neutral position and the rudder moves smoothly from the extreme position to the neutral one according to the differential equation

$$z = \ddot{x} + \dot{x} = x_0 \left(\frac{1}{\beta^2} - \frac{1}{\beta} \right) e^{-t/\beta} \tag{9.28}$$

This particular operation is explained on the basis of some secondary effects (time lags in the steering gear, etc.), which explains starting the rudder just after the passage through zero of the coordinate $\xi = x + \beta y$.

In view of this particular condition the deviation of the ship from her course decreases aperiodically according to (9.24), whereas in the other regions this decrease is oscillatory.

This study can be extended considerably by introducing the corresponding point transformation, determining its fixed point, and investigating the effect of the time lag, etc.

9.6 TOPOLOGY OF RELAY SYSTEMS

Assume that a relay has the well-known characteristic shown in Fig. 9.11 which (in suitable units) is characterized by three values of its control action: u_0, 0, $-u_0$.

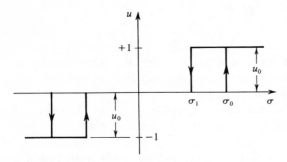

Fig. 9.11

In the dead zone (between $-\sigma_0$ and $+\sigma_0$) any value of σ may occur without any effect on the control.   As soon as $\sigma = |\sigma_0|$, the value U_0 is brought into play and remains constant if $\sigma \geqslant \sigma_0$.   If σ decreases, the disappearance of the control action U_0 occurs for $\sigma_1 < \sigma$ and if σ continues to decrease, as soon as $\sigma = -\sigma_0$, the control action $-U_0$ sets in and the same sequence of actions continues for σ increasing.

The non-single-valued determination of $U(\sigma)$ in the intervals (σ_1, σ_0) and $(-\sigma_1, -\sigma_0)$ is due to hysteresis.

The ratio $k = \sigma_1/\sigma_0 < 1$ is sometimes called the *coefficient* of the *return* of relay.

We shall apply the point-transformation method in connection with this nonlinear characteristic when a relay controls, for instance, a followup system.

Omitting some obvious constructional details, it is clear that such a control system is characterized by the system

$$I\ddot{\varphi} + \lambda\dot{\varphi} = -MU(\sigma) \qquad \sigma = \varphi + B\dot{\varphi} \qquad (9.29)$$

where φ = angle

I = moment of inertia

λ = coefficient of velocity damping

σ = control action responsive to φ and $\dot{\varphi}$

M and B = consts

If one introduces some dimensionless coefficients (this is of no direct interest here), it is possible to reduce (9.29) to the form

$$\ddot{x} + \dot{x} = -u(\xi) \qquad \xi = x + \beta\dot{x} \tag{9.30}$$

Finally, differentiating with respect to some suitable "dimensionless time" and setting $y = \dot{x}$, one can simplify the equations still more, which results in the system

$$\dot{y} = -y - u(\xi) \qquad \dot{\xi} = (1 - \beta)y - \beta u(\xi) \tag{9.31}$$

where $0 < \beta < 1$.

Since in this case there are two regions in which the characteristic is not single valued, it is useful to have a three-sheet phase plane, as shown in Fig. 9.12.

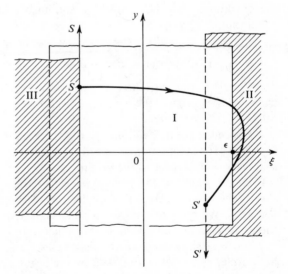

Fig. 9.12

In the middle region I, $|\xi| < \epsilon$ and it is supposed that $u = 0$. This corresponds to the neutral position of the relay.

Sheets II and III are superimposed on I, as indicated, with certain overlappings. Thus II corresponds to $\xi > \lambda\epsilon$ and III corresponds to

$\xi = -\lambda\epsilon$.   Sheet II corresponds to $u = +1$ and III corresponds to $u = -1$.

The motion of the representative point R from I to II or to III occurs at the frontier of I, that is, either for $x = +\epsilon$ or for $x = -\epsilon$.

As to the return (to sheet I), it takes place either for $x = +\lambda\epsilon$ or for $x = -\lambda\epsilon$, $\lambda < 1$, taking into account the hysteresis.

Note that although the variables ξ and y are continuous at the transition points (from one sheet to the other), their derivatives are not continuous at these points.

We shall not give a detailed analysis of what happens (see Andronov and Chaiken [1]), but will give only the principal conclusions.

In strip I (that is, for $u = 0$), Eqs. (9.31) are

$$\dot{y} = -y \qquad \dot{\xi} = (1 - \beta)y \qquad \text{whence} \quad \frac{dy}{d\xi} = -\frac{1}{1 - \beta} \tag{9.32}$$

In this strip all points of the abscissa axis are positions of equilibrium, which are stable, since R, moving in sheet I, describes the rectilinear trajectories: $\xi + (1 - \beta)y = \text{const}$; these trajectories are directed *toward* the abscissa axis.   All trajectories whose points satisfy the conditions $|\xi + (1 - \beta)y| < \epsilon$ end finally at these positions of equilibrium.

For sheet II (that is, $u = +1$), the equations are:

$$\dot{y} + y = -1 \qquad \dot{\xi} = (1 - \beta)y - \beta \tag{9.33}$$

Clearly in this case there are no positions of equilibrium, and the trajectories approach the line $y = -1$, $\xi = -t + \text{const}$ asymptotically.

Hence the point R will necessarily leave sheet II and will reenter I. On sheet III the situation is exactly the same as in II in view of the symmetry with respect to the origin.

Having resolved the general aspect of trajectories in these three sheets, the rest is merely the application of the point-transformation method.   We refer to Andronov and Chaiken [1a] for the details of these calculations and give only the conclusions.

It can be shown that there exists a closed trajectory (a nonanalytic limit cycle, as shown in Fig. 9.13 by the heavy line) to which all nonstationary trajectories approach.   One of these trajectories is shown by a thin line; the points s^* and s'^* are fixed points of the transformation; their calculation is the same as in Secs. 9.3 to 9.5.

This form of operation is often encountered in applications.   As an example we indicate the scheme of Fig. 9.14, in which 1 is the object to be controlled, 2 is the sensitive element (an instrument releasing impulses to the relay), 3 is a relay, 4 is a constant-speed servomotor, and 5 is a feedback connection.

If this scheme is intended for a followup action, the parameter μ will be the angle through which the servomotor turns, so that $d\mu/dt$ is the speed of the servomotor. Since the relay merely reverses the speed,

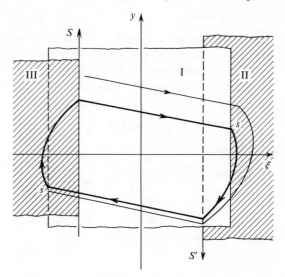

Fig. 9.13

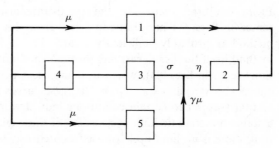

Fig. 9.14

one has the following relations:

$$\frac{d\mu}{dt} = \begin{cases} +\dfrac{1}{T_\epsilon} & \text{for } \sigma > \sigma_0 \\[2ex] 0 & \text{for } |\sigma| < \sigma_0 \\[2ex] -\dfrac{1}{T_\epsilon} & \text{for } \sigma < -\lambda\sigma_0 \end{cases} \qquad (9.34)$$

where σ_0 is the width of the dead zone and $0 < \lambda < 1$ is the "coefficient of the return" of the relay.   The nonlinearity (of the nonanalytic type) is thus located in the quasidiscontinuous characteristic of the servomotor working with reversals of speed.

The remaining parts of the scheme are continuous, namely,

$$T_a \dot{\varphi} + k\varphi = \mu \qquad \delta\eta + \varphi = 0 \qquad \delta = \eta - \gamma\mu \qquad\qquad (9.35)$$

The first of these equations relates to the motor, the second to the sensitive element, and the last to the feedback connection.

The scheme is thus an indirect regulation by means of a constant-speed servomotor capable of reversing its rotation by means of a relay.

If one changes the variables:

$$\varphi = \frac{T_a}{k^2 T_s} x \qquad \sigma = -\frac{T_a(1/\sigma + \gamma k)}{k^2 T_s}\xi \qquad T_s\dot{\mu} = -u \qquad t = \frac{T_a}{k}t'$$

$$(9.36)$$

Eq. 6.7 reduces to the system

$$\ddot{x} + x = -u(\xi) \qquad \xi = x + \beta\dot{x} \qquad\qquad (9.37)$$

and the argument developed in the beginning of this section can be applied to this scheme.

9.7   CONCLUSIONS

From the brief theory of the point-transformation method (presented in Secs. 9.1 and 9.2) and a few examples (Secs. 9.3 to 9.6) the method is probably sufficiently clear.   The difficult part is not the method itself but lies in carrying through very long and tedious calculations (e.g., in Sec. 9.3), which in many cases permit constructing two curves $s = s(s')$ and $s_1 = s_1(s')$.   If these curves have a point of intersection (subject to certain conditions indicated at the end of Sec. 9.3) a stable nonanalytic limit cycle exists; if these curves have no intersection, there is no limit cycle (no self-excited oscillations).

According to whether one tries to avoid the oscillation or to have it, one can dispose of the parameters in one of two ways.   The problem is thus formulated in a sufficiently general manner.

On its face the method seems to be complicated for applications insofar as its computational part is concerned (e.g., the calculations mentioned in Sec. 9.3).   It must be noted, however, that these calculations need to be made once and once only, and what is important for practice is not the calculations but rather their results arranged in the form of certain criteria (see the end of Sec. 9.3).

In practical calculations the matter generally reduces to simpler problems, which have for an object the establishment of the regions (or "sheets" of the phase plane) in which the piecewise analytic phenomenon is governed by different differential equations.

Once this point is reached, further progress greatly depends on the possibility of *simplifying the equations* by introducing some kind of "dimensionless unit." No general rules can be given, but one must say that a certain progress has been made even here (see Gorskaya [3]).

The history of this particular approach to the theory of nonlinear servomechanisms reflects to some extent the situation. In fact, the method was suggested by Andronov [1] around 1937 and for nearly 20 years there was no further progress. Finally a systematic study of point-transformation theory with the corresponding reduction to the fixed-point theorem was undertaken (1958), and this ultimately resulted in another systematic study of a great variety of nonlinear servomechanisms (1959), of which we have indicated a few examples.

The fact that the method ultimately leads to a topological representation is both its advantage and its drawback.

The advantage is that the *qualitative* character of the phenomenon involved is represented in a very clear manner. The drawback is common to all topological methods, and that is the impossibility of obtaining any *quantitative* conclusions.

Unfortunately, in the nonlinear and the *nonanalytic* domain the quantitative results are beyond our reach at present. Only recently has this question begun to be systematically studied [in the work of Aiserman and his school (Chap. 8)].

REFERENCES

1. Andronov, A. A., and S. E. Chaikin: "Theory of Oscillations," Moscow, 1937 (in Russian); English translation by S. Lefschetz, Princeton University Press, Princeton, N.J., 1949.

1a. Andronov, A. A. Witt, and S. E. Chaikin: "Theory of Oscillations," 2d ed., Chap. 8, Moscow, 1959.

2. Geleszov, N. A.: *J. Tech. Phys. Moscow*, vol. 13, no. 495, 1948, and vol. 20, no. 78, 1950; *Radiophysics*, vol. 1, no. 1, 1958.

3. Gorskaya, N. S. et al.: "Dynamics of Non-linear Servomechanisms," Fizmatgiz Moscow, 1959.

4. Koenigs, N. G.: *Bull. Sci. Math. Astron.*, vol. 7, Dec., 1883; Recherches sur les integrals de certaines equations fonctionelles, *Am. Sci. Ecole Norm. Sup.*, vol. 1, 1884.

5. Minorsky, N.: *Compt. Rend. Acad. Sci.*, vol. 255, p. 1374, Sept. 10, 1962.

CHAPTER TEN
FUNCTIONAL
TRANSFORMERS
AND ANALOGS

10.1 INTRODUCTORY REMARKS

Problems of functional transformation have played an increasingly important role in modern control systems, and it is useful to give a short outline of this now enormous field; for details see references, particularly [2].

In general these problems present themselves in the following manner. Given a certain law represented by a function $F(t)$, determine another law represented by another function $\Phi(t)$ such that

$$\Phi(t) = G[F(t)] \tag{10.1}$$

In this case G is the desired *operator of the functional transformation in question.*

This field apparently originated about 30 years ago (Minorsky [4]), but only during the last decade or so have these developments gained momentum. In one of the recent texts on this subject (Kogan [2]) about 140 international references, covering only the last few years, are indicated.

We shall not attempt to go into this subject in any detail but shall indicate only a few basic points which may be helpful in ascertaining connections between these developments and the theory of nonlinear control systems.

One of the early approaches can be described with reference to a scheme of integration by which a functional transformation of the form (10.1) can be effected by means of the integral relation

$$\varphi(t) = \int_0^t f(s)\, ds \tag{10.2}$$

Consider, for example, the following (somewhat idealized) arrangement. An alternating magnetic flux of a uniform density is produced in a certain area $ABCD$ (Fig. 10.1) at right angles to the plane of the

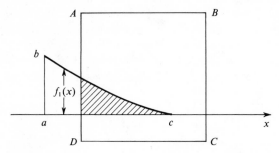

Fig. 10.1

paper. A flat coil abc consisting of a few turns of wire wound on an insulating material and limited on bc by the desired function $f(x)$ can be displaced along the axis x coinciding with ac. Clearly, the shaded area represents $\int_0^x f(s)\, ds$, and the voltage E induced in the coil M is proportional to the value of this integral, that is, in the root–mean-square values

$$\varphi(x) = E = \bar{e}_1 A = \bar{e}_1 \int_0^x f(s)\, ds \tag{10.3}$$

where $\bar{e}_1$ is the emf induced in the coil per unit flux area and A is the area of the coil. If E is applied to the grid of an electron-tube amplifier working on a substantially linear part of its characteristic, it will record the function $\varphi(x)$ or $\varphi(t) = \varphi[x(t)]$ if the coil is moved at a constant speed $dx/dt = c$.

Thus, for instance, if the coil is a rectangle (bc is a straight line parallel to the x axis), $\varphi[x(t)]$ will vary linearly with t; if the coil is triangular (one side parallel to the x axis), $\varphi[x(t)]$ will be a quadratic function of t, etc.

A similar scheme—using a luminous flux instead of an ac magnetic flux—can be worked out on the same principle; in such a case instead of the coil abc it is sufficient to have an opening in a shutter whose upper part bc is shaped in accordance with $y = f(x)$, the remaining arrangement being the same. In an optical functional transformer of this kind the function $\varphi(x)$ appears as a luminous flux penetrating into a photointegrator. The latter is merely a sphere with a white surface inside; the luminous flux penetrating inside the sphere after many reflections gives rise to an *average* luminous intensity proportional to $\varphi(x)$.

A photoelectric cell placed inside the sphere (not in the direct path of the luminous beam) then registers this average intensity, which, again, through a linear amplification reproduces the desired transform $\varphi(x)$ of the original function $f(x)$. A number of such schemes were used in the early days of the analog technique for the purpose of automatic (graphical) integration of differential equations mostly on the principle of a pendulum controlled by suitably chosen functions $\varphi(x)$.

Consider the differential equation of a pendulum

$$I\ddot{\theta} + \beta\dot{\theta} + C\theta = 0$$

and assume, for example, that instead of $C\theta$ one introduces a moment according to the function $\varphi(\theta)$ determined by the above procedure. With a proper shape of the coil M (or shutter) one can introduce a variety of functions $\varphi(\theta)$ and investigate the motion of the system.

$$I\ddot{\theta} + \beta\dot{\theta} + \varphi(\theta) = 0 \qquad\qquad (10.3a)$$

for different forms of $\varphi(\theta)$. One can also do this with respect to the term $\dot{\theta}$ with a proper timing of the damping current so as to have a differential equation

$$I\ddot{\theta} + \beta\varphi(\dot{\theta}) + C\theta = 0 \qquad\qquad (10.4)$$

The number of possibilities are, in fact, limitless. The difficult point is not in the fundamental idea but in its realization—for example, in securing the linearity of amplification, etc. Around 1936 schemes of this nature were a matter of scientific curiosity, but about 20 years later they developed into an enormous applied science, which is currently used for many applications, including problems of automatic control (Kogan [2]).

10.2 RECENT DEVELOPMENTS

At present, functional transformers, or analogs, are extensively used mostly in an electrical (electronic) form, and the number of possible combinations are, in fact, very large.

The fundamental idea is to introduce a certain "model" of the scheme in which one is interested.

Suppose that the differential equation of a component link of a control system is represented by the system

$$\dot{x}_i = f_i(x_1, \ldots, x_n, t) \qquad i = 1, \ldots, n \tag{10.5}$$

To a certain input, the form of the output defines the requisite functional transformation. Suppose that we are interested in reproducing on the model the behavior of the actual system with variables y; this leads to the relation

$$y_i = M_i x_i \qquad i = 1, \ldots, n \tag{10.6}$$

M_i being some scale factor. Besides the variables, the time scale is also to be transformed, so that

$$\tau = M_t t \tag{10.7}$$

τ being the "time" for the model. Since $dx_i = dy_i/M$ and $dt = d\tau/M_t$, Eqs. (10.5) will take the form

$$\frac{dy_i}{d\tau} = \psi_i(y_1, y_2, \ldots, y_n, \tau) \tag{10.8}$$

The physical nature of the model is not important, and an electrical circuit, for instance, may serve as a model of a mechanical system (or another kind).

As an example suppose that the structural scheme of the control system consists (Fig. 10.2) of two inertial links and one integrating link.

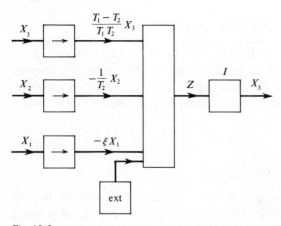

Fig. 10.2

For the former the operator is of the form $k/(1 + pT)$ and for the latter is of the form k/p. As just mentioned, the physical nature of the model is of no importance so long as the *operators* are the same for both the control system and its model.

If the controlled quantity is X and the corresponding model quantity is X_0, the operational ratio is

$$\frac{\overline{X}(p)}{\overline{X}_0(p)} = \frac{K(p)}{1 + k(p)}$$

$$= \frac{k_1 k_2 \xi_0}{p(1 + pT_1)(1 + pT_2)} \bigg/ \left[1 + \frac{k_1 k_2 \xi_0}{(1 + pT_1)(1 + pT_2) p} \right]$$

$$= \frac{\xi}{(1 + pT_1)(1 + pT_2) + \xi} \qquad \xi = k_1 k_2 \xi_0 \qquad (10.9)$$

where T_1 and T_2 are the time constants of the inertial links whose operators are $(1 + pT_1)$ and $(1 + pT_2)$, respectively, and k_1, k_2, and ξ_0 are the amplification factors.

Hence for the original $X(t)$ one has

$$\left[\left(1 + T_1 \frac{d}{dt} \right) \left(1 + T_2 \frac{d}{dt} \right) \frac{d}{dt} + \xi \right] X(t) = \xi X_0(t) \qquad (10.10)$$

Developing these relations, one obtains

$$T_1 T_2 \dddot{X} + (T_1 + T_2) \ddot{X} + \dot{X} + \xi X = \xi X_0(t) \qquad (10.11)$$

Writing this differential equation as an equivalent system, one has

$$\dot{X}_1 = X_2 \qquad \dot{X}_2 = X_3$$

$$\dot{X}_3 = Z = - \frac{T_1 + T_2}{T_1 T_2} X_3 - \frac{1}{T_1 T_2} X_2 - \xi X_1 + \xi X_0 \qquad (10.12)$$

One must then build a structural scheme of the model according to (10.12). The first two equations may be regarded as the differential equations of the integrating links with inputs X_2 and X_3, respectively, and outputs X_1 and X_2; the last differential equation requires a more complicated scheme in the analog (Fig. 10.2). It may be regarded as an equation of an integrating link the output of which is X_3; to its input is applied the quantity Z, which is equal to the sum of four terms [as seen from Eq. (10.12)] obtained as the output of an adding link to the input of which are applied the corresponding components.

The first component $-[(T_1 + T_2)/T_1 T_2] X_3$ is obtained by passing the quantity X_3 through an amplifying link A with the coefficient of amplification $-(T_1 + T_2)/T_1 T_2$; the other components are obtained

in a similar manner.   The external perturbing action ξX_0 is applied
from the outside (block: extension).   This scheme does not show yet
where the inputs to these blocks come from.   Note, however, that
X_1, X_2, and X_3 are outputs from the blocks.   Hence, if one applies
these outputs to the corresponding inputs, one obtains the requisite
model.   Figure 10.2 is the integrating link.

10.3   PHOTOELECTRIC FUNCTIONAL TRANSFORMERS

In recent years there have been numerous developments trying to
incorporate the functional transformation in the design of the phototube itself.   Since such devices are available in a great variety of forms,
we mention only their principle.

Figure 10.3 shows a cathode-ray tube (1), which has on the lower
part of its screen an opaque material and is limited on its upper end

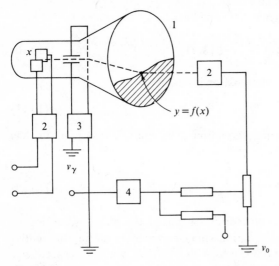

Fig. 10.3

by a predetermined curve $y = f(x)$.   Along the axis of the tube is
placed an electronic multiplier (2).

For a given horizontal displacement x of the electronic beam
established by the voltage on the vertical deflecting plates, there corresponds a voltage on the horizontal plates sufficient to reach the vertical
deflection y predetermined by the curve $y = f(x)$.   This is accomplished
by an appropriate followup circuit (not shown), which adjusts the

horizontal plate voltage (that is, the variable y) so that the beam is kept just at the edge of the opaque material for a given deflection x. In this manner the functional transformation appears in the form of the voltage across the horizontal plates, and this (through a suitable amplifier) can be used wherever it is needed.

The drawback of this scheme is that it is adapted for only one function: $y = f(x)$. If it is desired to have a greater variety of functions (or change them during the operation of the control system), the contour with the curve $y = f(x)$ can be placed outside the vacuum tube with an analogous followup control which holds the electronic spot at the edge of the curve $y = f(x)$.

Since these devices have different constructional details, we shall not elaborate on the matter further. It is useful to mention, however, that although the idea of such phototube functional transformers is very simple, there is a series of constructional features which renders their use delicate.

10.4 USE OF DIODES FOR FUNCTIONAL TRANSFORMATIONS

The use of diodes has progressed considerably in connection with functional transformations, and for that reason it is useful to outline this subject briefly (for details see [2]).

Given a single-valued continuous function in a certain interval (having, perhaps, a finite number of discontinuities of the first type), one can approximate it by the expression

$$y = y_0 + a_0 x + \sum_{i=1}^{n} b_i(x - x_{i0}) \qquad x_{10} < x_{20} < \cdots < x_{n,0} \qquad (10.13)$$

where

$$b_i = \begin{cases} 0 & \text{for } x \leqslant x_{i0} \\ B_i = \text{const} & \text{for } x > x_{i0} \end{cases}$$

x_{i0} being the initial point of an interval i. The significance of this formula is obvious if one recalls that a curve $y = f(x)$ can be replaced by a polygon (Fig. 10.5); each time when, following the polygon, one crosses an apex of the polygon, the slope of linear segments changes discontinuously by a quantity B_i.

This mode of approximation is often used in connection with diodes; in such a case one can use analogies, considering, for instance, the input quantities to be x_i and the output quantities to be y_i.

In this manner formula (10.13) acquires the obvious physical significance

$$e_{out} = e_0 + a_0 e_{in}^0 + \sum_{i=0}^{n} b_i(e_{in} - e_{in}^n) \tag{10.14}$$

where e_{out} and e_{in} are the output and input voltages, respectively, and e_{in}^0 is the initial value of the input for the given segment of the polygon approximation. One can write (10.14) in terms of currents by introducing conductivities, but we shall not elaborate this further.

The fundamental idea is as follows. The current of a diode may be regarded approximately as linear (at least in a certain interval) and hence can be represented by a straight line in the diagram $x_1 y$ in which x is the input voltage and y is the output current. For different combinations of parameters the voltage-current characteristics of diodes can have different aspects with respect to the origin, as seen from Fig. 10.4

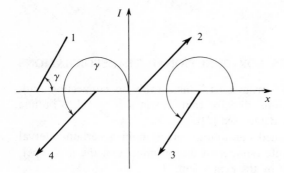

Fig. 10.4

If one also takes into account that these characteristics may have negative slopes γ (this would require inverters), one can readily see that with the proper timing of the firing of subsequent diodes, one could produce characteristics of the type (10.13). This means *to construct predetermined nonlinear characteristics by pieces.* Thus, for instance, an even function shown in Fig. 10.5 can be obtained by a change of the input voltage from $-e_{in}$ to $+e_{in}$. For different values of e in this interval, there will be a definite sequence of firing of different diodes, and to this, in turn, will correspond different outputs whose sequence [in direction and magnitude, as well as in location in the (e_{in}, I) plane] will give precisely the curve K in question by producing the "pieces" $AB, BC, CD, \ldots$, etc.

Such general functional transformers based directly on the geometric approximation of a curve by a polygon are rather complicated because of the multiple channels used for diodes, particularly if one wishes to obtain a certain accuracy.

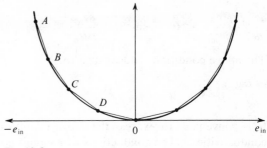

Fig. 10.5

In many control problems it is desired to introduce definite functions, for example

$$y = \sin x \qquad y = \cos x \qquad y = x^2 \qquad y = x^3, \ldots$$

In such cases it is often preferable to have special schemes that do not involve the general interpolation formula (10.13) but use schemes for multiplication, division, and similar operations that do not require such universal schemes.

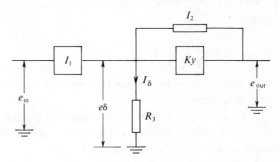

Fig. 10.6

A sufficiently general scheme that is relatively simple is shown in Fig. 10.6. In this scheme

$$I_1 = f_1(e_{in}, e_\delta) \qquad I_2 = f_2(e_{out}, e_\delta) \qquad I_1 = I_\delta + I_2$$

$$e_\delta = R_3 I_\delta \qquad e_{out} = -k_y e_\delta$$

(10.15)

For a large k_y system, (10.15) reduces to the equation

$$f_2(e_{out}) = -f_1(e_{in})$$

(10.16)

This equation represents the general form of a functional transformation of this type.   For the static stability (existence of a negative feedback) of this scheme, it is necessary that

$$\frac{de_{out}}{de_\delta} \frac{df(e_{out})}{de_{out}} < 0 \quad \text{since} \quad \frac{de_{out}}{de_\delta} = -k_y < 0 \tag{10.17}$$

The above condition reduces then to

$$\frac{df_2(e_{out})}{de_{out}} > 0 \tag{10.18}$$

It is convenient to express the above relation (10.16) in terms of the conductivities.   The conductivity of a circuit is defined by the slope of the inverse volt-ampere characteristic.   One can call $dI/de = Y(e)$ the *differential conductivity* of a nonlinear circuit.   Hence, differentiating (10.16) with respect to e_{in}, one gets

$$\frac{df_2}{de_{out}} \frac{de_{out}}{de_{in}} = -\frac{df_1}{de_{in}} \tag{10.19}$$

On the other hand, by definition,

$$\frac{df_2}{de_{out}} = Y_2(e_{out}) \qquad \frac{df_1}{de_{in}} = Y_1(e_{in})$$

Hence

$$de_{out} = -\frac{Y_1(e_{in})}{Y_2(e_{out})} de_{in} \tag{10.20}$$

This equation represents the relation in a nonlinear resolving amplifier in a differential form.

One can translate these relations for the piecewise linear representation, in which case the differential relations in (10.20) must be replaced by the difference relation

$$\Delta e_{out} = -\frac{\Delta Y_1}{\Delta Y_2} \Delta e_{in} \tag{10.21}^1$$

where Δe_{in} represents the difference of inputs of the initial and the terminal points of the ith stretch.   For n stretches one obtains

$$\sum_{i=1}^n \Delta Y_2 \, \Delta e_{out} = -\sum_1^n \Delta Y_1 \, \Delta e_{in} \tag{10.22}$$

---

[1] We omit the subscript i in what follows in order not to overburden notations (for example, Δ_{in} instead of $\Delta_{in,i}$, etc.).

10.5 MULTIPLYING SCHEMES

Here again the progress for the last decade or so has been so rapid that it is possible to say only a few words regarding the principles involved. We cannot describe the schemes themselves, since they are too numerous.

One of the earlier approaches was to use the algebraic identity

$$4xy = (x + y)^2 - (x - y)^2 \tag{10.23}$$

This means that the operation of multiplication can be replaced by the operations of algebraic addition and squaring. This amounts to addition (or subtraction) of electrical quantities with subsequent squaring. For the last-mentioned purpose one can use, for instance, the "quadratic region" of the characteristic of an electron tube or a quadratic (parabolic) characteristic obtained by means of diodes.

As another example, consider an arrangement based on the use of the relation:

$$xy = a^{(\log_a x + \log_a y)} \tag{10.24}$$

In this case the functional transformation is different; that is, it is required to determine the logarithm of the independent variable. This is often accomplished by means of a logarithmic functional transformer in the feedback circuit of the amplifier.

Since the logarithmic function is determined only for positive values, devices of this kind can be used only when the factors x and y do not change signs. In the case in which a change of signs takes place, one can add to x or to y a positive number sufficient to secure the positive sign for either (on the condition that the necessary quantity is subtracted later in order to obtain the correct value of the product).

Thus, for instance,

$$(x + a)(y + b) = \text{antilog } [\log (x + a) + \log (y + b)]$$

From this,

$$xy = -ab - ay - bx + \text{antilog } [\log (x + a) + \log (y + b)] \tag{10.25}$$

The logarithmic multipliers also permit raising a quantity to a certain power or extracting roots. Most of these schemes are based on formula (10.24) and the well-known experimental fact that the grid characteristic of an electron tube is (very nearly) of the form:

$$U_g = k \log I_g \tag{10.26}$$

This formula is accurate enough if I_g is small, that is, for large values of resistors in the grid circuit. It permits obtaining relations by adding voltages, say:

$$U_1 + U_2 = k(\log I_{g1} + \log I_{g2}) = k \log (I_{g1}I_{g2})$$

In this manner the summation of voltages may be interpreted as representing the product of currents.

There are a considerable number of multiplying schemes which cannot be given here (see Kogan [2]).

Dividing schemes are also very numerous; one of them is obvious: it results from the formula $x/y = x(1/y)$. That is, a quotient reduces to the product of one of the factors (x) by the inverse of the other: $1/y$.

10.6 REALIZATION OF DIODE SCHEMES

There are a considerable number of schemes that use diodes for functional transformations. Figure 10.7 shows a scheme with grounded

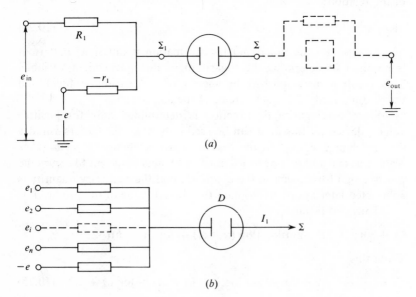

(a)

(b)

Fig. 10.7

diodes. If one neglects the resistance of the diode in comparison with resistances R_i and r_i, and designates by e_{in} the input voltage[1] for which

---

[1] Instead of $e_{\text{in},i}$.

the diode changes its conductivity, one obtains the following expression for the current characteristic (see Ref. 2):

$$I_1 = \begin{cases} \dfrac{e_{in}}{R_1} - \dfrac{e_{in}^0}{r_1} & \text{for } e_{in} > e_{in}^0 \\ 0 & \text{for } e_{in} \leqslant e_{in}^0 \end{cases} \tag{10.27}$$

Hence for $e_{in} > e_{in}^0$ one has

$$\frac{dI_1}{de_{in}} = \Delta Y_1 = \frac{1}{R_1} \tag{10.28}$$

so that (10.27) takes the form

$$I_1 = \begin{cases} e_{in}\,\Delta Y_1 - e_{in}^0\,\Delta y & \text{for } e_{in} > e_{in}^0 \\ 0 & \text{for } e_{in} \leqslant e_{in}^0 \end{cases} \tag{10.29}$$

where $\Delta y_i = 1/r_i$. The quantity e_{in}^0 is obtained from the condition of equality of two potentials Σ_1 and Σ, assuming (with a reasonable accuracy) that the summation of currents of the diode elements is obtained by the summation of (resolving) amplifiers. Hence

$$e_{in}^0 = \frac{R}{r}\,\bar{e} = \frac{\Delta y}{\Delta Y_1}\,\bar{e} \tag{10.30}$$

where $\bar{e}$ is the biasing voltage. This shows that e_{in}^0 can be greater, equal, or less than $\bar{e}$ when $e_{in} < e_{in}^0$, the potential at the point Σ_1, is determined by the expression

$$e_{\Sigma_1} = e_{in}\frac{\Delta Y_1}{\Delta Y_1 + \Delta y} - \bar{e}\frac{\Delta Y}{\Delta Y_1 + \Delta y} \tag{10.31}$$

The voltage e_Σ decreases when e_{in} increases. For $e_{\Sigma_1} = e_\Sigma$ the diode conducts, and the potential of the point Σ will be different from that of the point Σ by the voltage drop in the diode. Since the latter is small, the two potentials become nearly equal.

By means of such diode elements one can obtain the summation of several voltages if one connects several voltages through equal conductivities $\Delta Y = 1/R$ to the point Σ_1. (See Fig. 10.7b.) In fact, using the same assumptions previously used, the current characteristic for the scheme shown will be

$$I_1 = \begin{cases} 0 & \text{for } e_{\Sigma_1} > 0 \\ \Delta Y \sum\limits_{1}^{n} e - \bar{e}\,\Delta y & \text{for } e_{\Sigma_1} \leqslant 0 \end{cases} \tag{10.32}$$

$$e_{\Sigma_1} = \frac{\Delta Y \sum\limits_{i=1}^{n} e_i - \bar{e}\,\Delta y}{n\,\Delta Y + \Delta y} \qquad \Delta y = \frac{1}{r} \tag{10.33}$$

A combination of several such units permits obtaining functional transformations of a sum of input voltages, which is of importance when several arguments are involved, such as

$$e_{out} = f(e_1 + e_2 + \cdots + e_n) \tag{10.34}$$

Diode schemes of this nature (i.e., with grounded diodes) can produce characteristics in all four quadrants; there are two groups of such diodes: (1) diode elements working on switching in; and (2) those working on switching out. The first ones are those in which for the increase of $|e_{in}|$ the differential conductivity increases from zero to a certain constant value $\pm\Delta Y$; for the second, the increase of $|e_{in}|$ produces a decrease of the differential conductivity by a constant value $\pm\Delta Y$.

There is no difficulty in calculating the parameters of a scheme with grounded diodes; in fact after the piecewise linear approximation of a given nonlinearity is established, one knows the e_{in} and ΔY required; hence for a given $\bar{e}$ the calculation reduces from (10.35) for the determination of Δy:

$$\Delta y_i = \frac{\Delta Y_i e^0_{in,i}}{\bar{e}} \tag{10.35}$$

where i is the number of the diode. The current characteristics of the diode element can be represented in the form

$$I_1 = \begin{cases} 0 & \text{for } e_{in} \leqslant e_{in}^0 \\[2mm] \dfrac{e_{in} - \bar{e}R/r}{R + r_d(1 + R/r)} & \text{for } e_{in} > \bar{e}_{in} \end{cases} \tag{10.36}$$

(In these notations the index i is omitted and $\bar{e}$ means biasing.) Setting

$$R + r_d\left(1 + \frac{R}{r}\right) = R^* \qquad r = r_d\left(1 + \frac{R}{r}\right) = r^*$$

the preceding expressions can be written as

$$I_1 = \begin{cases} 0 & \text{for } e_{in} \leqslant e_{in}^0 \\[2mm] \dfrac{e_{in}}{R^*} - \dfrac{\bar{e}}{r} & \text{for } e_{in} > e_{in}^0 \end{cases} \tag{10.37}$$

The fundamental feature of these diode elements is that for the zero slope of their current characteristic ($\Delta Y_i = 0$) the current through the diode vanishes ($I_i = 0$). In view of this, for the representation of the characteristics with regions in which $\Delta I_i = 0$ one must use additional circuits starting with $I_i \neq 0$. In view of this it is preferable in such cases to use diode elements based on the principle of limitation. Figure 10.8 shows two typical schemes of this kind.

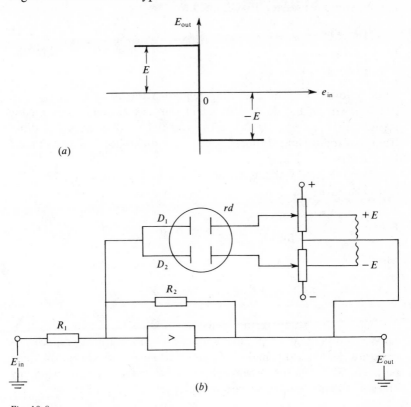

Fig. 10.8

For the scheme shown in Fig. 10.8*a*, considering previous notations, one has

$$I_1 = \begin{cases} \dfrac{\Delta Y\left(e_{\text{in}} + \dfrac{\Delta y}{y_d}\,\bar{e}\right)}{\dfrac{\Delta y}{y_d} + 1 + \dfrac{\Delta Y}{y_d}} & \text{for } e_{\text{in}} < e_{\text{in}}^0 \\[4mm] \bar{e}\,\dfrac{\Delta y\,\Delta Y}{\Delta y + \Delta Y} = \text{const} & \text{for } e_{\text{in}} \gg e_{\text{in}}^0 \end{cases} \qquad (10.38)$$

where

$$\Delta y = \frac{1}{r} \qquad \Delta Y = \frac{1}{R} \qquad e_{\text{in}}^0 = e\,\frac{\Delta y}{\Delta y + \Delta Y} \qquad (10.39)$$

(Here "in" stands for input, index i is omitted, and r_d is the resistance of the diode.)   If one neglects the resistance $r_d = 1/y_d$ of the diode, the preceding expression is simplified to

$$I_1 = \begin{cases} \Delta Y\, e_{\text{in}} & \text{for } e_{\text{in}} \leqslant e_{\text{in}}{}^0 \\[2mm] \bar{e}\,\dfrac{\Delta y\, \Delta Y}{\Delta y + \Delta Y} = \text{const} & \text{for } e_{\text{in}} > e_{\text{in}}{}^0 \end{cases} \qquad (10.40)$$

As it follows from the preceding relations, the slope of the current characteristic of the diode element in this case depends only on the resistance determined by ΔY.   The calculation thus does not differ from that for grounded diodes.   The only difference is that $e_{\text{in}}{}^0$ must be less than $\bar{e}$.

For the diode characteristic shown in Fig. 10.8a we have the relations

$$I_1 = \begin{cases} e_{\text{in}}\, \Delta Y^* & \text{for } e_{\text{in}} \leqslant e_{\text{in}}{}^0 \\[2mm] \bar{e}\, Y_2 & \text{for } e_{\text{in}} > e_{\text{in}}{}^0 \end{cases} \qquad (10.41)$$

where

$$e_{\text{in}}{}^0 = \frac{Y_1 + Y_2}{Y_1}\,\bar{e} \qquad \Delta Y^* = \frac{1}{R_1 + R_2} \qquad Y_2 = \frac{1}{R_2} \qquad Y_1 = \frac{1}{R_1}$$

To pursue this study further refer to Kogan [2, Chap. 5].   It is sufficient to say that a great many other extensions of these representations are possible; this makes the diode schemes very elastic for these purposes, although for piecewise linear representations involving many "pieces" the diode schemes become relatively complicated.

10.7   CONTINUOUS FUNCTIONAL TRANSFORMERS

In Sec. 10.4 we outlined the use of diodes in connection with building predetermined nonlinear characteristics by "pieces" of outputs of several diodes, with a proper adjustment for the instants of firing (see Fig. 10.5).   This is a purely piecewise analytic construction of nonlinear characteristics, as was explained in connection with Eq. (10.13).

In addition to this it is possible to obtain nonlinear control functions of a *continuous* type.   We have investigated such cases in connection with photoelectric functional transformers (Sec. 10.3) or, more generally, in the case of integrating devices (contours or shutters), as outlined in Sec. 10.1.

The simplest way of illustrating this approach is to investigate the problem of a generalized pendulum (Minorsky [4]).

$$A\ddot{\theta} + B\dot{\theta} + C\theta = 0 \qquad\qquad (10.42)$$

If A, B, and C are constant, (10.42) represents the differential equation of an ordinary physical pendulum with moment of inertia A, coefficient of velocity damping B, and coefficient of "spring constant" C.

If one provides a small mirror on such a pendulum that reflects the light from a luminous source on a moving photographic film, the record so obtained will give the *solution* of differential equation (10.42) directly.   For sufficient accuracy in the determination of such a graphical solution, certain constructional requirements must be fulfilled (small coulomb friction, sufficiently linear scale to avoid distortion, etc.).   We shall be interested here more in the theoretical aspects of these generalizations.

Consider the following scheme (Fig. 10.9c): inside a solenoid S (excited by a constant current i_1 in the winding w_1 and resulting in the

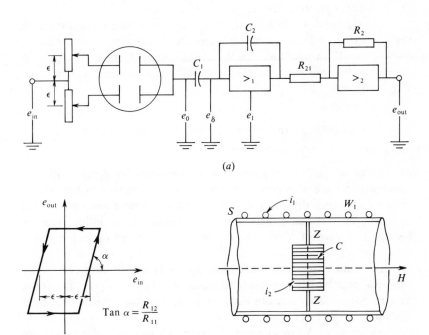

Fig. 10.9

uniform magnetic intensity H) is suspended about the axis z a coil C, which can also carry a current i_2 through some frictionless contacts (e.g., mercury) not shown.   As we know, the moment acting on C is

$$M = Ki_1i_2 \sin \theta \simeq Ki_1i_2\theta \qquad \text{for small } \theta \qquad (10.43)$$

The equilibrium ($\theta = 0$) occurs when the electromagnetic energy is maximum; hence, when coil C is coaxial with solenoid S and the currents in C and S are in the same direction, K is a constant and we assume that the angle θ of deviation from the equilibrium is small, so that $\sin \theta \simeq \theta$.

We have thus obtained a pendulum (assuming $B \simeq 0$) of the form

$$A\ddot{\theta} + M\theta = 0 \qquad (10.43a)$$

which does not yet represent anything of interest.

But suppose that the current i_2 in coil C is controlled by a contour (or a shutter), as was explained in Sec. 10.1.   For this purpose this element (contour or shutter) must be attached to C in some manner (e.g., be fixed on the axis z) and must be provided with a suitable push-pull circuit, in order to represent odd functions such as x^3, x^5, or some appropriate means for even functions.

Clearly in (10.43) instead of $M\theta$ one can introduce nonlinear terms such as $M\theta^3$, $M\theta^5$, . . . , or transcendental terms such as $M \log \theta$, Me^θ, ...   If, in addition, one varies the current i_1 in W according to some law, this will permit exploring a still larger number of equations. For example,

$$A\ddot{\theta} + f(t,\theta) = 0$$

To this class belongs, for instance, the well-known equation

$$A\ddot{\theta} + \alpha(1 + \cos 2t)\theta + C\theta^3 = 0$$

as well as a number of others.   Combinations involving nonlinear functions of $\dot{\theta}$ are also possible; $\dot{\theta}$ itself can be obtained either electrically or mechanically from a small constrained gyro associated with a piezoelectric circuit which can be modulated in a similar manner (either by means of a contour or, in the case of an optical control, by a shutter).

To summarize, pendulum analogs of this nature offer practically limitless possibilities for exploring any differential equation of the second order.   By coupling such analogs, one can explore nonlinear systems of higher orders.

As far as we know (Kogan [2, page 18]) this idea of a pendulum analog has been used in the U.S.S.R. for the investigation of the control of hydraulic turbines.

One cannot fail to notice that analogs of this nature represent high-precision instruments capable of yielding high-precision results. In many cases when only the qualitative part is of interest and the quantitative part is desired only to within a reasonable practical approximation, purely electrical analogs are simpler to produce and to handle.

The most commonly used analogs are those which are obtained by circuit elements. The major trend in this activity is to form certain combinations of relatively simple circuits so arranged that they represent the differential equation with which one can work.

Linear differential equations of a more or less high order appear first, naturally, since they are often encountered in control theory.

Consider a linear differential equation of the form

$$a_0 x^{(n)} + a_1 x^{(n-1)} + \cdots + a_{n-1} \dot{x} + a_n x$$
$$= b_0 y^{(m)} + b_1 y^{(m-1)} + \cdots + b_m y \quad (10.44)$$

where $y = F(t)$ is the external periodic excitation and $x^{(n)}, \ldots$; $y^{(m)}, \ldots$, are derivatives of the nth, $\ldots$, mth, $\ldots$, orders. The problem consists in investigating how such a system reacts to a complicated external excitation.

It is more convenient to represent the process, instead of by one equation (10.44) of the nth order, by an equivalent system of n equations of the first order, of the form:

$$b_i \dot{x}_i + \sum_{k=1}^{n} a_{ik} x_k + F_i(t) = 0 \qquad \begin{array}{l} i = 1, \ldots, n \\ a_{ik}, b_i \text{ consts}, b_i \neq 0 \end{array} \qquad (10.45)$$

The quantities x_i in (10.45) may be regarded as certain generalized coordinates and $F_i(t)$ as perturbations acting in the corresponding coordinates (degrees of freedom).

Finally, one can try to separate the differential equations not by their degrees of freedom but rather by their functional duties, for instance, by separating the equation of the object to be controlled from that of the controlling element per se.

One may have, thus, for the former the differential equation

$$a_0 \varphi^{(n)} + a_1 \varphi^{(n-1)} + \cdots + a_n \varphi = b_0 y^{(m)} + b_1 y^{(m-1)} + \cdots + b_m y$$
$$(10\ 46)$$

which is the same differential equation as (10.44). For the latter, if μ is the parameter of the regulation, one may have an analogous equation

$$C_0 \mu^{(s)} + C_1 \mu^{(s-1)} + \cdots + C_{s-1} \dot{\mu} + \mu = g_n \varphi + g_{n-1} \dot{\varphi} + \cdots + g_1 \varphi^{(n-1)}$$
$$(10.47)$$

For a static regulator one has the full differential equation (10.47). For an astatic regulator of the first order the term with μ drops out in (10.47); for that of the second order two terms, $C_{s-1}\dot{\mu} + \mu$, drop out, and so on.

One can also proceed by forming differential equations of the individual links, as shown in Fig. 10.10, which consists of two inertial

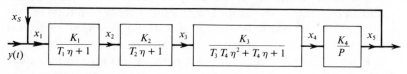

Fig. 10.10

links, one oscillatory link, and one integrating link.   The equations of motion in this case are

$$T_1\dot{x}_2 + x_2 = k_1x_1 \qquad T_2\dot{x}_3 + x_3 = k_2x_2$$
$$T_3T_4\ddot{x}_4 + T_4\dot{x}_4 + x_4 = k_3x_3 \qquad \dot{x}_5 = k_4x_4 \qquad x_1 = y(t) - x_s \qquad (10.48)$$

where x_i = coordinates
  $y(t)$ = external action
  T_i = time constants
  k_i = amplification factors
Sometimes one can write the dynamic equations directly.

For example, the linearized differential equations of an automatic pilot for aircraft are

$$\dot{\theta} = A_1\beta + A_2\delta + \frac{F}{mv} \qquad \ddot{\psi} + A_6\dot{\psi} + A_4\beta + A_5\delta = \frac{M}{I} \qquad (10.49)$$
$$\theta = \psi - \beta$$

and for the autopilot

$$T\ddot{\delta} + \lambda\dot{\delta} + \delta = i(\psi + T_1\dot{\psi} + T_2\ddot{\psi}) \qquad (10.50)$$

where ψ = departure from course to be steered
  β = angle of attack
  δ = rudder angle
  A_i = aircraft constants
T, h, i, T_1, T_2 = constants of autopilot
  M and F = perturbation moments
  I = moment of inertia
  The translation of these equations into analog form can be done in two different ways: (1) by increasing the order of derivatives; or

(2) by, on the contrary, decreasing it.   In case 1, one forms the scheme on the principle of subsequent differentiations accompanied by summation.   Figure 10.11 represents the structural scheme of a linear

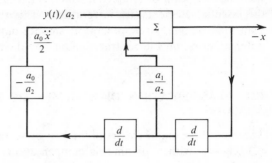

Fig. 10.11

differential equation of the second order

$$a_0\ddot{x} + a_1\dot{x} + a_2x = y(t) \tag{10.51}$$

In forming the analog by method 1, the procedure is applied to the coordinate x:

$$x = -\frac{a_0}{a_2}\ddot{x} - \frac{a_1}{a_2}\dot{x} + \frac{1}{a_2}y(t) \tag{10.52}$$

Assume that on the summation block Σ_1 all these components of the right-hand side of (10.52) act.   In the output one has x.

This quantity, after differentiations and multiplications [by $-a_0/2$ and $-(a_1/a_2)$], gives the components necessary for the summation block Σ.   With this scheme the fundamental elements of the scheme are differentiators, which are generally rather objectionable.

In method 2, one proceeds by subsequent integrations which are ultimately added.   This procedure is shown in Fig. 10.12.   In this case

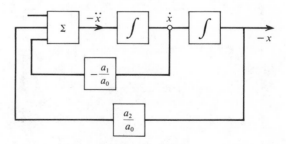

Fig. 10.12

it is necessary to solve the differential equation with respect to the highest derivative, after which all components are brought to the summation block by means of the corresponding feedback connections, with the exception of $(1/a_0)y(t)$, which is fed directly.   In this method the essential elements are integrators.   This scheme is less "jumpy" than the first one, since integrators smooth out disturbances, whereas differentiators, on the contrary, emphasize them.

10.8   CLASSIFICATION OF SCHEMES OF INTEGRATING ANALOGS

There are three major classes of integrating schemes: (1) the open type; (2) schemes with a parametric compensation; and (3) schemes of a closed type with a negative feedback.

To class 1 belongs the well-known mechanical scheme: disc-ball-cylinder transmission.   The disc rotates with a uniform velocity; the ball in contact with the disc can be displaced along its diameter so that the cylinder (in contact with the ball on the other side) has a variable speed (in magnitude and in direction) that depends on the position of the ball.

In this case one has the relation

$$y = \frac{kw}{r} \int_0^t x \, dt \qquad (10.53)$$

where y = angle of rotation of cylinder

$\qquad r$ = radius

$\qquad \omega$ = angular velocity of disc

$\qquad kx$ = distance of ball from center of disc

A corresponding electrical case would be the addition of three voltages e_1, e_2, and e_3, as shown in Fig. 10.13.   The currents flowing in

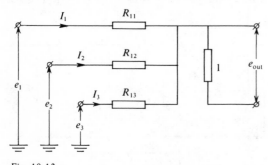

Fig. 10.13

the three branches are

$$I = e_{\text{out}} Y \qquad I_1 = (e_1 - e_{\text{out}}) Y_{11} \qquad I_2 = (e_2 - e_{\text{out}}) Y_{12}$$
$$I_3 = (e_3 - e_{\text{out}}) Y_{13} \tag{10.54}$$

where Y_i are conductances. Since $I = I_1 + I_2 + I_3$, a simple calculation gives

$$e_{\text{out}} = \frac{\sum_1^3 e_i Y_{1i}}{\sum_1^3 Y_{1i} + Y_c} \tag{10.55}$$

where $I = e_{\text{out}} Y_c$. This shows that the summation depends on the load and on the number of components.

In systems of class 2—with the parametric compensation—the fundamental idea is to introduce a correction proportional to (or, generally, as a certain function of) the output.

In fact, the relation between the input and the output quantities is

$$\bar{e}_{\text{out}} \cong \frac{Y_1(p)}{Y_3(p)} \bar{e}_{\text{in}} \tag{10.56}$$

where $\bar{e}$ are voltages (output and input) and Y are corresponding conductivities. If one considers the circuit shown in Fig. 10.14,

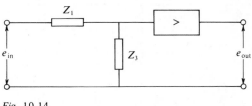

Fig. 10.14

formula (10.56) can be justified provided that the condition

$$\frac{Y_1(j\omega)}{Y_3(j\omega)} \ll 1 \tag{10.57}$$

is fulfilled.

Hence, if an amplifier is connected with a passive circuit (that is, a circuit without any sources of energy), one can eliminate the error inherent in the passive circuit by taking a certain amount of energy from the output and feeding it back into the input.

This is, of course, the old and well-known principle of "compounding," which is used for the voltage control in electric machines.

The same idea can obviously be used in electromechanical control systems. In fact, one has the relations

$$I\frac{d\omega}{dt} = K \qquad \frac{d\varphi}{dt} = \omega \qquad\qquad (10.58)$$

where ω = angular velocity of a motor M provided with a tachometer
generator TG (Fig. 10.15)
φ = angle of rotation
K = driving moment
I = moment of inertia

If one uses the first relation in (10.58), the angular velocity ω may be regarded as a measure of the integral of K; in the second relation the angle φ is the integral of ω.

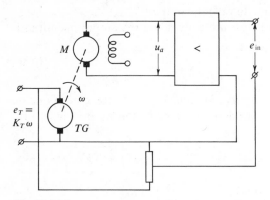

Fig. 10.15

In cases in which the input is a voltage, it is necessary to add a link to produce the transformation $K = kU$ and $\omega = k_1U$. The first transformation is usually obtained by means of a motor (dc or ac) and the second by means of a followup system. Since the parameters of these intermediate systems somewhat distort these theoretical relations, corrections are necessary if one aims at a high-precision performance.

Thus, for instance, instead of $\omega = k_1U$, in reality one has $\bar{\omega} = [k_1/D(p)]\bar{V}$, where $D(p)$ is a polynomial whose coefficients depend on the parameters of the followup system.

In view of this it is preferable to use the first relation: $I(d\omega/dt) = K$; $K = kU$, which involves integration. As an example, consider again the scheme shown in Fig. 10.15; the input signal (through an amplifier) is applied to the armature of a dc motor M with a separate excitation. The equation for the motion of the motor is

$$I\frac{d\omega}{dt} + \frac{M_0}{\omega_0}\omega = \frac{c\Phi}{R}U_a \tag{10.59}$$

where $I =$ total moment of inertia of rotating masses (reduced to shaft of motor)

$\quad M_0 = c\Phi I =$ starting moment

$\quad U_a =$ voltage applied to armature

$\quad R =$ resistance

If the tachometer generator is disconnected, one has the equation

$$I\frac{d\omega}{dt} + \frac{M_0}{\omega_0}\omega = k\frac{c\Phi}{R}e_{\text{in}} \tag{10.60}$$

k being a proportionality constant; this equation shows that the acceleration of the armature depends not only on the input signal but also on the speed.

If one introduces the emf of the tachometer generator, instead of e_{in} in (10.60) one will have

$$e_{\text{in}}^* = e_{\text{in}} + \alpha\omega \tag{10.61}$$

α being a proportionality factor from the tachometer generator voltage. Introducing in (10.60) the input voltage e_{in}^* (instead of e_{in}), one obtains

$$I\frac{d\omega}{dt} + \left(\frac{M_0}{\omega_0} - \frac{kc\Phi\alpha}{R}\right)\omega = \frac{kc\Phi}{R}e_{\text{in}} \tag{10.62}$$

If one adjusts the variable coefficient α so as to annul the parentheses in (10.62), instead of (10.62) one will have

$$I\frac{d\omega}{dt} = k\frac{c\Phi}{R}e_{\text{in}} \tag{10.63}$$

so that

$$\omega = \frac{kc\Phi}{RI}\int_0^t e_{\text{in}}\,dt \tag{10.64}$$

the constant k being determined by the condition mentioned above of reducing to zero the parentheses in (10.62). If this condition is obtained, a scheme of this kind will serve as an integrator; it will integrate the input voltage, which will give here the angular velocity of the motor.

The third class of integrating devices involves the use of a negative feedback. In recent years, this method has begun to be preferred, since one can disregard the accuracy of control in the main circuit so long as the feedback circuit is properly adjusted.

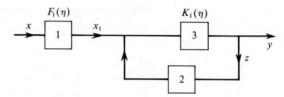

Fig. 10.16

Refer to the scheme of Fig. 10.16, which contains three links

$$\bar{x}_1 = F_1(p)\bar{x} \qquad \bar{y} = K_y(p)(\bar{x}_1 - \bar{z}) \qquad \bar{z} = F_2(p)\bar{y} \qquad (10.65)$$

where $F_1(p)$ is the transfer function of the input link, $F_2(p)$ that of the feedback, and $K_y(p)$ that of the amplifier.   One thus has

$$\bar{y} = \frac{K_y(p)F_1(p)}{1 + K_y(p)F_2(p)} \, \bar{x} \qquad (10.66)$$

If one takes a sufficiently large coefficient of amplification of the third link, one can write, approximately,

$$K_y(j\omega)F_2(j\omega) \gg 1 \qquad (10.67)$$

Under this approximation the relation between the output quantity y and the input x becomes simply

$$y = \frac{F_1(p)}{F_2(p)} \, x \qquad (10.68)$$

which shows that the relation between y and x is determined by the parameters of the feedback circuit as well as by those of the input circuit.

A system of this nature becomes a real functional transformer. In the particular case involving a large coefficient of amplification, in an open circuit, it permits solving the differential of the form

$$F_2(p)\bar{y} = F_1(p)\bar{x} \qquad (10.69)$$

As an example consider the scheme shown in Fig. 10.17. It represents a summation of the input signal with that from a tachometer generator through a resistor R.

The voltage e_δ at the junction point Σ is what is generally termed "the error function" of the followup scheme. This error signal is amplified and applied to the armature M of the motor (with a separate excitation, in order to reduce this error signal considerably).

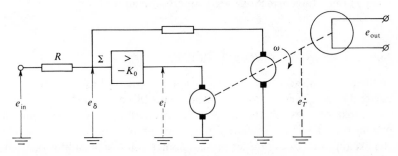

Fig. 10.17

A system of this nature guarantees a proportionality between the speed ω and the input voltage. One has the following relations:

$$\bar{e}_\delta = f_1(p)\bar{e}_{\text{in}} + f_2(p)e_T \qquad \bar{e}_\sigma = -\frac{\bar{e}_1}{k_0} \qquad \bar{e}_T = k_T\bar{\omega} \qquad (10.70)$$

where $\bar{e}$ = voltage of tachometer generator
  $\bar{e}_1$ = output voltage of amplifier
  k_0 = amplification factor
$f_1(p)$ and $f_2(p)$ are, approximately,

$$f_1(p) = \frac{\bar{e}_\delta}{e_m} \simeq \frac{1}{2} \qquad f_2(p) = \frac{\bar{e}_\delta}{e_T} \simeq \frac{1}{2}$$

Since $|e_1|$ is a finite quantity, for large k_0 the error e_σ is small. In such a case:

$$k_T\bar{\omega} = -\bar{e}_{\text{in}} \qquad \text{or} \qquad \bar{\omega} = -\frac{\bar{e}_m}{k_T} \qquad (10.71)$$

With the use of a reducing gearing operating a potentiometer the angle of rotation of the latter corresponds to a certain voltage. Since $\omega = a\, d\alpha/dt$, one has simply (see [2])

$$e_{\text{out}} = k_p\alpha = -\frac{k}{k_T\alpha}\int_0^t e_{\text{in}}\, dt \qquad (10.72)$$

k_p being a constant associated with the potentiometer.

To summarize, the output voltage *becomes the measure of the integrated value of the input voltage.*

The influence of the various parameters can be easily discussed.

The important point in connection with such schemes is that they become *real integrating schemes* that can be used with high-precision analogs once the corrections are properly introduced.

10.9   MORE ADVANCED PROBLEMS

In the preceding sections we have reviewed some of the analog methods currently used in connection with problems of control theory.

Most of these methods relate to ordinary problems of control engineering, and the use of analogs, although it considerably improves the existing art, does not yet present something which cannot be done otherwise, that is, *without* analogs.

There are, however, some *more advanced* problems in which the use of such contrivances *becomes essential*, since without them one either runs into very considerable computational difficulties or, simply, cannot proceed at all without stirring up formidable mathematical problems. It is precisely to these "ultradifficult" problems that the art of computers owes its existence.

This subject has acquired considerable importance in recent years and, properly speaking, goes much beyond the scope of control theory. It has, however, stirred up many new basic possibilities for control theory that could not have been predicted even a few years ago.

Since it is impossible to review this field systematically here, we shall limit ourselves to discussion of two recent developments in control theory in which electronic analogs introduced important contributions. They are: (1) difference differential equations; and (2) integral equations of the Fredholm type.

Difference differential equations   The history of difference differential equations is interesting; they were apparently discovered by Laplace (at the end of the eighteenth century). Euler even indicated the form of a complex exponential solution for them. Throughout the nineteenth century, however, very little was done on this subject. After World War I some interest in these questions was in evidence, but it was not until the end of World War II that the full sway of these developments was apparent.[1]

---

[1] See, for example, Bellman and Cooke [1], Pontriagin [9], and Pinney [8].

It will be useful to say a few words about the physical nature of the phenomena governed by these difference differential equations, since, as often happens in science, these equations were inspired by physics.

An ordinary differential equation expresses an *instantaneous equilibrium* of some physical quantities (forces, moments, voltages, currents, etc.) which are always considered *at the same instant t*. One can say that a differential equation *always deals with the present*.

The difference differential equation belongs to another class of the so-called *functional* equation in which the *past exerts its influence on the present*. There are problems in which the *whole past* (from $t = -\infty$ to $t = 0$) exerts its effect on the present ($t = 0$); these are the so-called "hereditary problems," and we do not consider them here. There is another class of problems in which only a *limited* past is of importance in shaping the present; this is the class of difference differential equations. Speaking more definitely, one can say that these are *problems with time lags h.*

More specifically we write an ordinary differential equation in the form, say, $a\ddot{x} + b\dot{x} + cx = 0$. To be more pedantic, one could write this as: $a\ddot{x}(t) + b\dot{x}(t) + cx(t) = 0$, emphasizing the fact that $\ddot{x}$, $\dot{x}$, and x are considered at the *same instant t*.

Here is a convenient point to bifurcate into the domain of the difference differential equation. Suppose that, whereas $\ddot{x} = \ddot{x}(t)$ and $x = x(t)$, on the contrary, $\dot{x} = \dot{x}(t - h)$, where h is a positive constant called *time lag*. In order to take this into account, it is useful to designate such a *retarded quantity* by the symbol $\dot{x}_h = \dot{x}(t - h)$; this is then the *retarded velocity;* likewise, the *retarded coordinate* will be $x_h = x(t - h)$, and so on. One can thus have difference differential equations of the form

$$a\ddot{x} + b\dot{x}_h + cx = 0 \qquad \text{or} \qquad a\ddot{x} + b\dot{x} + cx_h = 0 \cdots \qquad (10.73)$$

The first of these equations will then be a difference differential equation with a retarded damping; the second, a difference differential equation with a retarded restoring force, and so on.

The approach to this problem is almost intuitive; in fact, since $x_h = x(t - h)$, we assume that one can develop x_h in a Taylor series considering that the time lag h is small. If this series for x_h is substituted in one of the equations in (10.73) one obtains a differential equation of infinitely high order; this shows that the problem is *transcendental*.

If one looks for a complex exponential solution of the form e^z ($z = \alpha + i\omega$, $i = \sqrt{-1}$), a simple intermediate calculation (which we omit; see Myshkis [7, Chap. 21]) shows that the characteristic equation [in the case of the first equation in (10.73)] is

$$f(z) = az^2 + bze^{-hz} + c = 0 \qquad (10.73a)$$

and, for the second equation, it is

$$f(z) = az^2 + bz + ce^{-hz} = 0 \qquad (10.73b)$$

These equations are *algebraic transcendental;* a considerable amount of study has been devoted to them recently (Pontriagin [9]). It has been ascertained that such equations have, in general, an infinite number of complex roots, some of which may have positive real parts; this indicates the possibility of self-excited oscillations. Most of these transcendental frequencies are generally scattered over a large band of the frequency spectrum and for that reason are not objectionable; very often, however, one or two of them may happen to be in the neighborhood of the frequency in which one is interested.

The author came across a phenomenon of this nature during the tests of antirolling stabilization of a ship by the so-called "activated-tanks" method (Minorsky [5] and [6]). The method consists in activating the motion of the water ballast between the port and the starboard tanks by means of a variable-pitch impeller pump placed in the channel connecting the tanks. The angle of the blades was controlled by instruments responsive to the angular motion of rolling $(\theta, \dot{\theta}, \text{ and } \ddot{\theta})$. As long as the work of the impeller pump was within the limits of the hydrodynamic efficiency of the installation the result predicted on the basis of the differential equation was in accordance with the observed performance of roll quenching.

If, however, the impeller pump was driven to a point at which the cavitation in the cross channel would appear (with the incident time lag), this agreement between the theory and observed results disappeared entirely, and the blades of the impeller pump started oscillating with a frequency which did not exist in the frequency of the waves which were supposed to be quenched by the antirolling installation. At that time (June, 1940) this strange phenomenon was not understood, but at a later date, when it became clear that the difficulty was due to the fact that in the presence of cavitation the phenomenon was governed by a difference differential equation rather than by a differential equation, it was decided to check this hypothesis by the use of an electronic analog. The results obtained were found to be in satisfactory agreement with the observed data [5].

The analog was very simple and is shown in Fig. 10.18, in which LR_1R_2C is an ordinary oscillating circuit with constants adjusted to the values desired for the quantitative results (law of similitude) observed on the ship.

Across the resistor R_1 was connected an amplifier A whose output was connected to a special phase-shifting network P whose duty was to maintain a constant time lag h for a relatively wide band of frequencies. The output P was connected across R_2, as shown.

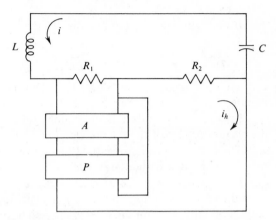

Fig. 10.18

Consider the following difference differential equation:

$$\ddot{x} + p\dot{x} + q(\lambda)\dot{x}_h + \omega_0^2 x = 0 \qquad (10.74)$$

λ being a variable parameter, which is the first equation of (10.73) with the difference that it also has an ordinary velocity damping $p\dot{x}$.

Consider meanwhile the analog shown in Fig. 10.18. The differential equation of the oscillating current is

$$L\frac{di}{dt} + (R_1 + R_2{}^2)i + \frac{1}{c}\int i\,dt = 0 \qquad (10.75)$$

Let us analyze the scheme of Fig. 10.18.   We take the ohmic drop across R_1 and apply it to the input of A, whose output is connected to the phase-shifting network P; the voltage across the output of P will be of the form

$$e(t) = \lambda R_1 i(t - h) = \lambda R_1 i_h \qquad (10.76)$$

where λ is the amplification factor (due to A) and the time lag h is due to P.

Instead of the differential equation (10.75), we have now a difference differential equation

$$L \frac{di}{dt} + (R_1 + R)i + S(\lambda)i_h + \frac{1}{c} \int_0^t i \, dt = 0 \tag{10.77}$$

This is also the difference differential equation of the form (10.74), in which the role of $p\dot{x}$ is played by the term $(R + R_1)i$ and that of $q(\lambda)\dot{x}_h$ by $s(\lambda)i_h$.

If one differentiates (10.77), divides the equation by L, sets

$$p = \frac{R + R_1}{L} \qquad q(\lambda) = \frac{S(\lambda)}{L} \qquad \frac{1}{LC} = \omega_0{}^2$$

and replaces i by x, the identity of (10.77) with (10.74) becomes manifest.

It was found at once that an analog of this kind indicates correctly the *qualitative* fact of the phenomenon of "retarded stabilization."

The first observation regarded the appearance of the phenomenon of the screen of a cathode-ray oscilloscope. It is well known that if one has a pattern of a Fourier series, then by "stopping" the fundamental (by means of a synchronizing network), one "stops" the whole pattern of harmonics on the screen, since all harmonics are in a rational ratio with respect to the fundamental.

With a difference differential equation this is not the case; since the problem is transcendental, harmonics generally *are not in any rational ratio* with respect to the fundamental. If one "stops" the fundamental wave on the screen, this does not "stop" the harmonics, which seem to "ride" on the top of the stationary fundamental wave. The quantitative part was still more interesting, since it gave with a reasonable degree of accuracy the predetermination of these irrational harmonics which were hampering the work of stabilization by this method.

It was interesting to observe that the electronic model of this kind, in spite of its simplicity, was sufficient to clarify the nature of these phenomena.

Integral equations Another example of a similar nature but with entirely different details relates to the stochastic theory of control processes (Valdenberg [11] and Solodovnikov [10]). This method depends on a computer for an automatic solution of the integral equation of the first kind, namely (see [10]),

$$R_{h\varphi}(t) - \int_0^\infty R_\varphi(\tau,\lambda) \, k(\lambda) \, d\lambda \qquad R(\tau,\lambda) = R(\tau - \lambda) \tag{10.78}$$

where $R_{h\varphi}$ and R_{φ} are correlation functions supposed to be known and $k(\lambda)$, the so-called *impulse transfer function,* is unknown; the computer must determine *it.*

The usual numerical procedure by iterations is long and tedious; a computer permits carrying out these operations very rapidly, since the iterations approach the limit and after this the same value of the unknown function is maintained. The whole procedure is thus completely automatic (Fig. 10.19).

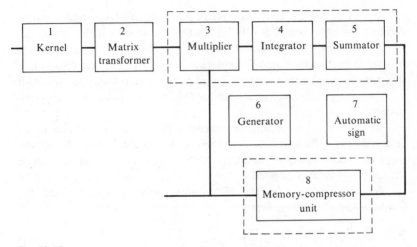

Fig. 10.19

The principle of operation is the method of successive approximations applied with respect to the unknown function $k(t)$; one can start, therefore, from some arbitrary value of $k(t)$, and the sequence of iterations will gradually improve its initial value until it will satisfy the integral equation (10.78).

In order to construct a computer of this nature one approximates the integral equation (10.78) by a system of equations

$$R_{h\varphi}(\tau_i) - \Delta\lambda \sum_{j=1}^{n} R_{\varphi}(\tau_i,\lambda_j)k(\lambda_i) = 0 \qquad i = 1, \ldots, n \qquad (10.79)$$

where $\Delta\lambda = \lambda_{\max}/n = \tau_{\max}/n$, and $\lambda_i = (\lambda_{\max}/n)i$. In these notations $\lambda_{\max}$ and $\tau_{\max}$ are sufficiently large values of λ and τ for which $R_{\varphi}(\tau,\lambda)$ and $R_{h\varphi}(\tau)$ are in the neighborhood of zero. Such values exist, since $R(\infty) \to 0$.

Using the notations:

$$R_\varphi(\tau_i, \lambda_j) = R_{ij}$$
$$R_{h\varphi}(\tau_i) = R_{h\varphi i}$$
$$k(\lambda_j) = k_j$$

system (10.79) reduces to

$$R_{h\varphi i} = \Delta\lambda \sum_{j=1}^{n} R_{ij}k_j \tag{10.80}$$

It can be shown that the matrix R_{ij} is symmetrical and positive definite, since the kernel of (10.78) has this property, which is assumed.

In the computer the replacement of (10.78) by (10.80) is obtained by approximating the functions entering in (10.78) by the corresponding step functions; the more "steps" used in these step functions in order to represent continuous functions in (10.78), the better the approximation.

Moreover, this computer employs the iteration procedure of Gauss-Zeidel, which differs from the usual iteration in that the adjustment of the iteration occurs after each step and not after the whole iteration has been processed.

In this version (Zeidel) the iteration process is built from the formula (details in Ref. [2])

$$k_i^{(m)} = \frac{R_{h\varphi i}}{\Delta\lambda R_{ii}} - \frac{1}{R_{ii}} \sum_{j=1}^{j-1} R_{ij}k_j^{(m)} - \frac{1}{R_{ii}} \sum_{j=i+1}^{n} R_{ij}k_j^{(m-1)} \tag{10.81}$$

The upper index (in parentheses) indicates the number of the iteration step.

The initial approximation is that the number of equations in this system is $n = 32$; this means that the functions entering into the integral equation are determined by 32 ordinates.

The computer itself consists of two principal parts: (1) the computer of integral transformations (*CIT*); and (2) the memory and "compressor" arrangement (*MCA*). Part (*CIT*) carries out transformations according to the form

$$F(x) = f(x) - \int_0^T k(x - s)\varphi(s)\, ds \tag{10.82}$$

It is supposed that all functions on the right-hand side are known. In reality $k(t)$ is unknown, but in the iteration process this function is approximated initially by some value, which in the course of the iteration procedure tends to the *correct* value. However, each step in the iteration procedure leading to *one* approximation requires 32 integrations in view of the above remark that $n = 32$.

Once one approximation has been obtained, it is "memorized" in the second part (*MCA*) of the machine; this memorized function (represented by 32 ordinates) is introduced into *CIT* for the following approximations.

In this way both parts (*CIT* and *MCA*) form a closed system guided by the convergence of the approximate value of $k(t)$ to the ultimate function satisfying the integral equation (10.78).

There is one noteworthy detail. As we just mentioned, for one single approximation (in the iteration series) one has to carry out 32 integrations, but for each such integration the value of the kernel is different.

In order to be able to introduce the value of the unknown function $k(t)$ under the integral sign for the following iteration step, it is necessary to "compress" this function (along the abscissa axis) 32 times. This is accomplished by increasing the rate of registering from the memory device 32 times as compared with the rate of recording. In this manner the second part (*MCA*) has not only the "memory" feature but also that of "compression" (i.e., change of scale in the ratio 1:32). There are a considerable number of other technical details for which Valdenberg [11] must be consulted. We shall follow the principal points only.

The functions introduced in this computer appear in the impulse forms, but it is possible (through the iteration) to follow the changes of these functions. Viewed from this angle the apparatus is based on a discrete action.

For the memory device use is made of photoelectric intermediate circuits, which result in charges on a large number ($32 \times 32 = 1,024$) of small condensers which appear as "memory cells." In each column of 32 such "memory cells" there is *one* which is charged and thus represents the memorization. In this way one charged cell in the column of 32 *defines the ordinate;* but, since there are 32 such columns, it is seen that there are 32 points which define the curve and each of them represents a charged condenser—a memory cell. If one could "see" these charged cells, one could "see" the curve; these curves change, however, from one iteration to the following one. Finally, in the long run the whole sequence of these variable curves converges to one unique curve, and this curve $k(t)$ is precisely the solution of the integral equation (10.78).

We shall not discuss a number of other details (for instance, how the curve defined by the sequence of small charged condensers is being taken into account in such a computer, etc.). These details are connected with the techniques used in television and allied topics and do not relate to the essential points of the scheme.

A device of this nature is not an analog in the above-defined sense, but is, rather, a *computer* arranged for an iteration solution of a system of difference equations by which the original integral equation is approximated.

10.10 CONCLUDING REMARKS

We have attempted to outline in this chapter a few salient points about analogs; these have found numerous applications in control theory during the last decade or so. Around 1936, when the author made some early contributions to this subject, the interest in these problems was practically nonexistent, but World War II stimulated further developments in control theory and thus stimulated also the remarkable advances in the field of mathematical machines. In fact, during the last decade about 140 publications have appeared on this subject (Kogan [2]).

To a great extent this activity was initiated by new developments in control theory. For example, in the theory of optimizing control it becomes necessary to introduce functional transformations by replacing a given characteristic by either its "quadratic" or "square root" counterparts. This also happens in many problems in which some *predetermined* nonlinearities are to be introduced or when these non-linearities are to be changed as the result of the operation of a control scheme.

In the early days of control theory [say, for example, at the time of the New Mexico steering tests (1923)] the "control space" (in the sense of the term used now) was an ordinary Euclidian space of θ, $\dot{\theta}$, and $\ddot{\theta}$, θ being the deviation of the system to be controlled from its predetermined equilibrium point. A "control point" under these conditions was generally determined by a certain linear function: $m\theta + n\dot{\theta} + p\ddot{\theta}$, m, n, and p being some constant parameters (Minorsky [5]).

With the appearance of a host of new problems and methods, one is more and more interested in "function spaces," in which a function obtained directly from experimental data must undergo some functional transformations before being used in a control scheme.

Instead of early schemes, which were based on some *fixed* differential equation, we are inclined to use more and more certain *functional* equations of which we know but little.   In such cases analogs permit "short cuts" by producing rapidly results which we cannot calculate easily and which sometimes cannot be calculated at all.

Owing to these devices we have begun *to use* certain domains in which our theoretical knowledge is, as yet, little advanced.

In other words, analog computers and similar devices, which give either solutions of certain equations graphically or give the corresponding figures (e.g., in the binary code), begin to appear as the *principal component* part—the brain—of modern control schemes.

The situation is still in a state of evolution, and the last word has not yet been said, but it is probable that the future advances in the control theory will be closely connected with, and to some extent dependent on, the corresponding advances in the theory of mathematical machines, which were outlined briefly in this chapter.

REFERENCES

1. Bellman, R., and Kenneth L. Cooke: "Differential-Difference Equations," Academic Press Inc., New York, 1963.

2. Kogan, B. J.: "Electronic Models and Their Applications," Fizmatgiz, Moscow, 1963.

3. Korn, G., and T. Korn: "Electronic Analogue Computers," McGraw-Hill Book Company, 1952.

4. Minorsky, N.: *Compt. Rend. Acad. Sci. Paris*, vol. 102, 1936; *Rev. Gen. Elec.*, vol. 30, May, 1936.

5. ——: "Non-linear Oscillations," D. Van Nostrand, Inc., New York, 1962.

6. ——: *Trans. ASME*, October, 1947.

7. Myshkis, A. D.: "Linear Differential Equations with Retarded Argument," Goztehizdat, Moscow, 1951 (in Russian).

8. Pinney, E.: "Ordinary Difference-Differential Equations," University of California Press, Berkeley, California, 1958.

9. Pontriagin: *Izv. Akad. Nauk SSSR*, vol. 6, 1942.

10. Solodovnikov, V. V.: "Stochastic Dynamics of Control Systems," Moscow, 1960, p. 313.

11. Valdenberg, Yu. S., cited in Ref. 10; published in The method of solving a certain class of integral equations by casing computers, *Automatika i Tele.*, no. 19, 1958, pp. 725–730.

APPENDIX
THE NEW
MEXICO TESTS

In Sec. 5.7 an outline of the "first problem of Bulgakov" in the terminology of Letov was given. Equations (5.34) and (5.35) were interpreted in terms of the applied problem of the automatic steering of a ship. This problem formed the object of research (in 1922 and 1923) by the author in connection with the automatic steering of the *U.S.S. New Mexico.*

The theoretical part of this control was described in the May 1922 issue of the *Journal of the American Society of Naval Engineers*, and the results of these tests were published in the May 1930 issue of the same journal. B. V. Bulgakov's work in connection with this problem was published in 1942 (*Doklady Akademic Nauk*, vol. 37).

The author's theory was, for obvious reasons, rather crude as compared with the present state of control theory.

Several circumstances, however, contributed to the ultimate success of these tests in spite of the oversimplified theory upon which they were based: (1) the smoothness of operation of the Waterbury hydraulic gear displacing the rudder; (2) the enormous moment of inertia of the ship, which was 32,000 tons; and (3) quiet weather.

These favorable conditions allowed the isolation of the fundamental dynamic actions in a practically pure form, and this permitted the results to come out fairly well even on the basis of a rather crude theory based on the consideration of a dynamic system with *one* degree of freedom.

Consider the angular azimuthal motion of a ship with moment of inertia I about the vertical axis passing through its center of gravity and subjected to actions of external moments $\Sigma\,M_e$. If θ is the angle of deviation of the ship from her set course, the differential equation of angular motion will be then

$$I\ddot{\theta} = -\sum M_e \tag{A.1}$$

There are in this case three external moments:

1. The so-called "resistance to turning" $M_e(\dot{\theta})$, which is a nonlinear function of $\dot{\theta}$, but for small motions one can linearize it by the expression $M_e(\dot{\theta}) \cong B\dot{\theta}$, B being an adequate linearizing factor.
2. The head resistance. It is shown in treatises on naval architecture that this is a *perturbing factor* which tends to emphasize the existing deviation; if one designates its moment by $M_e(\theta)$ and linearizes it by the relation $M_e(\theta) = C\theta$, one must introduce this term *with a minus sign.*
3. Finally, the third moment is due to the rudder, say, $R(\alpha) \cong R\alpha$, where R is again the constant of linearization. Thus the differential equation of *uncontrolled* motion will be, after the right-hand terms $-\Sigma\,M_e$ in (A.1) are transferred to the left,

$$I\ddot{\theta} + B\dot{\theta} - C\theta + R\alpha = 0 \tag{A.2}$$

In this form the differential equation is more or less useless, since it is supposed to be valid only for small deviations, but there is no certainty that the motion will be small as long as α, the angle of the rudder, is *not related* to the ship's motion. *The problem of automatic steering appears when α becomes related to the angular motion.*

Let us assume therefore that the rudder moment $R(\alpha)$ is of the form

$$R(\alpha) \cong R\alpha = m\theta + n\dot{\theta} + p\ddot{\theta} \tag{A.3}^1$$

that is, the rudder angle is a certain linear function of θ, $\dot{\theta}$, and $\ddot{\theta}$, the constants m, n, and p being at the same time certain coefficients of linearization; dimensionally (A.3) has the dimension of the moment.

The controlled motion of the ship will be then

$$I\ddot{\theta} + B\dot{\theta} - C\theta + m\theta + n\dot{\theta} + p\ddot{\theta} = 0 \tag{A.3a}$$

---

[1] It is noted that this form in the notations of recent authors, e.g., formula (4.1), is $\sigma = \sum_{k=1}^{3} c_k x_k$, where $x_1 = \theta$, $x_2 = \dot{\theta}$; $x_3 = \ddot{\theta}$, and the constants are $c_1 = m$, $c_2 = n$, and $c_3 = p$.

Or, combining the terms with θ, $\dot{\theta}$, and $\ddot{\theta}$, one has:

$$(I + p)\ddot{\theta} + (B + n)\dot{\theta} + (m - C)\theta = 0 \qquad (A.4)$$

It is noted that the control actions (characterized by the coefficients p, n, and m) enter *as if they were modifying the natural properties I, B, and C of the ship.* In the first place, it is clear that for a ship, the moment of inertia I grows in proportion to the *cube* of the linear dimension, whereas the resistance to turning grows only in proportion to the *square* of that dimension. One expects, therefore, that for a very large ship (and very small angular motions) I will be rather large in comparison with B. Hence it is advantageous to have $n > 0$ and $p < 0$; in view of stability, m must be positive, and, in addition, $m > |C|$.

These rather crude physical ideas were guiding the selection of the proper values for m, n, and p (and this was the most difficult part of the adjustments); one can find the details of these adjustments, as well as details of the behavior of the ship during the final test (September 27, 1923) in the *Journal of the American Society of Naval Engineers*, 1930.

We shall now try to correlate this crude theory with the more elaborate theory of Bulgakov, which is condensed in Eqs. (5.34) and (5.35). Clearly angle ψ in these equations is the θ of the equations in this section. If we use θ, as well as the other notations here, Bulgakov's equations become

$$I\ddot{\theta} + B\dot{\theta} + \mu = 0 \qquad (A.5)$$

$$\dot{\mu} = f^*(\sigma) \qquad \sigma = a\theta + E\dot{\theta} + G\ddot{\theta} - \frac{1}{e}\mu \qquad (A.6)$$

Clearly σ is $R\alpha$ in our notations and a, E, and G are respectively m, n, and p. Hence, in (A.6), the second equation becomes (in our notations)

$$R\alpha = m\theta + n\dot{\theta} + p\ddot{\theta} - \frac{1}{e}\mu \qquad (A.7)$$

Only the last term, $-(1/e)\mu$, makes a difference. In order to see this point it is necessary to analyze Eq. (5.6a), which shows that the signal σ (or $R\alpha$ in these notations) is continuously reduced by the "followup" actions $-\mu/e$. Hence, if the quantities θ, $\dot{\theta}$, and $\ddot{\theta}$ *vary slowly*, and the followup action, on the contrary, *varies rapidly*, it is sufficient to neglect the term characterizing the readjustments of the followup action and assume that the control moment *continuously follows* the resultant signal.   In such a case one can write

$$R\alpha = m\theta + n\dot\theta + p\ddot\theta \tag{A.8}$$

This makes our conclusions identical with those of Bulgakov.

In fact in the *New Mexico's* automatic steering installation the partial control actions $m\theta$, $n\dot\theta$, and $p\ddot\theta$ were in the form of certain voltages, so that the resultant voltage was controlling the field of a differential-equation generator; the latter, through two additional followup systems (one on the hydraulic gear and the other on the rudder), introduced the rudder action in the form of Eq. (A.8).

The problem was thus simplified in advance in view of the favorable conditions 1 and 2, mentioned at the beginning of this section.   The results of the text (*JASNE*, 1930) corroborated these predictions.

This does not mean, however, that the more elaborate theory formulated by Bulgakov is not necessary; on the contrary, its value would be clear in a more general case in which the simplifying circumstances existing during the *New Mexico* tests did not occur.

One remark should be made at this point.   An automatic steering device of the form of Eq. (A.4) has one basic limitation, namely, in its so-called "static error," when external disturbances (e.g., a wind from a beam) are acting.   In order to see this point we replace (A.4) with the equation

$$I^*\ddot\theta + B^*\dot\theta + C^*\theta = A \tag{A.9}$$

where $I^* = I + p$; $B^* = B + n$; $C^* = m - |C|$; and A is the external moment due, say, to the wind from a beam.   The abovementioned disturbance is expressed by the existence of a particular solution $\theta_1 = A/C^*$.   This means that the ship would have a *static correction* in its steered course according to the value of A.

In order to eliminate this inconvenience it can be shown (see *JASNE*, 1922) that instead of controlling the *angle* α of the rudder in accordance with Eq. (A.8), it is necessary to control the *rate* at which the rudder is operated.

In such a case one would have the equation

$$\frac{d}{dt}[R(\alpha)] \cong R\frac{d\alpha}{dt} = m\theta + n\dot\theta + p\ddot\theta \tag{A.10}$$

which gives

$$R\alpha = \int_0^t (m\theta + n\dot\theta + p\ddot\theta)\,dt = \int_0^t X\,dt \tag{A.11}$$

In this case, taking into account the external action A, Eq. (A.3a) would become

$$I\ddot{\theta} + B\dot{\theta} - C\theta + \int_0^t (m\theta + n\dot{\theta} + p\ddot{\theta})\, dt = A \tag{A.12}$$

If one differentiates this equation, one has

$$I\dddot{\theta} + B\ddot{\theta} - C\dot{\theta} + m\theta + n\dot{\theta} + p\ddot{\theta} = 0 \tag{A.13}$$

We reach thus the following important conclusions:

1. If one uses the "integral control" (A.11)[1] the order of the differential equation is raised by one unit [differential equation (A.13) is now of the third order].
2. *The effect of the external constant disturbance A is now eliminated* [Eq. (A.13)].

The second conclusion is the most important.

A generalization is immediate. If, instead of the integral control of the form

$$\int_0^t X\, ds, \qquad \text{where} \qquad X = m\theta + n\dot{\theta} + p\ddot{\theta}$$

one uses the control of the form

$$\int_0^t ds \int_0^t X\, ds \qquad \text{or} \qquad \int_0^t ds \int_0^t ds \int_0^t X\, ds_1, \ldots, \text{etc.,}$$

one can eliminate the *effect* of the uniformly growing disturbances $A = A_0 t$, $A_0 = \text{const}$, and so on.

These considerations are mentioned in *JASNE*, 1922, but this form of control was not used in the *New Mexico* experimental installation, and this matter did not receive any further attention at that time.

However a number of years later the idea of this "rate" or "integral" control was apparently "reinvented" and received the new name *astatic control*, the term *astatic* probably signifying the fact that the *static* error θ_1 is eliminated by this form of the "rate control."   Astatic systems are used extensively in modern control engineering, and they are characterized by an "order of astatism."   Thus in the case of (A.11)

---

[1] In modern terminology, instead of "integral control" one uses the term "astatic control."

we have

$$R\alpha = \int_0^t X\,ds \qquad X = m\theta + n\dot{\theta} + p\ddot{\theta}$$

Such systems are called astatic systems of the *first* order.   If

$$R\alpha = \int_0^t ds \int_0^t X\,ds$$

the astatic system is said to be of the *second* order, and so on.

It is seen thus that these more or less modern developments were also connected (somewhat indirectly) to the problem of automatic steering; this acted as a stimulus in the early development of control theory.

INDEX

This book was set in Times Roman by The Universities Press, and printed on permanent paper and bound by The Maple Press Company. The designer was Ben Kann; the drawings were done by B. Handelman Associates, Inc. The editors were B. G. Dandison, Jr. and J. W. Maisel. Robert R. Laffler supervised the production.